Alan Holtham has been involved in all aspects of woodworking for over 30 years. After graduating with a degree in Forestry and Wood Science, he established a specialist woodworking business that grew to supply tools and machinery to customers all over the world, as well as importing and processing timber for both retail and wholesale customers.

After 20 years at the 'sharp end' of retailing, he decided to take a step back and concentrate on sharing his accumulated knowledge and experience, setting up a dedicated film studio and workshop in 2000. Initially making instructional and promotional videos covering all aspects of woodworking machinery, the media business grew rapidly and Alan has now written hundreds of magazine articles and continues to write and present a variety of woodworking programmes on DVD.

He has appeared on many TV woodworking programmes, and regularly demonstrates tools and techniques on behalf of major machinery and tool manufacturers.

His simple, down to earth approach, fronts a personal ambition to demystify woodworking and bring it back as a mainstream interest for all, but particularly for youngsters whom he feels have been sadly neglected by an education system that places little credibility on teaching practical hand skills.

First published in 2007 by Trend Machinery & Cutting Tools Ltd

ISBN 978-0-9557935-0-9

COMPLETE ROUTING

Alan Holtham

Foreword

Some 60 years ago there was little to say about a router. It's birth was due to an operator finding the need to bring the tool to the job rather than heave large lumps of timber to his fixed head motor. But in a matter of years the possibilities of the hand router exploded into life. The saw was made to saw; a plane to plane and a drill merely to drill, but the router was found to be able to do all three jobs and much more in an extraordinary manner. Routing specialists such as Trend, devised clever jigs and cutters to give the router such value that, at the present time, any workshop without a router on their shelf would be considered backward to the extreme. No wonder the router has been termed "a workshop in itself"!

I wonder how many enthusiasts have devised their own special routing gadgetry in the privacy of their own workshop shed. This clearly is a unique feature of this amazing tool for it can inspire one to experiment and be creative. I should know, it is most fulfiling.

I have written books myself on routing techniques but this book by Alan stands ahead in every respect. Without hesitation, I predict that anyone possessing a router, whether it be a DIY person, Carpenter or Furniture Maker, all will find it a most valuable source of know-how information to regularly refer to.

Jim Phillips
Founder of Trend Machinery & Cutting Tools

November 2007

Acknowledgements

I am indebted to many friends and colleagues in the woodworking world for their help and advice during the creation of this book.

In particular my thanks go to Stephen Phillips of Trend who originally inspired the project and whose patience and guidance was much appreciated. I was also privileged to have the assistance of Jim Phillips, the 'guru' of routing, who willingly shared his immense knowledge and ensured that the technical details are all correct.

There are many others at Trend who also deserve thanks, Emma Harvey who toiled ceaselessly converting the mass of text and pictures into the excellent layout. Barry Flammia, Annette Kelly and Matt Shepherd in the Design Studio who worked wonders on my images.

Thanks also to the following:

Brimarc for the loan of tools and images of the Leigh dovetailer and Proxxon router. Woodrat for images of their unique machining centre, Wealden Tool Company for the Linenfold panel photos and Triton for the loan of equipment.

To everyone else who contributed in any way, my grateful thanks.

Alan Holtham

Preface

Complete Routing is the definitive reference manual for all router users, whether you are a complete novice or seasoned professional. Comprehensively illustrated with hundreds of clear photographs and action shots, this is a real 'hands on' book. Packed with practical information and tips, it tells you all there is to know about the incredible world of the router.

The book starts with an introduction to the router itself and outlines its development from earliest beginnings to the current hi-tech models of today. The main features and accessories are discussed in detail, providing you with an invaluable guide to choosing the correct router and then using it both safely and efficiently.

The book leads you gently through the process of actually getting started with the router, showing you in detail how to set it up and make some initial cuts. Subsequent sections cover the many different ways to guide the router, the use of jigs and templates and a host of other routing techniques, such as moulding, grooving, jointing and carving.

You are introduced to the vast range of tooling available for the router and given an insight into just what it can do for you. Guidance is provided to help select the right cutter for the job and then use and care for it properly.

To further enhance the versatility of the router, you are then introduced to the concept of using it in a fixed position, either under a table, in an overhead stand or a machining centre.

The final section provides a source of inspiration that should help you realise the true potential of the router and dramatically increase your woodworking aspirations and abilities.

Although sponsored by Trend Machinery, the world's leading router specialists, this book covers the whole range of general routing techniques and equipment, including many other brands, so its content is relevant no matter what your level of expertise or kit.

Enjoy!

Alan Holtham

CONTENTS

trend
trend

INTRODUCTION

Over recent years the hand held router has become the world's most popular power tool. With its seemingly limitless variety of applications, in a wide range of materials, the versatility of this tool cannot be overstated.

Both professional and amateur woodworkers have seen their abilities and aspirations substantially extended after buying a router.

It provides an extremely fast and accurate means of carrying out many woodworking operations and more importantly, it allows relatively unskilled users to quickly produce mouldings or joints that were previously the preserve of the highly skilled tradesman.

This is not to say that a router doesn't require any skill to operate. There are certain rules and procedures that must be followed for its safe and efficient use, but these are not difficult and with a little practice the complete novice soon becomes a total router convert. In fact, much of the skill is in setting up the router, rather than actually using it.

So what can you do with your new router? The list is endless, but just as a taster you can mould edges, trim, rebate, cut profiles, inlay and groove.

You can cut circles, ellipses, dados, carve shapes and drill holes. You will be able to

make a range of woodworking joints, shape decorative panels and for mass production work, repeat cut a particular profile using a template.

With the addition of a range of extra accessories or jigs, the versatility of your router is expanded even further and you can produce complex dovetail joints or turned components, cut hinge and lock recesses, rout stair housings and much, much more!

The router can be used either hand held, or mounted underneath a specially designed table to give you all the advantages of a spindle moulder.

If this isn't enough, you can even buy a specialised machining centre where the router is mounted overhead which brings a whole new dimension to many of the standard functions.

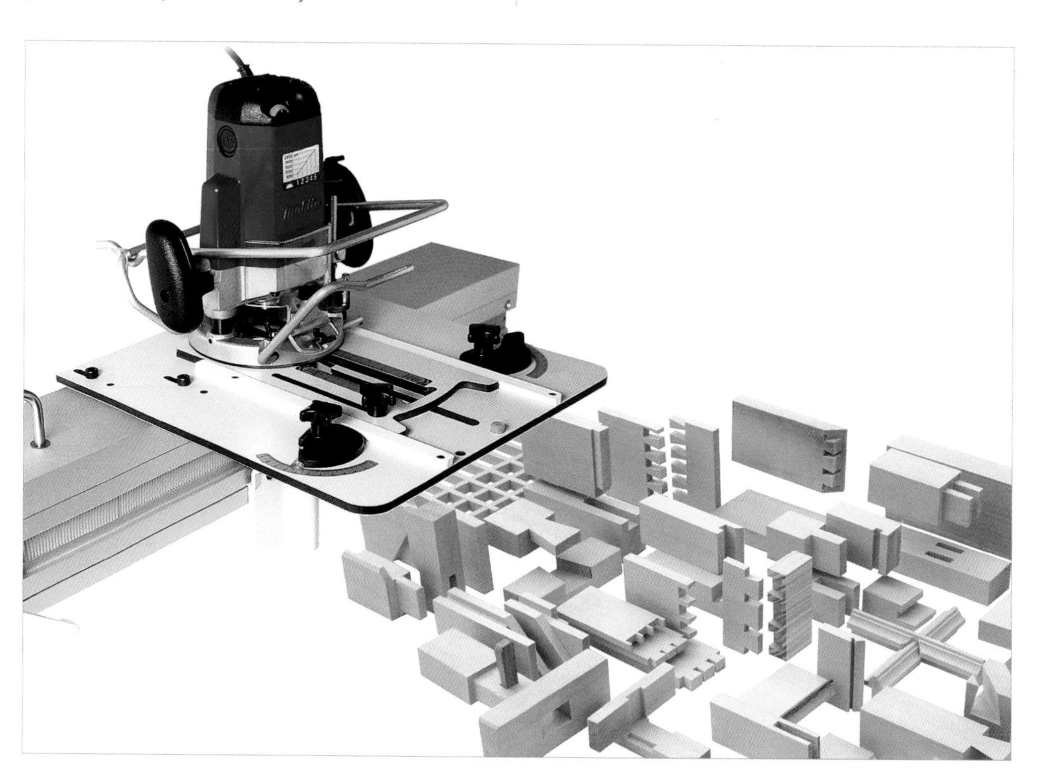

Router cutters have developed to keep pace with all these new uses and now you can safely machine not only wood but laminates, aluminium, plastics and resins such as Corian®.

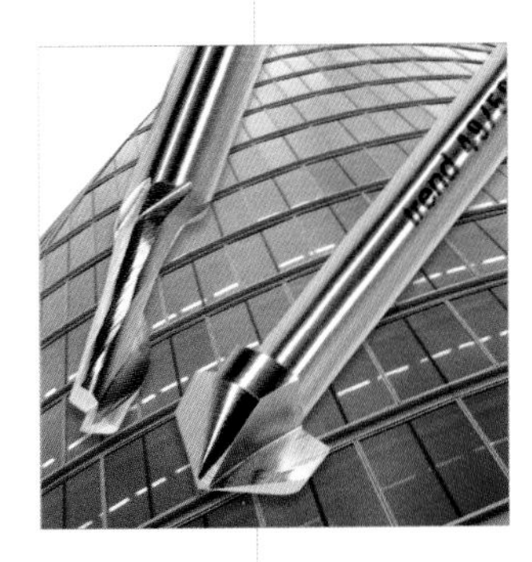

Its immense versatility doesn't have to be expensive either. In real terms, the cost of a basic router and a few simple cutters has dropped dramatically over the last few years and it is now a very affordable tool so you can get started without having to spend a fortune.

Once you have mastered the basics the rest is up to you, but remember that the router won't do all these wonderful things on its own, there has to be some input from you. So be adventurous and keep practising to build both your confidence and ability.

With only a little experience you will soon be using the router to transform both the making and the detail of all your woodworking projects, but do be warned, it can become seriously addictive!!

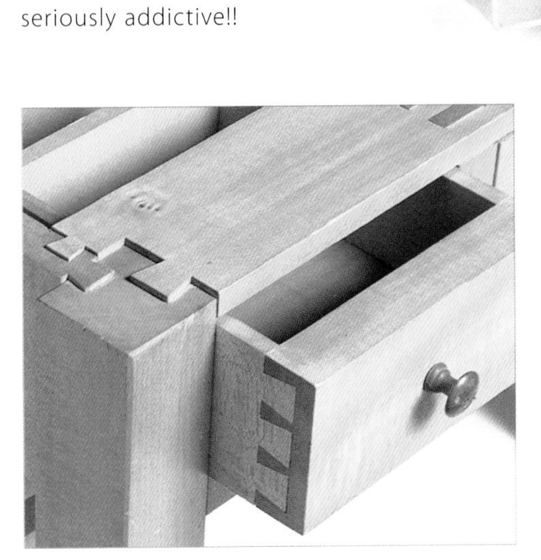

1. THE ROUTER

The growth and development of routing technology has been astonishing in recent years, an upward trend that will undoubtedly continue unabated, with hugely exciting implications for all woodworkers.

Historical development

Since the dawn of time, Man has always had the desire to fashion and shape wood. Early primitive stone tools were gradually replaced by metal ones, some of which were inserted into wooden blocks to allow for gripping with both hands. By moving these tools backwards and forwards over a piece of wood, grooves were formed and the router had arrived on the scene!

By the 19th century this had developed into the hand routing tool that became known as an 'old woman's tooth', which was used for ploughing grooves and rebates.

20th century plane makers refined this further into the classic hand router, though the basic functions remained the same.

Although the development of electrically powered hand routers for more complex shaping work started in the early 1900's, they were beyond the reach of the local joiner or cabinetmaker, who still had to painstakingly form profiles using hand moulding planes.

From these followed the more complex combination planes, whose series of interchangeable shaped cutters mimicked the principle of the modern router. But these were tricky to set up, slow to operate and were unsuitable for use with the newly emerging, but highly abrasive materials such as ply, blockboard and MDF.

However, a major step forward came with the idea of developing a shaping tool from a hand held motor with a sharp cutter mounted on the end of the spindle and this fundamental concept of the router has remained virtually unchanged to this day, and even the very early machines are still instantly recognisable for what they are.

The relatively late arrival of the powered router to the scene was entirely due to the speed limitations of the early series wound induction motors. Previously, wood machining work had to be carried out on spindle moulders which could only achieve the correct tooling speed by using large diameter cutter blocks.

These heavy floor standing machines were used by workshop based woodworkers for long runs of production work, but this necessarily involved bringing the work to the machine rather than vice versa.

For the next few decades things changed slowly, both with regard to the routers themselves and the tooling to fit in them. They remained as simple grooving and housing tools, for work where the quality of the finish was unimportant. It had already been established that the ultimate cutting performance was only obtained from tooling with a peripheral speed of around 1000 metres a minute, but the available motors were incapable of reaching anywhere near such high speeds.

The breakthrough came with the invention of the small series wound motor and this heralded the arrival of the powered hand router as we know it today.

Now, spindle speeds of up to 30,000 rpm are easily available, providing enough peripheral speed for cutters even as small as 1/8" in diameter.

This was the catalyst to the amazing growth in popularity of the router and wood machinists were quick to exploit its portability, quick cutter change and more particularly, the high quality finish. Routers became lighter and more compact and by the early seventies, plunge base models with electronic speed control added further to the range of possible operations.

The machines were now also made from lighter materials and electronic miniaturisation allowed them to be made much more compact, with consequent dramatic changes in the power to weight ratios.

Tooling continued to develop in tandem with the router, but it was the advent of tungsten carbide that solved the wear problems associated with abrasive materials such as plywood and MDF. Carbide tipping of cutters was a revolutionary advance in wood machining and it has now become standard practice.

There followed a positive explosion in the range of cutter types and profiles, adding further to the complete versatility of this most useful machine. Almost every conceivable profile can now be cut with a modern router and many industries are totally reliant on routers and associated tooling for their manufacturing processes.

More recent developments and mass production has further reduced the price of 'entry level' machines and cutters to a stage where they are totally affordable and machine routing is now well within the reach of even the occasional woodworker.

At the other end of the scale, we now also have completely automated CNC routers, capable of mass production in a range of different materials.

As for the future, the router is definitely here to stay and there is no stopping the mechanical and electronic advances of this unique tool. Motors will continue to improve with continuously rated, high frequency brushless models making the router quieter and more user friendly. Collets will probably disappear with keyless chucks allowing painless and spanner free tool mounting.

Tooling will carry on developing apace, with innovative concepts like replaceable tips, spiral tooling and diamond impregnated edges, filtering down from industrial manufacturing to the home user, just as the router itself has done.

The modern router, with its speed and efficiency of cutting in a huge range of new and traditional materials, has undoubtedly revolutionised the process of shaping wood, and there are exciting times ahead as the development continues.

Choosing a router

Whatever the model or type of router you eventually choose, the basic operating principle is always the same.

It is essentially a high revving motor into the end of which you fit a variety of shaped cutters or 'bits', all of which are held securely in a precision collet.

However, it can be very confusing trying to decide which particular router is the one for you. Manufacturers overwhelm you with all sorts of performance claims and the first time buyer can easily become bewildered by the vast array of models on offer.

Unfortunately, because of its very versatility, there is no such thing as the perfect router and you will have to accept some degree of compromise. Provided you remember the indisputable adage that you get what you pay for, you should not be disappointed.

The cost of a specific router will always indicate the quality of the engineering and materials that have gone into its manufacture.

This financial criteria is therefore one of the best to provide you with reassurance about the expected performance and long-term reliability of a particular model.

For instance, the armature on a good quality router will have been balanced after manufacture by careful machining so that it runs really smoothly and without any vibration at high speed.

Impressive looking routers at greatly reduced prices will not have had any of this quality control and inspection.

So don't always judge a machine by its visible features, as much depends on what you cannot see within the casing.

However, be aware that this is probably the one occasion when buying the biggest is not necessarily the best.

A really powerful and heavy duty machine may boast an impressive specification, but when you try and guide it along a delicate piece of edge moulding, then the sheer size and weight makes it very cumbersome to handle.

Tip

A smaller, lightweight machine will probably do the job just as well, but with much easier handling characteristics, and allow better visibility and control of the cutter.

The larger routers are normally reserved for heavier applications, such as cutting worktops, deep channelling and stair trenching, and for situations that require it to be mounted under a router table.

The smaller light and medium duty models are better suited for hand-held use, but beware of compromising too much, or you will end up buying a model that doesn't do either job particularly well.

It is inevitable that if you are even remotely serious about woodworking, then you will end up with more than one router and probably several, so a smaller but good quality model is probably your best starting point.

The other consideration is whether there is a range of accessories available to further enhance your router's use. Although cutters are interchangeable, the main machine accessories are often made for a specific model so make sure you buy into a system that will expand with your needs.

Fortunately, there is now a range of independent manufacturers who supply a vast array of useful accessories and jigs that fit almost all makes and models.

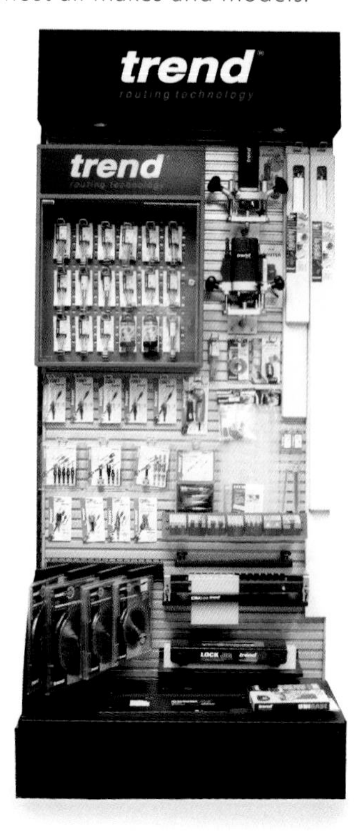

It also helps to buy from a reputable dealer who has been trained and approved by the router manufacturer. Such dealers can offer you a choice of models to suit your budget, as well as giving a reliable back-up service for spares and accessories.

Remember too, that at some time in the future your router may need servicing or repairing, in which case you may find it difficult to get help from a big DIY store or mail order house.

Once you start looking round for a router, you will notice huge differences in the type and positioning of switches, plunge locks, depth gauges etc, all factors that determine the ease of handling of the router and which may affect your specific application.

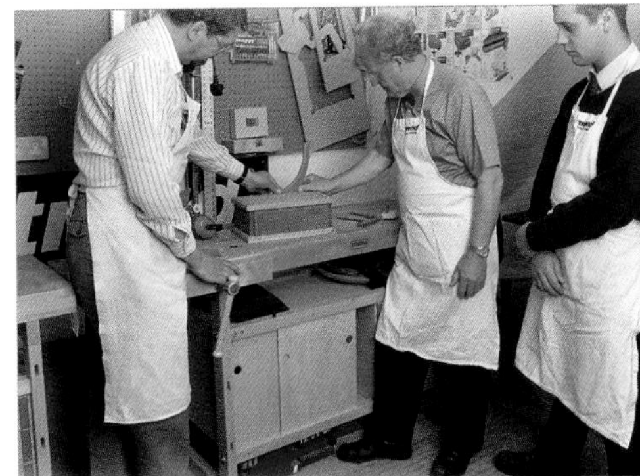

Tip

So before you finally commit yourself, do try and find the opportunity to actually try out as many different models as possible.
This is much easier these days, as many tool dealers and manufacturers host open days and shows, or offer specialist tuition courses where you can gain real 'hands on' experience.

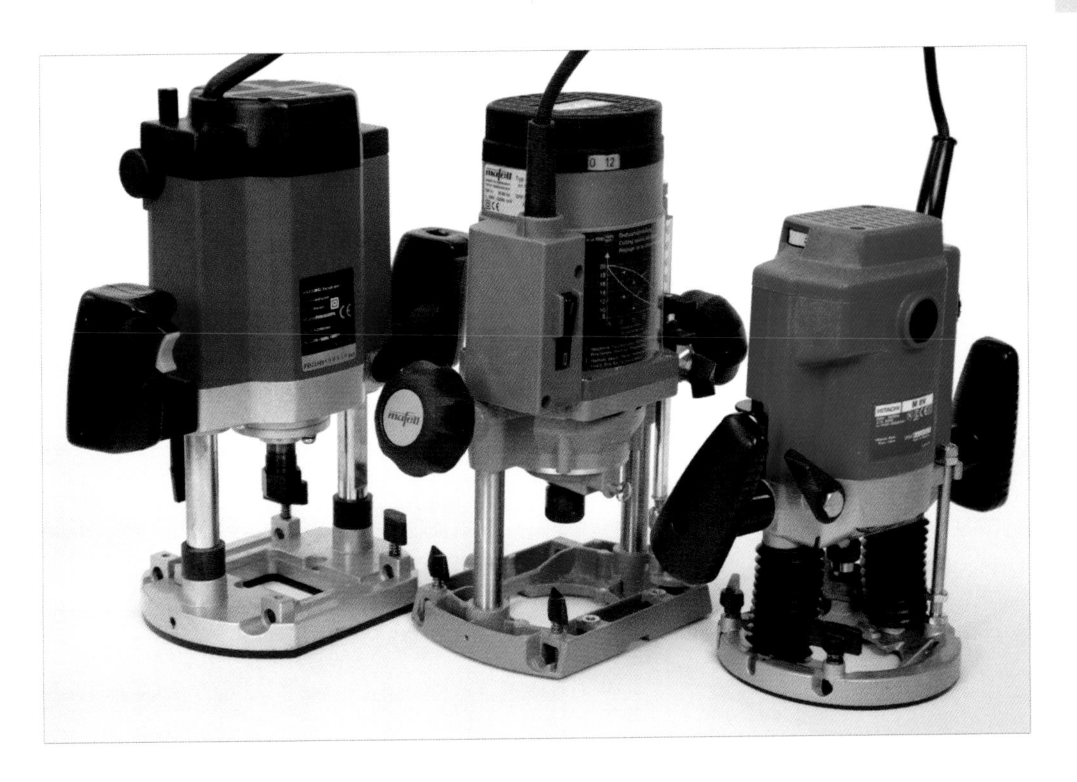

Router classification

Types of router

There are currently two styles of router available, either fixed base or plunge.

As the plunge router has overwhelming advantages compared to a fixed base model, this book is entirely devoted to the use of plunge models, used in both portable mode and when mounted under a router table.

Early machines were all of the fixed base

type, where the base clamps firmly to the body of the detachable motor forming a rigid unit.

Depth of cut is achieved by releasing the motor in the base, sliding it up or down, then re-clamping.

These routers have more limitations than the plunge type, particularly when you have to start a cut in the middle of a piece of work.

However, it can be argued that their very rigidity imparts a degree of stability not possible with the plunge router.

What is indisputable is that a fixed base router is more dangerous to use, as the cutter is always exposed below the base.

Today, the majority of routers sold into the European market are of the plunge type.

These have the motor mounted on a spring loaded base that allows the cutter to be plunged into the work at the start of the cut **1** & **2**, and then retracted safely back into the base at the end **3** & **4**.

This plunge mechanism ensures that the cutter enters and leaves the work at 90° leaving a clean and square cut. The depth of plunge can be controlled with a series of preset stops and the depth is easily locked with either a dedicated lever or by twisting one of the handles.

Power and capacity

Routers are usually classified by their power and the maximum collet capacity they will accept. e.g. 750 watt, 1/4" shank or 1800 watt, 1/2" shank.

Power is by far the most important factor that will determine how the router performs. It is measured either in Horsepower (HP) or in watts. There are 746 watts to one horsepower. The power quoted on the machine label is usually just the input power which is not what is delivered at the cutting edge.

It is the output figure that actually represents the power available for cutting, once any friction has been overcome.

From this it is apparent that the better the quality of manufacture the smaller the difference will be between the input and output figures and the more efficient the router will be.

Power will also determine how easily the rotational speed of the cutter is maintained under load. As soon as the motor starts slowing, the peripheral speed will drop and the resultant finish will suffer.

More power means less speed variation under load and therefore cleaner cutting.

You can find routers ranging from tiny 100 watt versions, up to massive 2600 watt heavy duty models so the choice is wide open.

Having settled on a particular power, the operator has to work within that envelope, but can control how the power is delivered by varying the size of the cut, the feed speed and of course by using only very sharp cutters.

Collet capacity is another useful indicator of a router's capabilities. The most universal

sizes are 1/4" and 1/2", though 6mm, 8mm, 3/8" and 12mm are also available.

Only heavy duty routers are designed to take the 3/8", 12mm and 1/2" shank cutters, the lighter duty models being restricted to 1/4" or 8mm.

There is of course no problem fitting a smaller collet into a heavy duty router, but you cannot fit a bigger collet into a small router.

It would perhaps be useful to break this huge range of power down into distinct classifications and give an indication as to uses within the group.

Tip

The diameter of the cutter shank determines how strong it will be. A large diameter cutter mounted on a thin shank will be weaker and more susceptible to higher flexing and bending stresses.

Heavy duty routers

These are usually rated around 2000 watts and are suitable for all cutter shank diameters up to 1/2", though the sheer power and high torque may lead to cutter failure if you start using small shank cutters carelessly.

They are suitable for the production of joinery components such as doors and frames, structural framing, staircases and general building work. Although they can safely be used, hand-held routers of this power tend to be large and heavy which makes them unwieldy and awkward to handle in portable mode.

Heavy duty routers are therefore ideally suited for use inverted in a router table or in an overhead stand and this is actually essential when using some of the large diameter cutters.

Medium duty routers

With input ratings between 750 and 1200 watts these routers will accept only the smaller collets, usually 1/4" but sometimes up to 8mm.

They are suitable for general furniture construction, cabinet making, and decorative moulding and inlay work.

The majority of DIY projects will be covered by a router of this size and they are powerful enough for use in machining centres or specialised jigs.

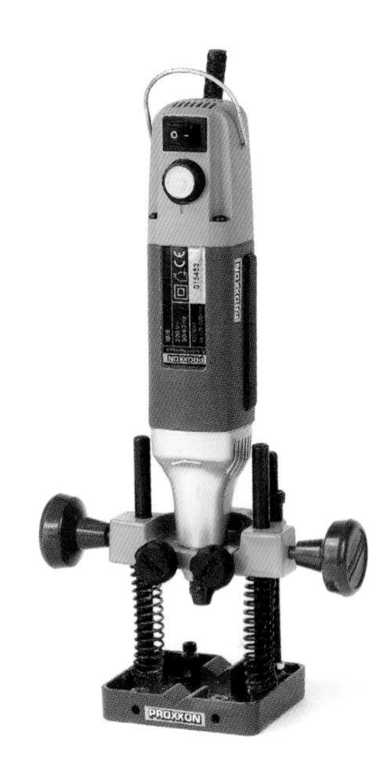

Light duty routers

This category covers the input range between 400 and 750 watts, and their lower power restricts these routers to 1/4" collets.

They should only ever be used with cutters up to a maximum of 30mm diameter, but then only for light cuts.

Many light duty routers have a removable plunge base which allows the motor to be used separately, or for fitting into a drill press for overhead routing and drilling applications.

The motor collar is normally a standard size of 43mm to allow for this.

Although being low on power there is a definite place for these routers in the workshop.

Their very lightness makes them suitable for fine and intricate work such as inlaying, as well as veneer and laminate trimming, the motor body can also be used hand-held for carving operations.

Short runs of basic moulding, grooving or rebating are quite possible, provided the router is used sensibly and not overloaded.

Micro routers

These are usually high speed modelling drills mounted in specially designed plunge base. With a power output around 200 watts they are ideal for fine hand craft operations like carving, drilling and grinding.

Many of the micro routers use a chuck rather than a collet system to hold the unique range of cutters designed for such miniature work.

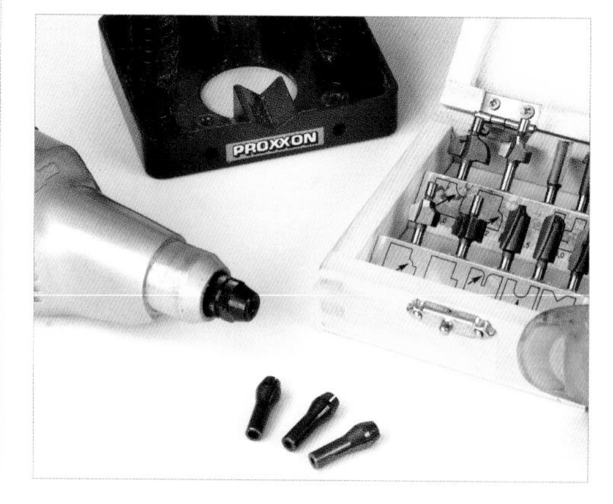

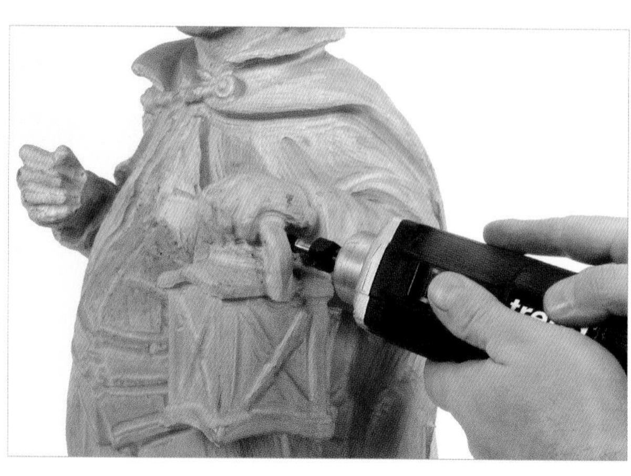

Laminate trimmers

These are essentially a light duty router, but modified solely for trimming purposes in the construction of laminate faced furniture.

However, they are still a precision tool with various types of non-plunge bases which have micro adjustments for cutting depth, roller guides for circular work, and riser plates or skis for vertical and horizontal laminate edge trimming.

Laminate trimmers are designed for use with smaller diameter cutters, their input ratings are around the 500 watt mark with just a single speed.

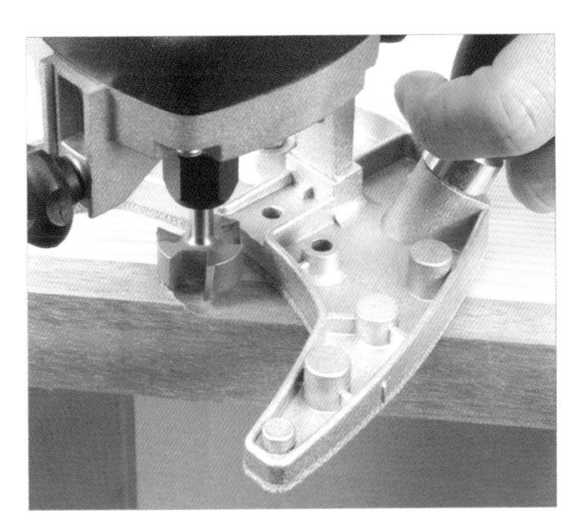

Features and controls

Most routers share the same broad range of features and controls, all of which are designed to help you operate the machine both accurately and safely.

However, the layout and ease of operation of these controls does vary enormously from router to router and you will find some arrangements suit you better than others.

Factors such as the size of your hand, grip strength and whether you are left or right handed can make a tremendous difference to the handling when you are using the router. For this reason it is always best to get a 'hands on' test of a router before you finally buy it. If all the controls are easy to operate you will then be able to concentrate fully on the work, rather than battle with the switch or plunge lock.

Side handles

These are used to steady and manoeuvre the router during a cut and must therefore be comfortable to grip. On smaller routers they are usually simple round knobs, but on larger, more powerful machines they tend to be elongated.

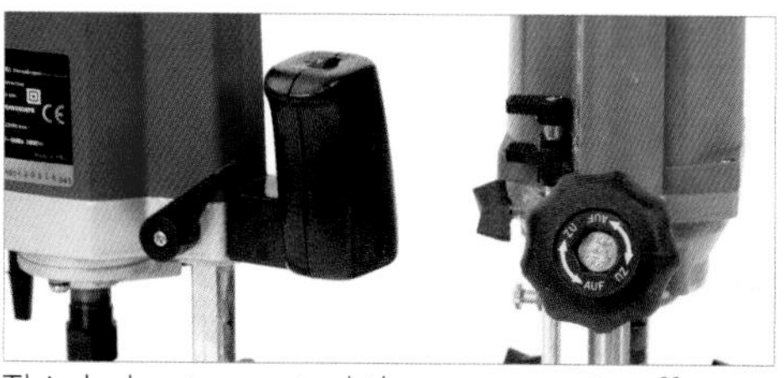

This helps to control the gyroscopic effect of the spinning motor, which tries to turn the router in the operator's hands when it is lifted out of a cut.

Some machines may also allow you to adjust the orientation of their handles for maximum comfort.

D shaped main handles are easy to use and make the router very controllable, but this arrangement tends to be restricted to fixed base routers only.

There is some debate as to the positioning of the side handles. Having them low down on the router body gives you much better control for hand work, but in this position they may possibly interfere if you start using the router along a straightedge or in some jigs. I have never found this to be a real problem, but in any case such handles are usually removable.

Better routers have both the plunge lock and on/off switch built into the side handles, so as well as providing a comfortable grip for guiding the router, these handles have to be shaped to allow easy access to these controls.

Plunge lock

This locks the movement of the spring loaded router body on the plunge bars to determine the depth of cut. As the router is often plunged into the work at the beginning of a cut, it is important that the lock lever can be operated easily without pushing the router off line as you do so.

Every manufacturer seems to have their own design of plunge lock, with some being very much easier to use than others.

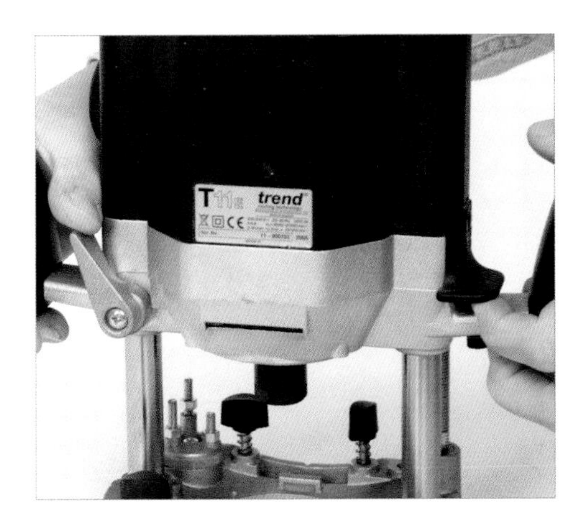

There are three main variations of lock mechanism:

i. A separate lever

ii. A latch built into the handle

iii. A twist lock on one of the side handles

The latter two options are the easiest to operate, particularly if you are trying to adjust the router mid cut. Personally, I have always found that a twist lock on one of the side handles is the most intuitive, but try them all out and make sure you find one that suits you.

On/Off switch

Router switches vary almost as much as the plunge lock types, but whatever the design, it is vital that it is easily accessible without removing your hand from the side handle.

For this reason switches that are actually built into the handle are best and those that incorporate a safety lock-off button are better still.

These require you to operate the side button before the router can be switched on and therefore prevent the possibility of accidental starting if you pick up the machine carelessly, or knock it as you put it down on the bench.

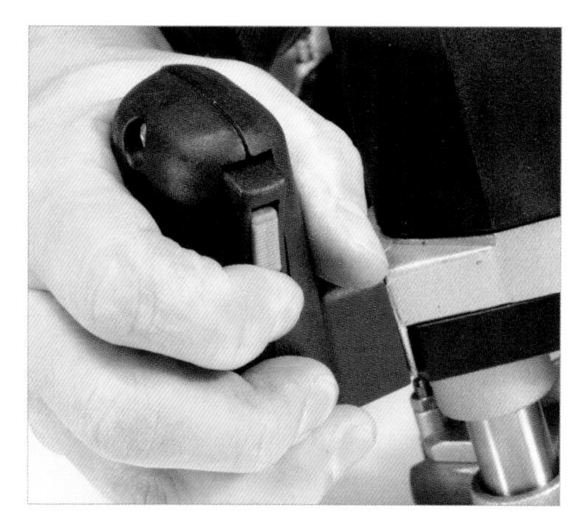

The 'dead man' switch that requires continual holding to operate may seem a safer option, but it becomes tiring for long runs and is awkward if you want to use the router mounted under a table. In this case you have to hold it on using a separate trigger lock and then operate the machine via the safety switch on the table.

Also, some operations may require you to change hands part way through a cut, for example when circle cutting. In which case, the router will stop and restart if you are using a dead man switch and this may leave a distinct cutter mark or burn unless you are very careful.

More conventional switches include toggle or slide switches, usually shielded against accidental knocking on, but do make sure you can access this type of switch and operate it with one finger. You should not have to change your grip to operate the on/off switch.

Depth stop

On a plunge router it is essential to have a depth stop that can be preset for your maximum cut. On cheaper routers this is just a simple rod with a crude graduated scale.

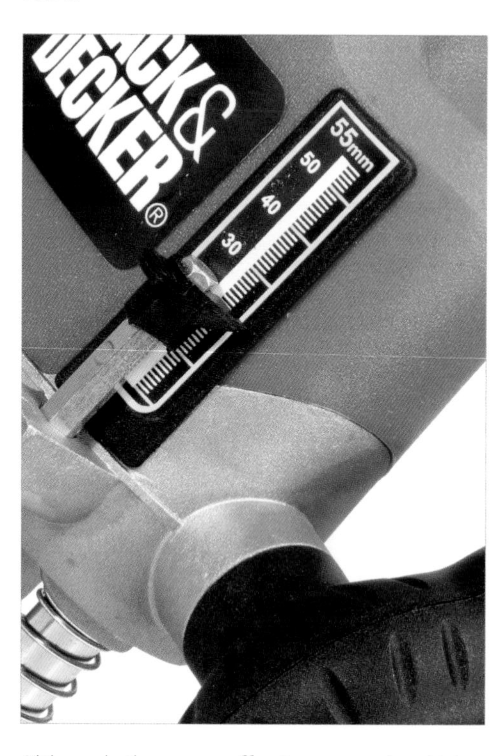

Although these are effective, care should be taken with the scale, as it can bear no relation to the amount of cutter projection.

Better routers allow you to zero out the depth scale with the bit touching the work surface before you start. These then give you a true reading for the depth of plunge, rather than a comparative one.

Some form of micro adjustment built into the depth stop is useful if you are making precise cuts, for example when inlaying.

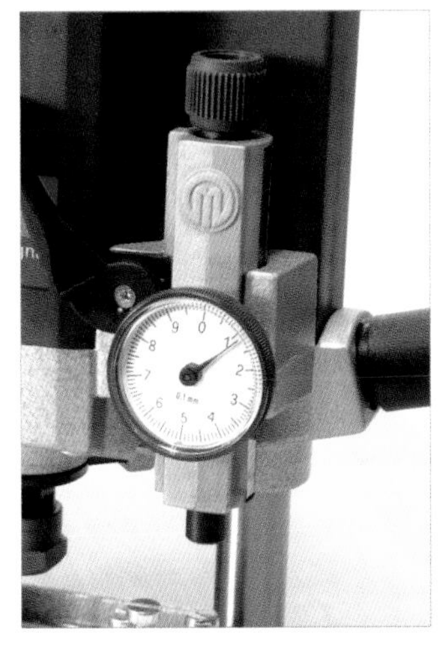

In this case, a geared adjustment mechanism which incorporates a vernier or dial gauge makes accurate setting a simple process without having to physically measure the amount of cutter projection.

Most routers use the depth stop in conjunction with a multi position turret, which allows several depths to be preset.

This allows quick resetting of the cutting depth when routing in stages, or for stepped recessing for cabinet fittings.

The turret simply rotates on a 'click' location stud to line up under the depth stop, each tower of the turret being individually adjustable for height.

Variable speed control

The router operates at very high spindle speeds in order to produce a clean and precise surface finish. The ideal is a peripheral speed on the cutter of around 1000 metres per minute, which necessitates spindle speeds in excess of 20,000 rpm for smaller cutters.

Large diameter cutters have a far higher peripheral speed than smaller ones, so in order to maintain the correct and safe cutting speed, it is necessary to have some control over the spindle speed.

Cutters that are run too fast will burn both the wood and themselves. Conversely, those that are run too slowly will also leave a poor finish and may even snatch at the work.

Most manufacturers now offer their routers with electronic variable speed control, which allows the spindle speed to be adjusted to suit the cutter in use, and/or the type of material being cut.

Early variable speed controls were very simple but prone to failure, and many lost power at low speeds.

Modern electronic controllers now incorporate load compensation systems that allow the pre-set spindle speed to be monitored and automatically compensates for any change in speed as the load on the cutter varies.

As well as providing a much more uniform finish on the work, the 'soft start' and smooth running characteristics of this type of control reduces the initial jerk experienced when starting up a high speed motor. The motor gradually ramps up to full speed rather than instantaneously kicking in at full revs. This makes it far more comfortable to work with in comparison to a single speed machine and also reduces the stress on both motor and bearings.

The control for speed is usually a simple rotary dial, which shows several speed positions. You will have to find the actual speed for each position by looking in the router handbook, as they all vary. Some machines may actually have it marked on the motor body. In reality, experience will soon allow you to make adjustments whilst you work, as the precise speed is not critical provided the finish is good and the cutter is not burning the material.

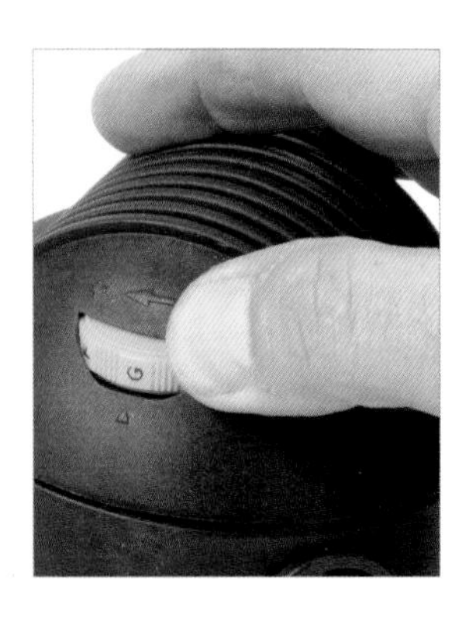

Spindle lock

For fitting or removing cutters it is necessary to hold the spindle still whilst operating the collet.

Older routers had no provision for locking the spindle, so cutter changing required the use of two spanners, one to hold the spindle, the other to operate the collet.

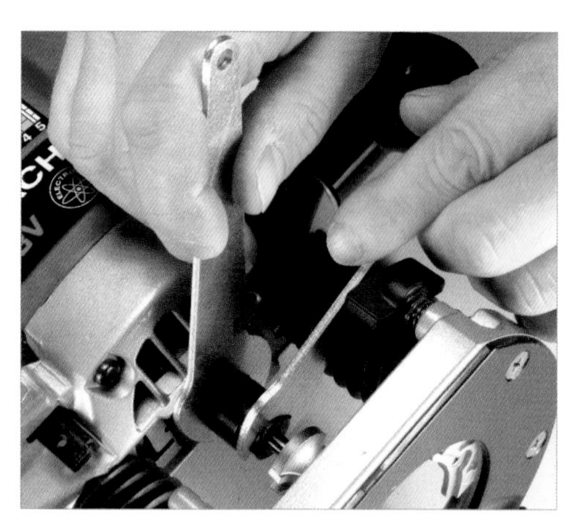

Newer machines now incorporate a sliding spindle lock that allows much easier and quicker cutter changing, requiring only a single spanner.

Baseplate

The baseplate is another important component of the router.

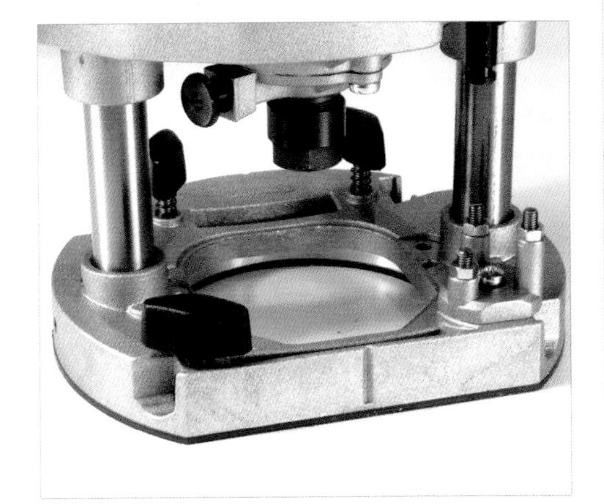

It must be strong enough to take the vertical plunge columns and is machined to take a range of accessories like the side-fence, template bushes and dust extraction hood.

The actual shape of the base is not critical, some are completely round, whilst others have one or two flat faces.

However it is vital that the baseplate is concentric to the cutter, to allow you to guide the router against a straightedge or jig.

The size of the central hole is another important consideration. Obviously the bigger this is, the larger the cutter you can fit, provided it is within the power envelope of the router.

A large cutter opening will also allow better visibility of the cutting edge during a cut.

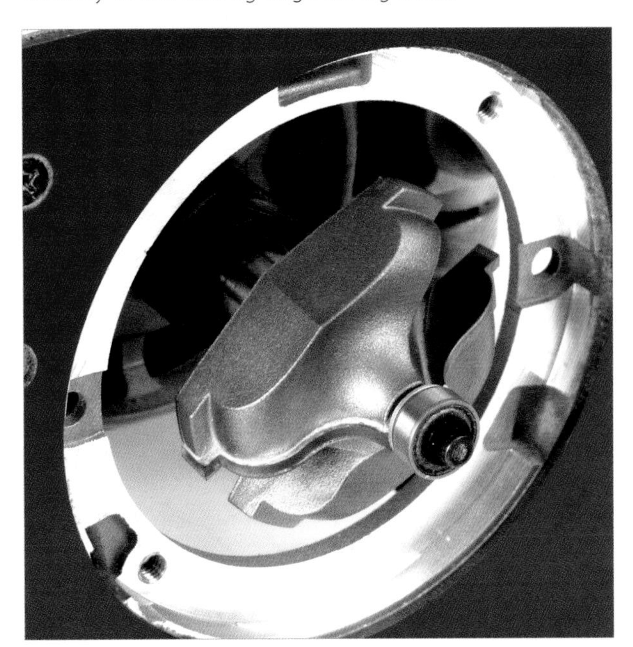

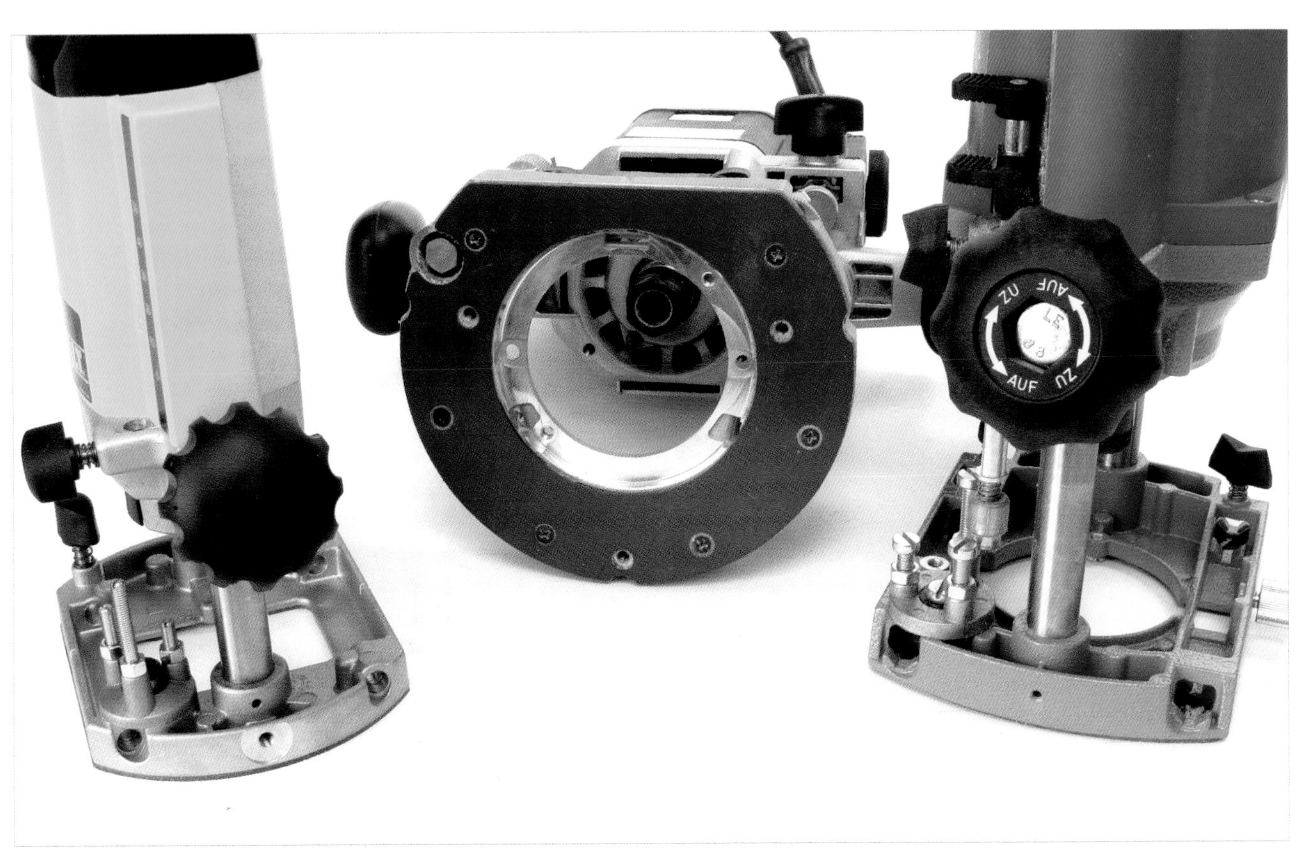

However, if the cutter opening is too big, there may be problems with regard to support when you are working with narrow stock, or on the corner of boards.

A large base opening should have the facility to mount a reduction plate so standard guide bushes can be fitted for template operations.

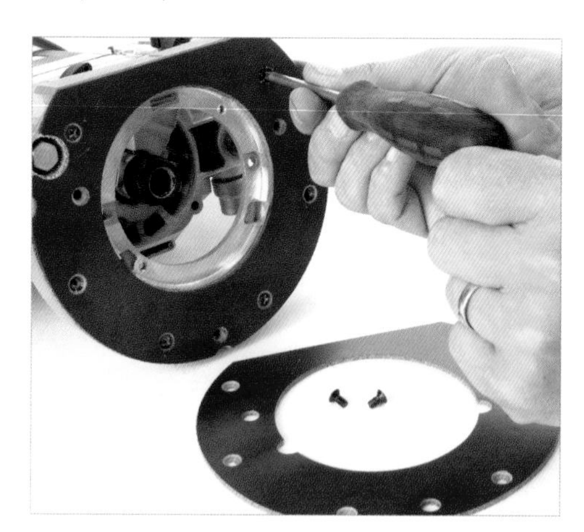

The plastic sub-base should be replaceable as it will inevitably wear or chip, and as it is the datum of the whole routing process, it must be in good condition at all times.

You will often need to attach your own shop made sub-bases to fit jigs or templates, or you may wish to fit the router under a table, so the base needs to be drilled and tapped to accommodate these requirements.

Once again, every manufacturer seems to have their own system for this but Trend have developed their own base configuration, (TBC) which other manufacturers now seem to be adopting.

This allows you to fit a whole range of jigs and accessories without having to keep drilling and tapping the base yourself. If your machine is not TBC, you can buy a universal sub-base called a Unibase to convert it. This then affords the utmost versatility for fixing accessories and guide bushes to virtually any make or model of router.

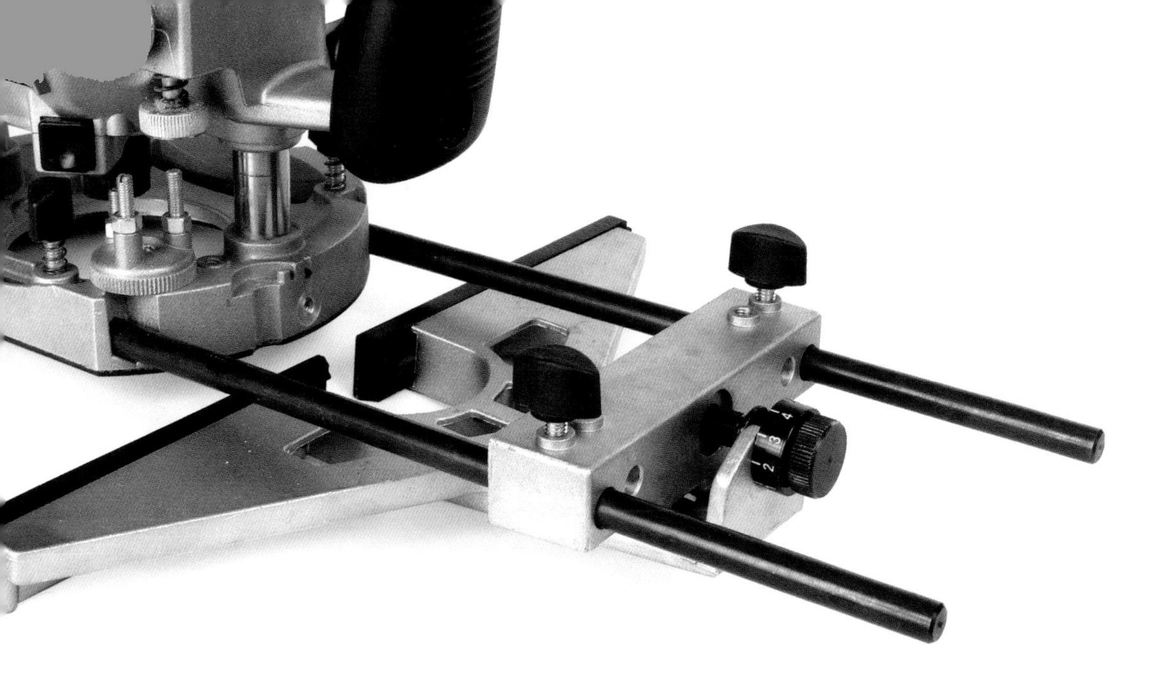

Side-fence

Your router should come with a side-fence that acts as a guide for making grooves, rebates or moulding cuts parallel to the edge of straight-sided work pieces.

The quality and construction of these fences seems to vary enormously, from a plain but adequate one, to a very sophisticated version.

For precise work, the side-fence should be fitted with a micro adjuster and the faces should be adjustable to allow the cutter aperture to be closed up for maximum support.

If you feel your router fence is a let down compared with the rest of the machine, there are several very good quality independently made fences that are available to fit virtually all makes and models, but although excellent, these are often very expensive.

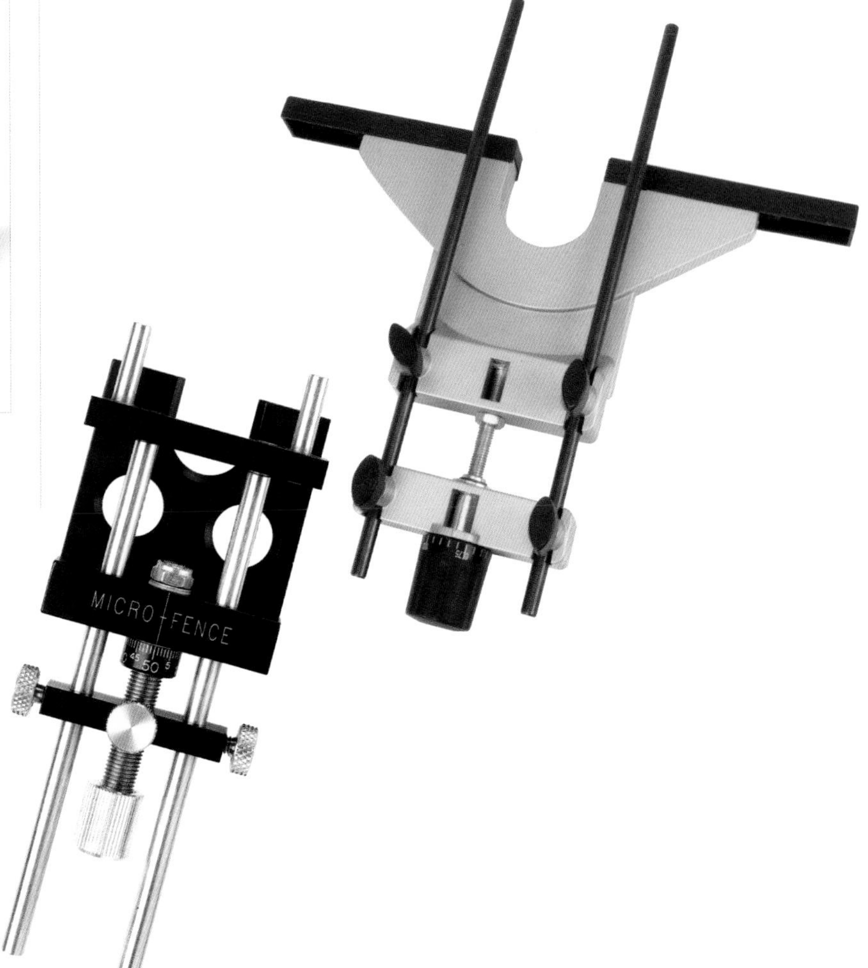

Dust extraction

Dust extraction has become quite an issue with all modern power tools and it is particularly important on a router.

Cheaper machines usually have some form of detachable hood fitted, which although made of clear plastic does restrict visibility of the cut and sometimes interferes with cutter changing.

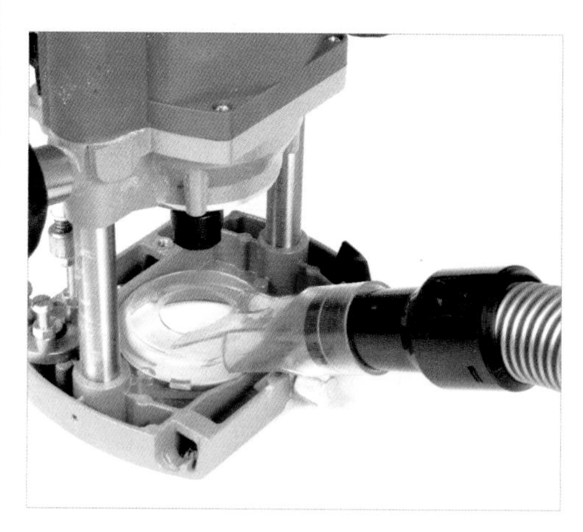

The dust spout on the hood needs to be attached to a suitable vacuum extractor via a flexible hose, which can make the set-up slightly cumbersome.

There are a few professional routers with built in extraction ports, taking the dust out through an enlarged plunge column. These are much more convenient to use but this is reflected in the cost of the router.

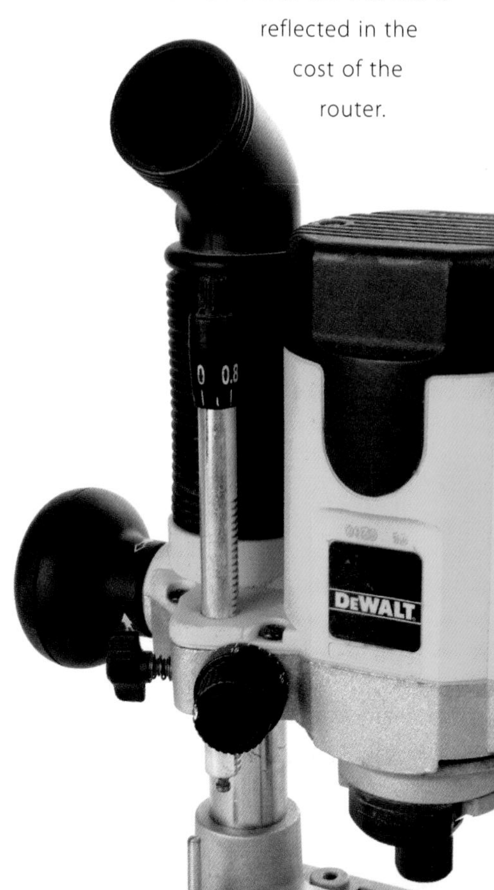

Fine height adjuster

Some routers already have a fine height adjuster built in to the body of the machine, but if not, there is probably one available as an accessory, they just fit onto one of the turrets of the depth stop.

They are essential for making precise adjustments, particularly when the router is mounted under a table and you will not be able to use some of the additional jigs, like the dovetailer, without one.

Collets

Cutters are held in the end of the router spindle using a precision ground collet which is machined to take one specific shank diameter only.

The collets are available in both metric and imperial internal sizes to suit the range of available cutter shank diameters. Being so size specific, you will have to change the collet to suit each shank. In the UK the common collet sizes are 1/4" and 1/2" whereas the rest of central Europe seems to have settled on 6mm, 8mm and 12mm as the standard.

Generally, your router will be supplied with one or more collets appropriate to its capacity. Wherever possible, buy spares and replacements from the original manufacturer or from a specialist routing supplier.

Always choose top quality collets as cheap substitutes can cause irreversible damage to both the router and the cutter shank. There are many different designs of collet, each with its own method of gripping the cutter.

The better the quality of collet the better the alignment of the cutter will be. Remember that a tiny amount of eccentricity on a cutter revolving in excess of 20,000 rpm will set up significant vibration.

As well as being uncomfortable to use, this will affect the long term life of the router bearings and a poor quality collet may well cause the router bit to cut oversize and will also have a detrimental effect on the quality of finish.

For maximum support the collet needs to have as big as possible surface area in contact with the cutter shank. This is the key to the whole business of cutter security and will prevent any suggestion of cutter 'creep', where the cutter gradually moves in the collet during use.

Compare the collet sizes from a budget router and a top of the range model to see the differences. The better quality one is at least twice the length of the other and it goes without saying what the effects will be as regards bit holding, leverage and consequent vibration.

The best collets are made from high quality tempered sprung steel that will withstand constant tightening and un-tightening.

Softer, poor quality collets will quickly wear to a 'bell mouth' that reduces both alignment and grip and in extreme cases may allow the cutter to spin in the collet, which will damage both the cutter and the collet.

The number of slits in the collet has quite a bearing on its ability to grip. Collets with just a few slits cannot provide a uniform grip on the shank and often won't release the cutter properly.

This problem is exacerbated by the use of poor quality cutters, which may have wide tolerances in their shank diameter.

The consequent uneven pressure will mark or burr the cutter shank, leading to other problems.

Multi slit collets have an equal number of slits machined alternatively from the top and bottom edges. This produces a flexible cage that grips the cutter shank with firm, even pressure around the full circumference of the shank.

Collet systems

There are effectively three types of collet, the simplest of which is the one piece system. This screwed collet fits directly into the armature of the motor, the tapered housing squeezing down on the collet as you tighten up. But it does have some limitations, not the least of which is that any damage to the collet also damages the motor spindle so repairs can be expensive.

A more common system is the two piece collet which uses a separate locknut to compress the collet down onto the cutter shank. This is probably the most common system on the lower specification routers and is quite adequate provided you treat it with care.

Better machines will have a full length collet with its tightening nut permanently held in place. These are typically made from top quality steel with multiple, long slits for maximum cutter security, and have the advantage that they will release the cutter from the collet as you un-tighten.

This often causes confusion because it actually works via a double lock system. This means that when you first un-tighten the locking nut, the cutter remains firmly in place and the unwary start trying to force it out. In fact you have to keep unscrewing the nut until it goes tight again and then use a spanner for a second time to finally release the cutter. This is by far the best system when you get used to it and reduces any tendency for the cutters to jam in the collet.

Good quality collets are not cheap, but you can convert a big collet to a smaller one using a tubular reducing sleeve.

Although these are more economical than the cost of a new collet they often fail to grip the shank securely and can result in cutter misalignment.

Collet extensions allow the cutter to protrude further from the base of the router and increase the depth of cut, particularly when mounted in an inverted router table.

However unless the extension is machined to an extremely high standard, it is unlikely to hold the cutter in true alignment to the spindle axis and may cause vibration. So only use them where absolutely necessary.

Maintenance and trouble shooting

Your router is a precision machine that is usually made to work extremely hard in adverse conditions, so it makes sense to try and prolong its life with a routine of regular preventative maintenance. Little and often is the key to keeping the router in good shape.

The main enemy is dust and debris and this then often gets mixed with resin deposits from the timber to form a hard deposit that sticks to casings, screw threads and moving parts.

If you ignore it, the router becomes stiff and jerky to operate, the switch gradually seizes up, the cutters start jamming in the collet and all enjoyment in its use is lost.

Basic maintenance is not difficult and there is no need to dismantle the machine. All you have to do is give it all a thorough cleaning on a regular basis. However, repairs are best left to a qualified service engineer particularly if the router is still under guarantee.

When you are cleaning the router don't be tempted to blast it all over with a high pressure air line, as this just tends to force more debris deeper into the machine and could damage the delicate windings and other electrical components as well as embedding dust into the grease packed bearings.

Even with the use of extraction, dust is pulled into the router by the cooling fan so try and suck it back out through the ventilation slots with a vacuum cleaner.

Do the same on the outside components of the router having first loosened it all with a small stiff brush.

If the resin deposits are severe use white spirit or a proprietary resin remover to break them down, but keep these solvents well away from the internal motor parts and the plastic casings.

Here is a checklist for more specific cleaning and maintenance.

Plunge columns

It is essential that the router plunges freely and without jerking, so make sure there are no sticky deposits on the plunge columns, scraping them off with a plastic scraper or a piece of stiff card.

Never use wire wool or abrasive paper on these columns as this will leave scratches that actually aggravate the problem further. Once clean, apply a coat of thin oil or preferably a dry lubricating spray (PTFE) to keep them sliding smoothly.

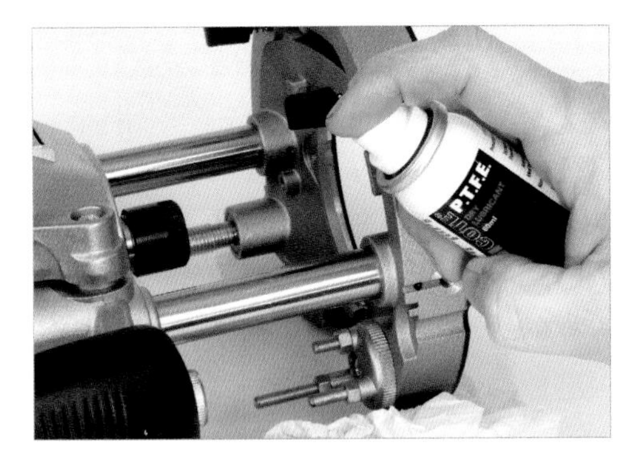

Regularly check for side play in the plunge columns, any excessive play can only be cured by replacing the plunge bushes. Also make sure that the plunge lock operates smoothly and is not marking or burring the face of the columns.

Bearings

The top and bottom bearings are packed with grease and sealed for life, so do not try and lubricate them in any way or you will do more harm than good.

Potential bearing problems are usually first detected with your ears. Any change in speed and motor noise when it is free running, particularly intermittent noise, should immediately arouse suspicion.

Then check for unusual vibration whilst cutting. Modern bearings are actually very reliable, but they have to work particularly hard on a router, so if you have any doubts have them changed immediately by a qualified service engineer, or you will end up with expensive damage to both the spindle and armature.

Tip

Physically check the spindle for play by trying to waggle it with a long cutter in place and feel for any rough spots as you turn it by hand. Make sure the router is unplugged!

Motor brushes

Excessive sparking from the area around the brushes may indicate damage or wear, so they must be replaced before the commutator on the motor spindle is damaged.

Changing or inspecting the brushes is a simple process and only requires you to remove the brush caps or the top motor casing. Check the manufacturer's manual.

Make sure that when you replace the brushes the springs are not damaged or trapped so that the brush can slide freely in its housing.

There may be some initial sparking from new brushes as they 'bed in' and loose carbon dust breaks away, but this will soon disappear as the brush assumes the shape of the commutator.

Switch

The switch is one area particularly susceptible to dust build up and it should be given a thorough cleaning with a vacuum cleaner in the same way as the motor housing.

Slide switches in particular seem to suffer from intermittent operation if dust accumulates on the grease of the contacts.

These are usually easy enough to dismantle and clean but get it properly serviced if you don't feel confident doing it yourself.

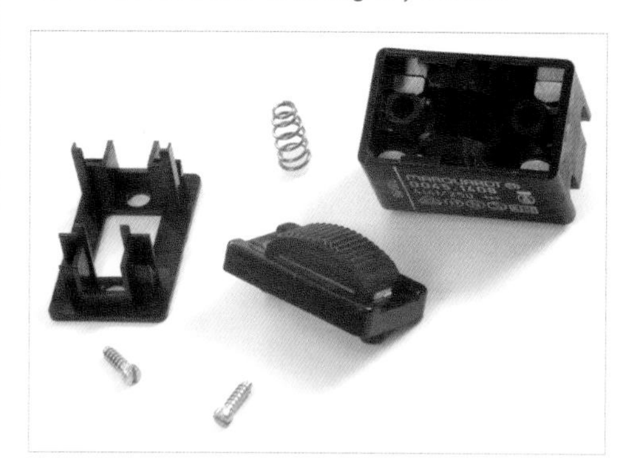

Clamp screws

All the clamping screws for the fence rods and depth stop should be fitted with anti-vibration springs to ensure that they don't work loose whilst the router is running, particularly if you are not using the fence.

The danger is that they gradually unscrew and then drop into the revolving cutter, so make sure the springs are in place and replace any that are missing.

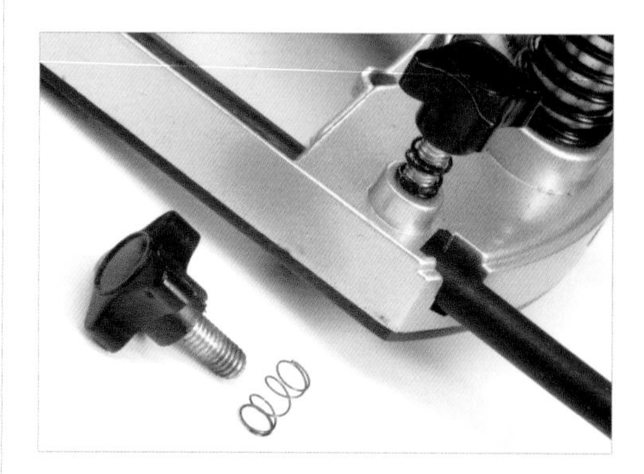

Baseplate facing

The plastic facing on the router base is designed to ensure that it doesn't mark the surface of the timber as you run the router over it. However it can quickly wear or become contaminated with resin. Any severe scratches can be flatted off with very fine abrasive paper wrapped over a flat block and resin deposits removed with a suitable solvent. Then spray the base with PTFE spray to help it slide freely over the workpiece.

Collets

We have already seen just how important the collet is for smooth and accurate running of the router and poor collet maintenance has been shown to be one of the most common causes of cutter damage and breakage.

Regular inspection and cleaning of the slits of the collet is essential and you can now buy inexpensive kits that contain the necessary resin remover and corrosion inhibitor, as well as purpose made brass brushes for each collet size. This will remove any resin deposits or sawdust that could prevent the collet closing down evenly and gripping properly. Warning signs are brown markings on the cutter shanks, shank slippage, bit or collet seizures and in extreme cases, shank breakage.

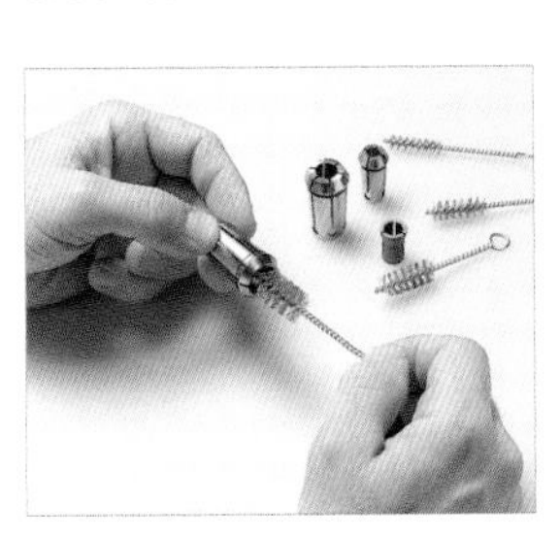

Check that there are no burrs or scratches on the tapered faces and that the internal spindle taper and locknut thread are clean and undamaged, as these are all factors that can affect the security of the cutter in the collet. If either the collet or locknut is found

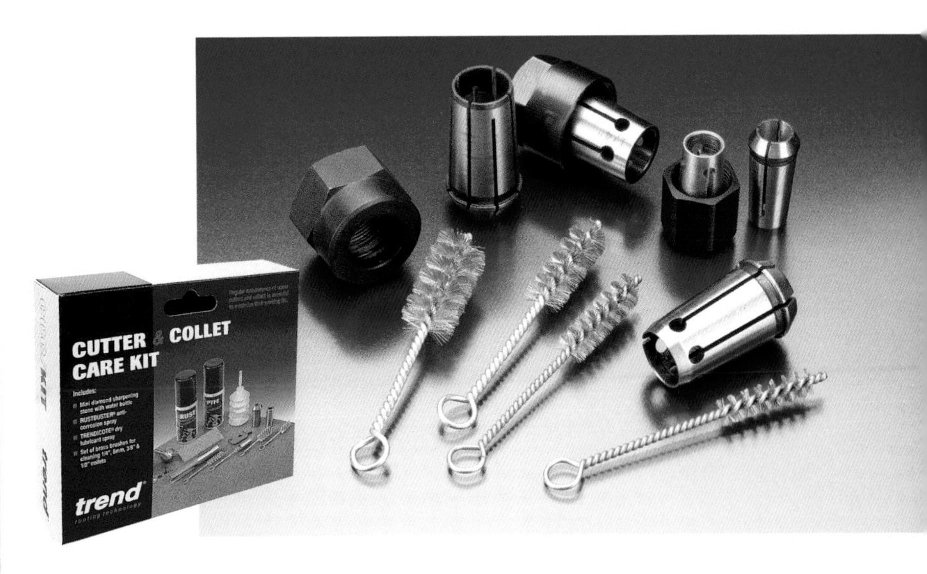

to be faulty they must be changed as soon as possible. Do not use cutters with damaged shanks, particularly in new collets as this just transfers the problem.

Power cable

Constant movement of power tools often leads to fatigue and damage to the mains lead, particularly in the area where it enters the motor or plug. Like switch problems this is often characterised by intermittent starting and running. Examine the cable and strain relief area carefully and replace if necessary.

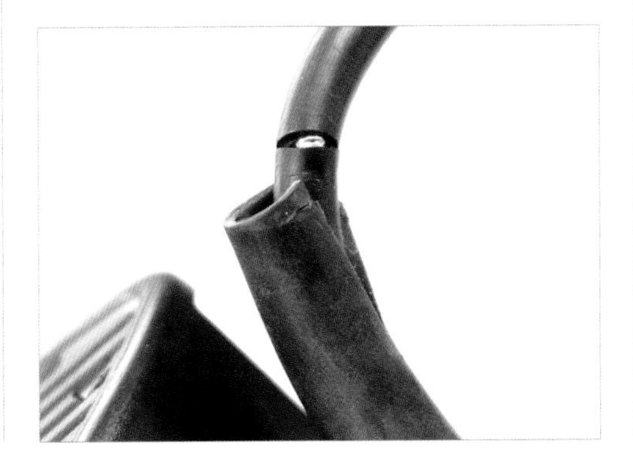

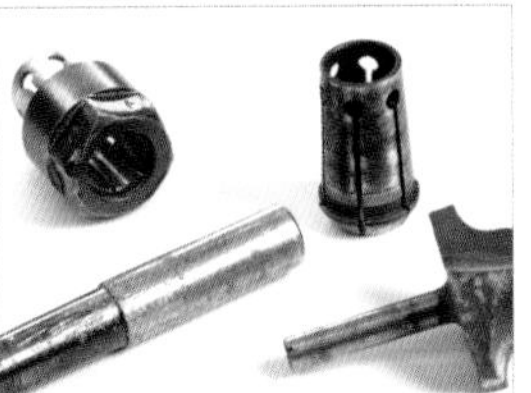

Tip

Remember that the continual heating up and cooling down from using blunt cutters can eventually affect the temper of the spring steel in the collet and reduce its elasticity. If you find that your collet is starting to need excessive tightening before it will grip, it is time to replace it.

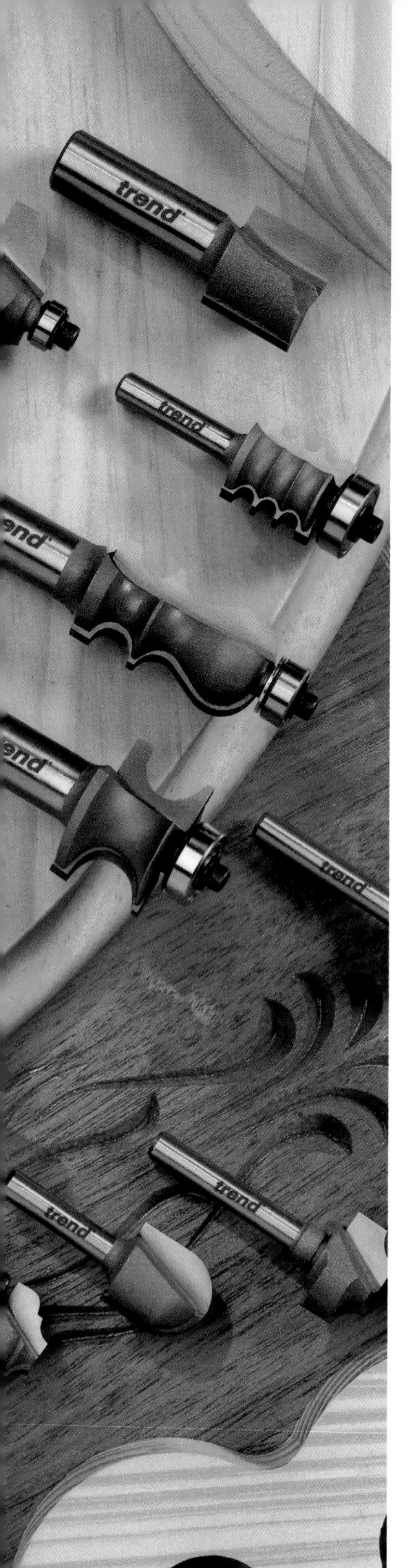

2. ROUTER CUTTERS

Since it is the router cutter that does all the work in producing your chosen profile, it is worth looking in some detail at the various types of cutter, as well as their construction and most importantly, their care and maintenance.

Cutter terminology

You also need to understand some of the basic terminology relating to cutters or 'bits' as they are often called. There is no distinction between these two terms and they will be used synonymously throughout this book.

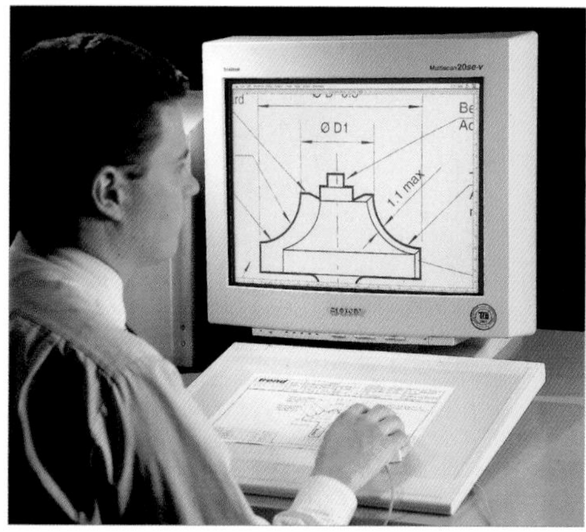

Years of intensive research and development have led to a massive proliferation in the range of cutters available to both the professional and amateur user, and this progress seems set to continue further, with more innovative designs and profiles being added all the time.

Much of this development is initiated for the benefit of the industrial sector, but some of the advances do filter down to the level of the home woodworker and various cutter ranges are now on offer, differing in both price and quality to cater for their various needs.

However, cutters still tend to be relatively expensive items, especially the larger and more complex profiles, so it is worth choosing carefully before you buy.

Better quality cutters are more likely to do the job efficiently and will continue to give good service for many years, so they are always more cost effective .

It is difficult to over emphasise the amount of work a router bit will do in its life, but at 28,000 rpm the edge will make 466 cuts per second! Multiply this up over several years of use and you can see why you need to buy the very best quality.

Some cutters are designed for just one specific use, but with careful selection you can often cut several different profiles from one cutter to increase the cost effectiveness even further.

Router cutters are designed to produce a really smooth clean finish, which can only be achieved by grinding them to very precise cutting and clearance angles. These angles represent the optimum compromise between sharpness and durability, as well as optimising overall strength and waste clearance.

As they are capable of removing a lot of material, it is important that this waste, in the form of tiny chips, is removed quickly and efficiently.

One of the other main criteria in cutter design is to minimise friction, which is generated both by the cutter passing through the timber and by the build up of waste being trapped behind the cutting edge.

Excessive friction will cause the cutting edges to overheat, leading to tempering and consequent loss of sharpness, as well as scorching the surface of the cut.

Cutting edges

As with all cutting tools, the edge is ground to provide maximum sharpness, but at the same time retaining enough support to make sure that the keen edge is retained for as long as possible.

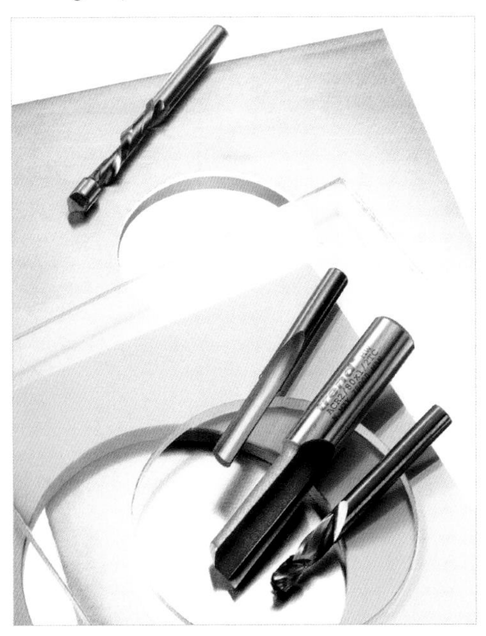

Cutters may have one, two or multiple cutting edges, which are referred to as flutes. Each edge on a multi-bladed cutter must be ground to the same height and angle to ensure they do the same amount of work. Any inconsistency here will reduce the efficiency of the cutter and also affect the balance, causing vibration that will affect the quality of the cut.

Tip

Cutters without any bottom cut facility can only be fed into the work from the side or edge, they will just burn if you try and plunge them into the surface.

Some cutters are designed for plunging into the work and these need bottom cutting edges. They are much harder to manufacture, as it is difficult to grind the small tip area properly. Cutters designed specifically for boring or plunge work have a separate tip or tips, brazed across the bottom of the cutter.

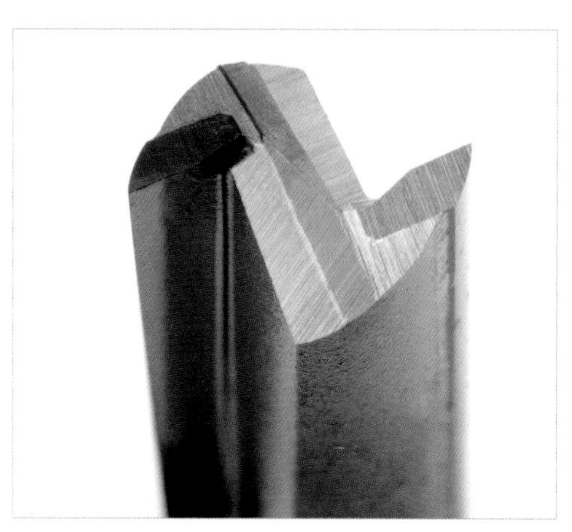

Rake angle

This is the angle at which the cutting edge meets the surface of the workpiece and will vary on different cutters, depending on the application. An acute or positive rake angle will give a fast cutting action and remove material quickly, ideal for work in solid timber. A lower or negative rake angle will produce a slower cut with more of a scraping action. This configuration is more suited for laminate trimming and edge finishing work.

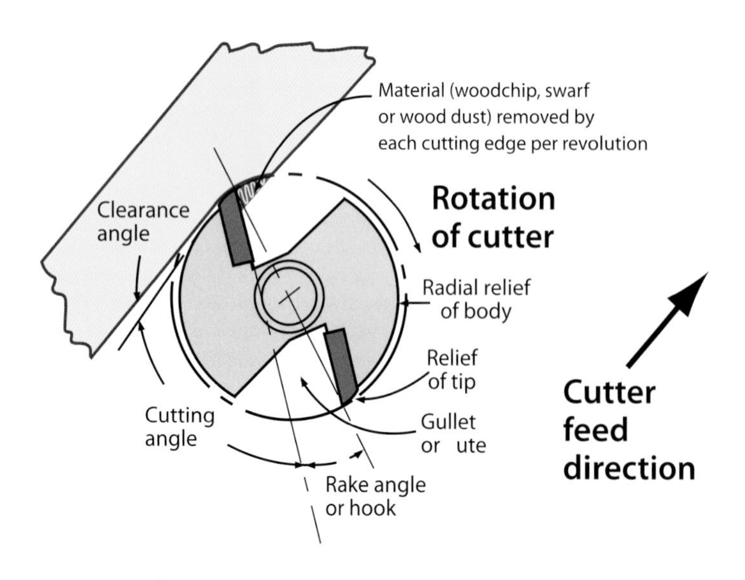

Clearance and radial relief angles

The clearance angle is the angle immediately behind the cutting tip, whilst the radial relief refers to the angle over the remaining back face of the cutter.

Both these angles are necessary to prevent the area behind the cutting tip rubbing on the face of the work and to stop waste becoming trapped.

Shear and spiral angles

The cutting edge of a straight flute cutter produces an impact cut against the face of the workpiece every time it revolves, leaving the surface as a series of tiny hollows or ripples. This finish is virtually undetectable and is good enough for most woodworking applications. However, a finer and smoother finish can be obtained by using shear cutters that have the flutes set at an angle to the vertical axis.

This shear angle produces a slicing action that minimises the hollowing effect and cuts the timber much more cleanly, particularly important if you are machining veneer faced boards. They also cut more smoothly and with far less vibration.

Spiral cutters take this one stage further and produce a super-smooth finish, as they are able to make a continuous uninterrupted cut, entirely eliminating any ripples. They are most suited for cutting hard materials such as dense hardwoods, aluminium and plastics and are particularly effective for plunge through cut-outs. They do however create more torque and make the router slightly more difficult to control for hand held operations.

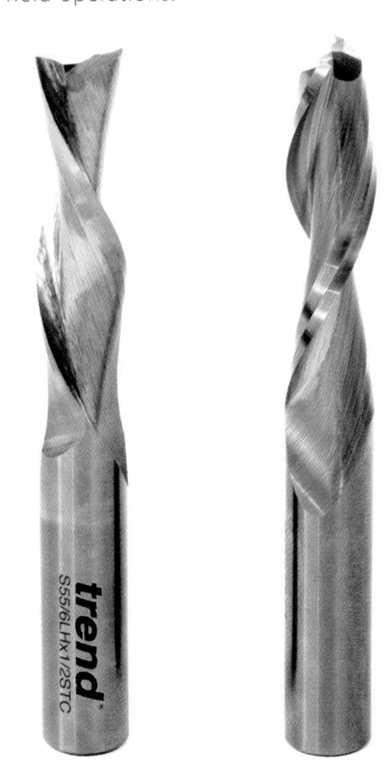

They can be either down-cut or up-cut depending on the direction of spiral. Down-cut spirals will force the chips down into the work, but will minimise spelching and breakout along the top edge of the work. Up-cut versions obviously give better chip dispersion, but can feather the top and may also try and lift the work.

Cutter balance

It is vital that all cutters are dynamically balanced so that they rotate true to the axis of the shank. Any small amount of run-out will set up vibration that is magnified by the speed of rotation and shows up as chatter marks on the cut surface. As well as being uncomfortable to work with, continued use of poorly balanced cutters may also damage the router bearings.

Chip limiting

To meet modern safety standards EN 847, cutters should be produced with the main body just slightly less in diameter than the cutter edge.

This limits the amount of 'bite' that the cutter can take to 1.1 mm on cutters above 16mm diameter, reducing the risk of the cutter either snatching or kicking back.

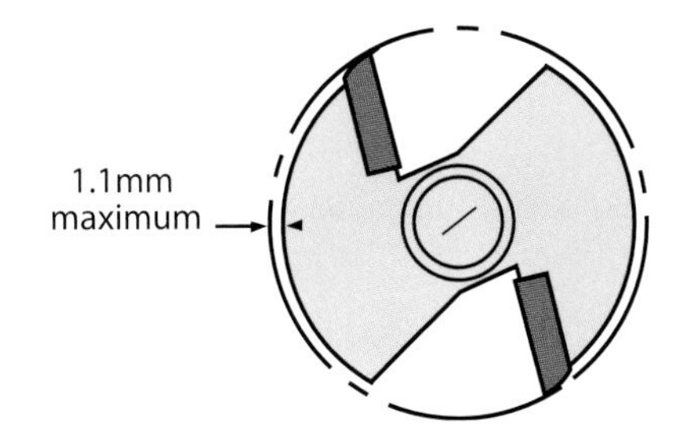

The extra weight of these safety cutters does have other advantages as well. They cut more smoothly with less vibration and any excess heat is quickly dissipated by the extra metal, which will also improve the edge holding characteristics.

Cutter shank diameters

Most router cutters are available with a choice of shank diameters, usually 1/4", 3/8" or 1/2". However for strength purposes some of the bigger profiles are only available on 1/2" shanks. Routers below about 1200 watts are usually restricted to smaller diameter shanks.

A more recent introduction has been cutters with 8mm shanks that allow larger and more complex profiles to be used in smaller capacity machines, but you should always check that they are not too big for the power output of the router. There are some other metric sized shanks available as well, so care must be taken to match the shank size perfectly to the diameter of the collet. Metric shanks will not fit in imperial collets and vice versa, although they may look very similar.

Plain and bearing guided cutters

For most hand-held routing applications, you can use plain cutters that are guided by the fence, or some other type of guide like a guide bush fixed to the router base. This will then follow the edge of a pre-cut template or pattern.

Guided cutters have either a solid pin on the end, or a bearing fitted above or below the cutting edges.

You can then run this against the existing workpiece edges whether straight or curved. Again, one can use it running along a template to cut out a particular shape.

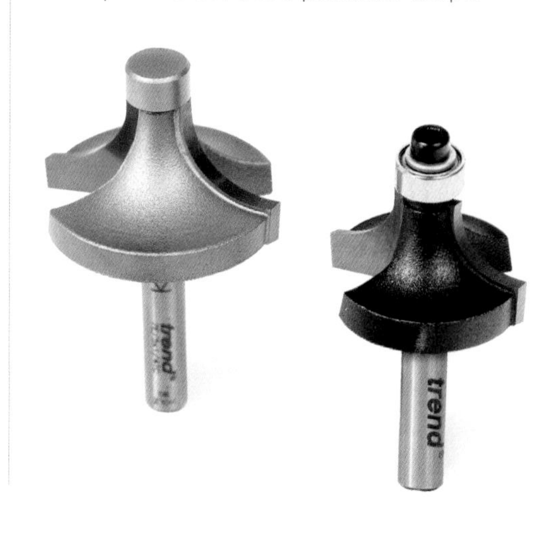

Flutes and cutting speed

The cutting speed of the router is not only dependent on the rotational speed of the router itself, but also on the number of cutting edges or flutes on the cutter.

Single flute cutters are usually produced in straight profiles only. Because the flute is relatively large, and the cutter is generally much stronger, they have good chip clearance properties and can be fed into the wood at a faster speed.

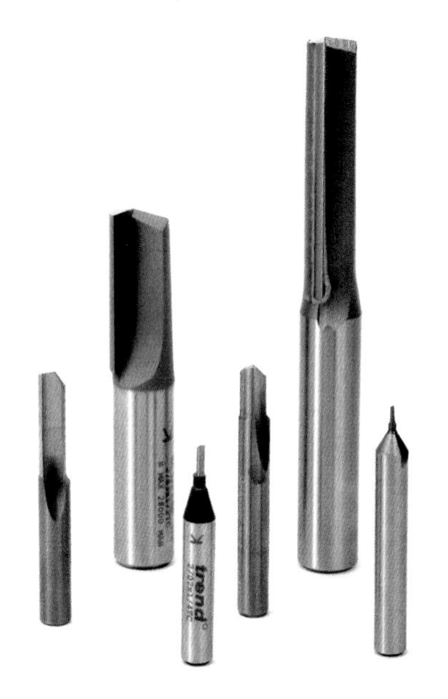

However the cutting speed is slower and the finish is therefore not so good, so their use is restricted to less critical applications or roughing out cuts.

Two flute cutters are used for most woodworking operations and will instantly double the cutting speed. i.e. with the motor set at 26000 rpm you will get 52,000 cuts per minute.

This produces a much cleaner and smoother finish, particularly if an underpowered router is not maintaining the correct speed under load.

There are some three-flute cutters available as well, but these are restricted to fine trimming applications where only a small amount of waste is being removed from the edge of the work.

Multi flute cutters are intended for use with low speed motors and drill attachments, typically around 3000 rpm maximum. They are often no more than burrs or rasps and are renowned for their poor waste clearance and not designed for a good surface finish. They are however ideal for carving and grinding and used extensively freehand on wood and metal. The latter for deburring welds.

Tip

Pin guides have the advantage that they can be used to profile intricate shapes as the pin is so small, but they do generate a lot of frictional heat and may mark or even burn the timber if they are not used with care.

Safe working speeds

Smaller router bits can be used safely up to their maximum speed, which is usually in the region of 28 – 30,000 rpm. However, as the cutter diameter gets bigger the peripheral speed increases dramatically, and excessive speed makes a hand held router difficult to control safely.

As well as the danger factor, excessive speed will also cause the cutter to burn rather than cut, so it is useful to try and match the speed to suit a particular cutter.

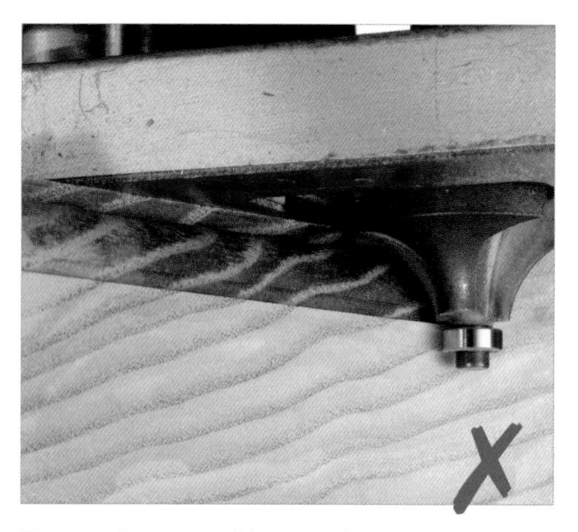

This is why a variable speed router is essential.

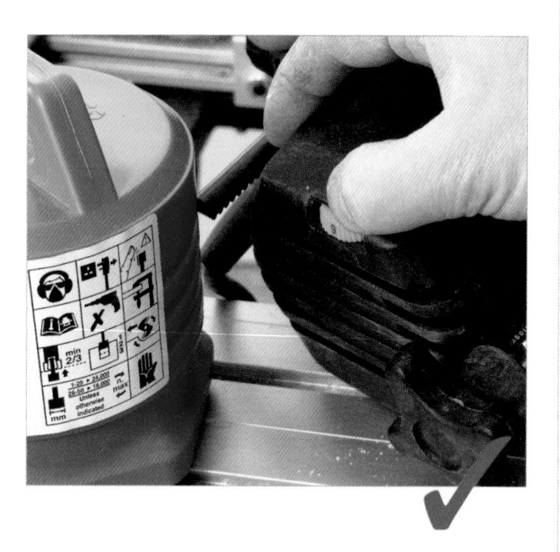

Unfortunately, there are no hard and fast rules here, as you have to factor in things like motor power, workpiece material and feed speed, all of which have an effect on cutting speed. As a general rule, it is usually recommended that cutters are run within the following guidelines.

Diameter	Speed rpm
Up to 24mm	28,000
25 – 30mm	24,000
31 - 50mm	18,000
51 – 67mm	16,000
68 – 86mm	12,000

However, always follow the manufacturer's recommendations for operating speeds. Cutters over 40mm diameter should normally only be used in a router that is either fixed under a table or overhead in a machining centre.

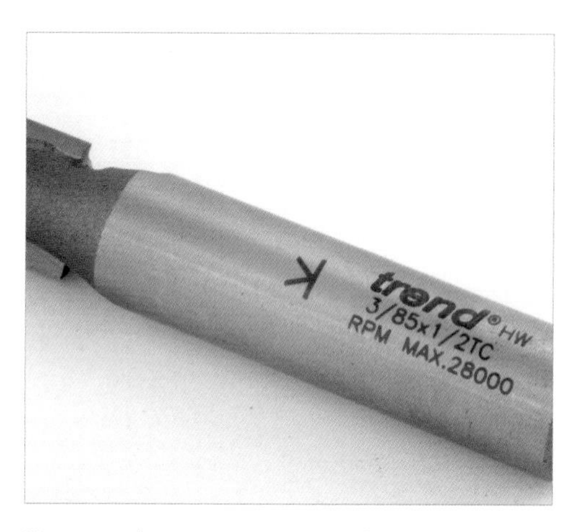

New regulations are now making it compulsory to show maximum speeds on the cutter shank, as well as the insertion point. Avoid cutters that do not show this information.

Cutter composition and quality

Router cutters were originally all made from High Speed Steel (HSS) but these have now largely been superseded by Tungsten Carbide cutters either in solid tungsten or usually tungsten tipped (TCT). These have far superior edge holding properties, particularly when working with very abrasive man-made materials.

However, the increasing use of routers within a range of manufacturing industries has lead to the development of cutters coated with new materials such as Polycrystalline diamonds and edges of solid tungsten carbide, as well as tooling with replaceable tips. These are primarily designed to maximise the benefits of CNC routing and although initially very expensive, they are more economical for demanding applications, where long life and minimal downtime when changing cutters is crucial.

High Speed Steel HSS

The best router cutters are produced by turning the cutter body to the required profile and then grinding the flute and clearance angles before finally honing the edges to a mirror finish. Poorer quality cutters are often just machined from cast steel.

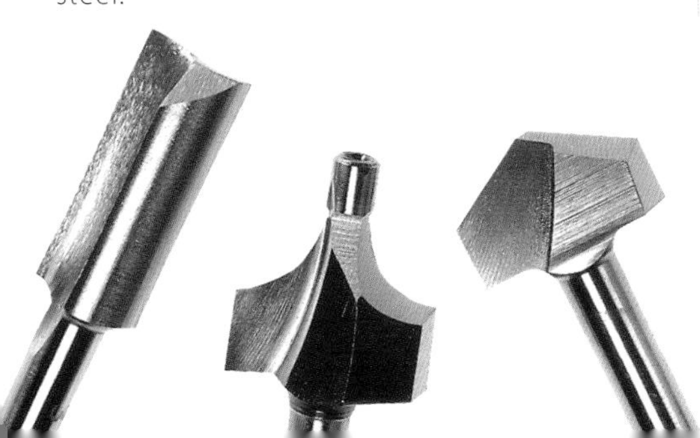

The advantage of HSS is that the cutters can be sharpened to a very keen edge and will leave a super smooth finish on good quality timbers. They are particularly effective on softwoods and the edge can be quickly re-honed on an ordinary oilstone.

However, this sharpness is soon dulled when the cutter is used on hard or abrasive timbers and it will burn and ruin after just a short time if you try and cut materials like MDF or plywood.

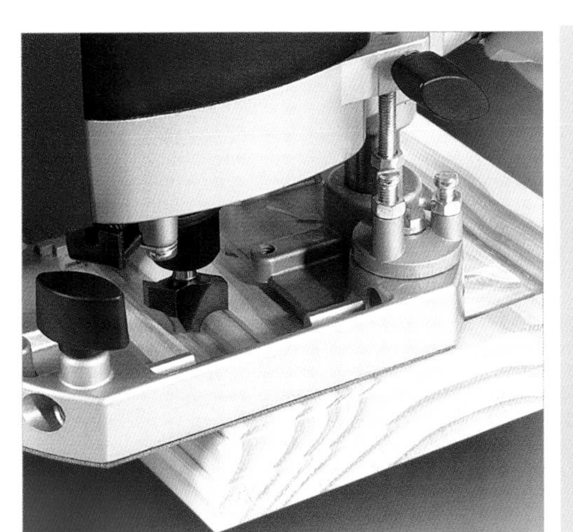

Tip

HSS cutters are most suitable for fine and detailed work that requires a very clean and precise finish straight from the cutter, dovetailing in soft woods and panel raising being good examples.

HSSE cutters

Cutters made from a special grade of HSS have been developed for cutting, drilling and slotting various grades of non-ferrous metals and plastics, particularly in the window industry.

These leave a very clean finish, even on hard finishes such as anodised aluminium, but any work in most of these materials will require the use of a coolant or lubricant.

Tungsten Carbide Tipped TCT

These are produced in a similar way to HSS cutters, but the flutes are machined to accept tungsten carbide tips, which are then brazed in place and ground to form cutting edges.

Although very hard and wear resistant, tungsten is a grained material and therefore quite brittle, so it cannot be honed to such a fine edge as HSS. However, it is the cutter of choice for general routing applications and provided the edges are regularly honed, will produce an excellent finish. Although more expensive, TCT cutters will retain their edges far longer than the equivalent HSS ones. Estimates vary but they will probably last 15 to 25 times longer. The downside is that they are more difficult to sharpen when they do eventually need it. Although you can use a diamond or ceramic slipstone to hone up the edges, they will ultimately need a professional regrind to maintain their best performance.

Solid Tungsten Carbide STC

Solid tungsten carbide cutters are produced from a particularly hard grade of carbide, to produce the necessary machining and performance characteristics. Being turned, milled and ground from solid material they are stronger, can be re-sharpened many times and can be ground to produce better plunge cutting than TCT cutters.

As their manufacturing costs are relatively high, they are normally only available in small sizes, but they do produce a good finish suitable for most woodworking applications and are recommended for machining aluminium alloy and hard plastics.

Tip

You must use a tungsten cutter for any work in resin-bonded materials like MDF, as they are the only ones hard enough to withstand such abrasive materials.

Polycrystalline Diamond PCD

These cutters are made by bonding man-made diamonds onto tungsten carbide tips under extreme pressure and heat. The resulting cutting edge will outlast conventional tungsten many times over. They are very expensive to produce and their expense is only justified in specialised production applications, or on CNC fixed head routers with automatic feed. PCD currently represents the pinnacle of cutting performance available with today's manufacturing technology.

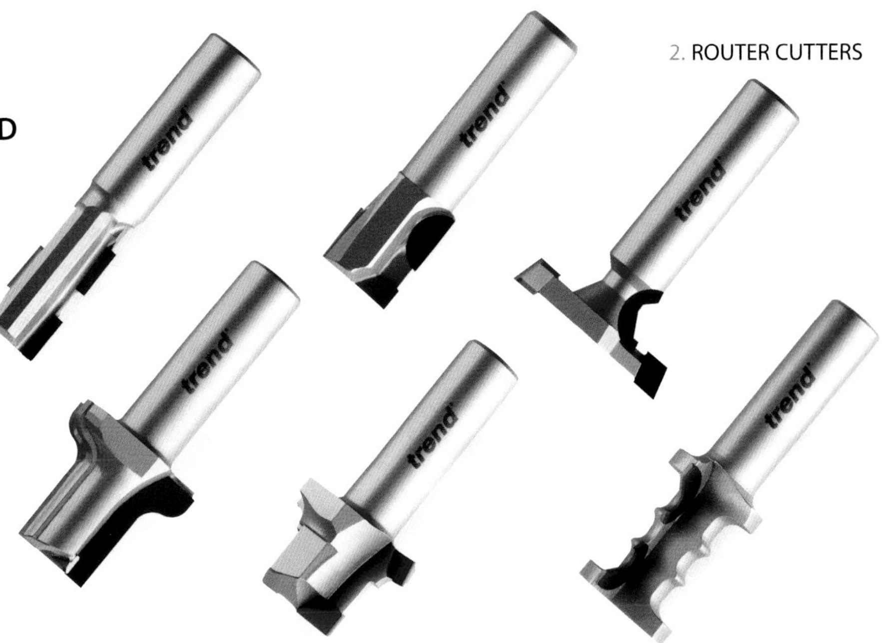

Replaceable blade cutters

These are precision ground cutter spindles onto which you can fit removable solid tungsten carbide blades. The blades are held in place with small screws and each one is ground on two or four of their cutting edges, so you can quickly turn them round to expose a new cutting edge after the first has dulled down.

The advantages are obvious, particularly in a production set-up where the blades can be replaced without disturbing the router or depth settings, therefore minimising expensive downtime.

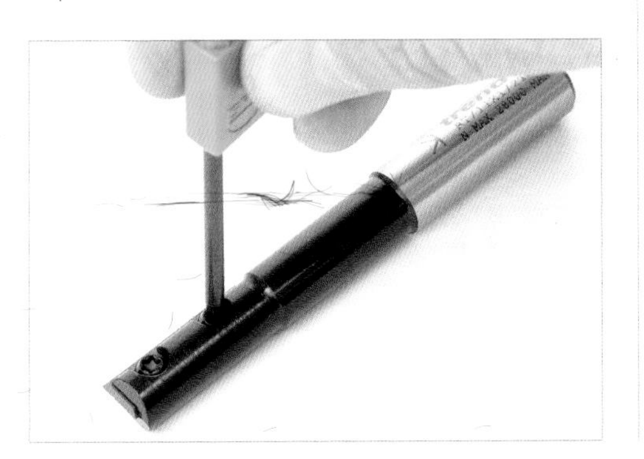

The blades are relatively cheap as well, so the economic advantages are enormous, particularly with very abrasive materials that quickly dull the edge. However, they are only available in straight and angled profiles and some are not suitable for plunge cutting.

Multi profile replaceable blade cutters

This system allows you to fit a variety of different profiled solid carbide blades into a holder that is available with and without a bearing guide.

Two blades are fitted to the body and they are designed to provide integral chip limitation to minimise kickback.

As no brazing is required a higher grade of tungsten carbide can be used, resulting in superior edge holding and durability characteristics. The blade range includes a good selection of decorative profiles, making it a very economical option for the home user needing quality cutters at minimal cost, when the small amount of down time involved in changing over the blades is unimportant.

Choosing and buying cutters

There are thousands of router cutters on the market, many looking exactly the same but with vastly differing price tags. The newcomer can therefore be excused for being confused and bewildered by the choice. Even if you know what you want, there are some qualities that you just cannot determine by looking at the cutter, so for ultimate performance you should only buy top quality tooling.

For this reason it is always better to stick to a well proven manufacturer and a reputable dealer to provide reliable advice with a good back-up service.

Poor quality cutters will successfully machine wood, but what they will not guarantee is durability, consistency of performance or quality of finish.

For this you need superior cutters made from the best materials, ground and machined to precise tolerances, with the correct clearance and relief angles. It goes without saying that all this comes at a cost and you will have to make some value judgements based on the projected amount of use, but do try and think long term when you buy and remember that you always get what you pay for.

Whilst the following description of the checks you need to make before buying a cutter may seem excessive, the process is not really that complicated and with just a little experience may soon become intuitive.

Tip

When choosing a cutter, a good rule of thumb is that the cutting edge length should not exceed three times the diameter and if you can get away with less, then so much the better.

Selecting a cutter

For a start, think carefully about the length of cutter you need as biggest is not always best. The aim is to try and maintain accuracy and minimise vibration, but at the same time maximise safety.

So it is not always advantageous to buy a cutter with long cutting edges if you don't need them. In fact, if you start cutting really deep in one pass the cutter will deflect and vibrate excessively. For deep cuts, plunge in gradually with several shallower passes. The longer the cutter is, the more this vibration is likely to occur and in extreme cases you can actually snap the cutter, usually at the point between the flutes and the shank. Shorter bits are obviously more stable and will cut smoothly.

Another strength consideration involves the shank diameter. Always choose the largest diameter shank that your router will take. There is rarely any significant difference in cost, but the extra stability involved is proportionally huge.

A 1/2" shank has a cross sectional area that is four times that of a 1/4" shank which says it all in terms of strength.

Don't think that buying a small diameter shanked cutter and then bushing it up to fit a bigger collet is a way round this. These bushes can never grip the cutter as accurately as a collet and they inevitably introduce yet another source of vibration, so avoid them if at all possible.

The choice of cutter grade is also critical. For most jobs, TCT is the only option for its excellent edge holding properties in a broad range of different wood based materials. But not all tungsten carbide is of the same quality, and just being labelled TCT doesn't necessarily signify a good cutter. The grade of carbide has improved markedly on the top quality bits and in recent years a micro-grain carbide has been introduced which can be sharpened to a fine edge without becoming brittle or chipping, a recurring problem with early cutters.

There can be as much as a ten times difference in the edge holding properties between different grades of carbide, so always insist on micro-grain. Only choose HSS if you want a superfine finish in softwood and are able to keep the edges in shape with regular honing.

The case for deciding between a single or two flute cutter is even more clear-cut. If a fast feed speed is your most important consideration then go for a single flute version, but it is nearly always better to go for a two flute cutter, which will leave a noticeably superior finish to its single flute counterpart.

If the cutter of your choice is available in shear or spiral form then this is another way of making the cut smoother and cleaner, particularly in tricky, end-grain trimming work.

They also reduce the load on your router and are more comfortable to use for long periods. However, this option is more

expensive than a straight two flute cutter and you will only be able to hone the shear type.

Armed with all this information you can now choose the type of cutter you want, but how do you go about checking the quality?

Although you cannot tell much about the raw material of the cutter just by looking at it, there are other visible signs on the cutter like machining quality, grinding angles and surface finish that will give a good indication as to quality. A manufacturer is unlikely to buy the best quality material and then spoil it by poor machining. A careful examination is likely to reveal whether the cutters are up to standard or not and it is a worthwhile operation, as the quality is reflected in both your subsequent work and safety.

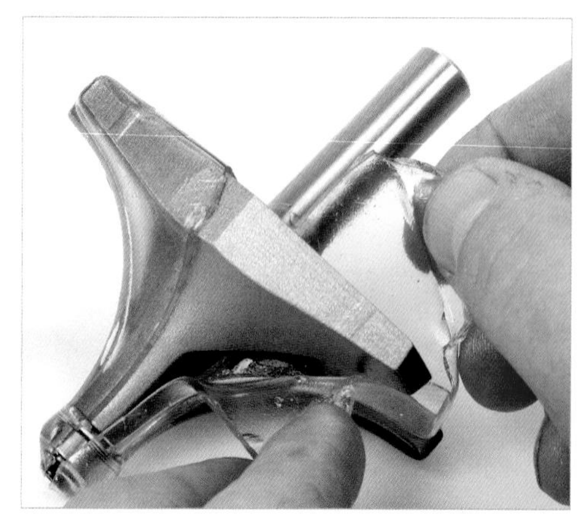

Most new cutters come covered with wax, which although protective can also hide manufacturing imperfections. Remove this carefully after slitting it with a knife, but beware as it is very easy to cut yourself as you slide the wax free, so consider wearing gloves for this operation.

Then have a really close look at the cutter. See if the cutting edges are really sharp and make sure that the brazed tips do not overhang the end of the flute other than by the ground bevel, as this can cause them to flex under load. Check that the surface of the edges are not chipped or pitted and the edges themselves are honed smooth and polished. The best way to do this is to rub your fingernail down the ground angle. If it feels rough or wavy the edge is not properly machined.

It needs to be a mirror finish otherwise the cut surface will be equally rough and resin will soon start to build up in the grooves and affect the quality of cut.

Each cutting edge must be ground to the same angle to ensure that they are doing an equal amount of work, so they must be precisely the same size and shape.

Cheap cutters have very thin carbide tips that leave little scope for re-sharpening. As well as giving longer life, a thicker tip will give much more support to the edge and will stay sharp longer.

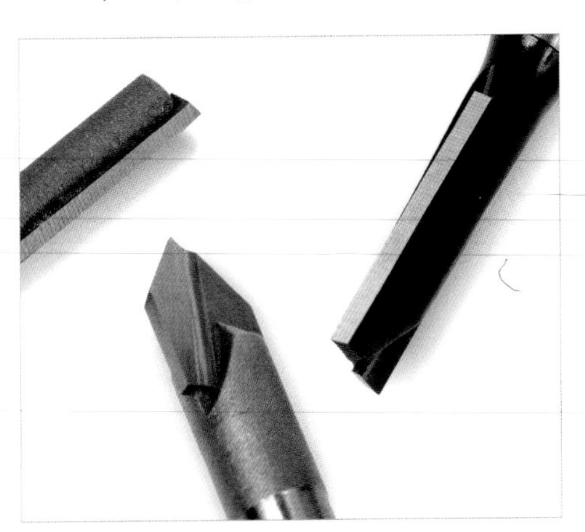

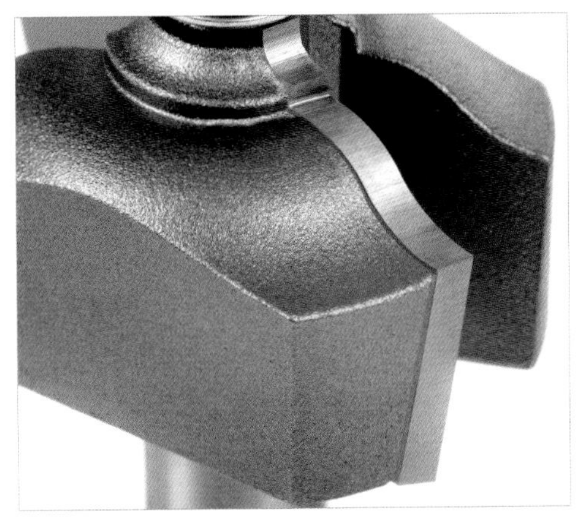

Check that the brazing on these tips is clean and that there are no gaps or voids, or the tip may detach itself under load. Poor quality brazing will also affect the ease of chip clearance.

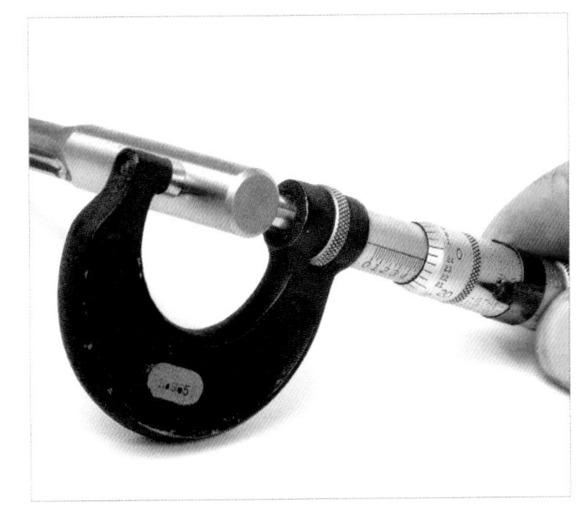

The shank should be smooth and perfectly true, with a nicely chamfered end and most importantly, dead on size. If you have any doubts, check the diameter with a micrometer, as an undersized one will very quickly damage the collet. Then if possible, put the cutter into the router and feel how it spins, it must run free of any vibration.

If you are buying a bearing guided cutter, check that the mounting pin is strong enough to support the bearing and that the holding screw tightens sufficiently to get a good hold, but the bearing itself should have minimal play whilst still turning freely.

Finally, I like to see the cutter supplied in some nice packaging that allows for subsequent protection and storage, and where necessary, instructions for use should be included, particularly with the more complicated profiles.

Cutter sets

I am often asked if cutter sets are worth buying, or should you buy separate cutters? The answer is a cautious 'yes' to sets, as they can be a great way to get started. If you are a confused newcomer, the sheer enormity of the range of individual cutters is very confusing. Many people are scared off thinking they will need to spend a fortune on dozens of cutters when actually the reverse is true. So by all means start with a basic set of good quality cutters, eight or ten will probably cover 90% of your initial needs and you can then buy different or better quality ones as you become more proficient. The following cutters will give you a good start and I would recommend that you buy them all in TCT:

1/4" and 3/8" straight two flute
3/8" rounding over/ovolo with bearing
3/8" Radius
45° Vee
Bearing guided rebate
Chamfer
Bearing guided trimmer
Roman ogee
Dovetail

Avoid buying the very complicated and expensive cutters until you have a specific need for them.

Cutter care and maintenance

You will soon accumulate a serious investment in cutters for your router, so it is important to do everything possible to keep them in good condition. Regular maintenance will preserve the cutting performance and enhance the life of the tool. As with all edge tools, you should sharpen them as soon as you notice they are losing their edge. *"Little and often is always the best policy with any form of sharpening"*.

One of the main causes of cutter failure is overheating, which is usually initiated by machining with a blunt cutter. This slows the feed rate, the chips stop clearing properly and then start jamming behind the cutter flute. This generates frictional heat, which then accelerates the dulling process, and you are in a downward spiral that will eventually ruin the cutter and could possibly damage the router. Meanwhile the work will show a poor surface finish with torn grain and burn marks that are impossible to remove.

Maintenance

Cutter care is obviously an important issue, so start by storing them properly. Tungsten is notoriously brittle and will chip or shatter with only the slightest knock. Never leave them ratting around loosely in a box or drawer.

Store them either in their original packaging

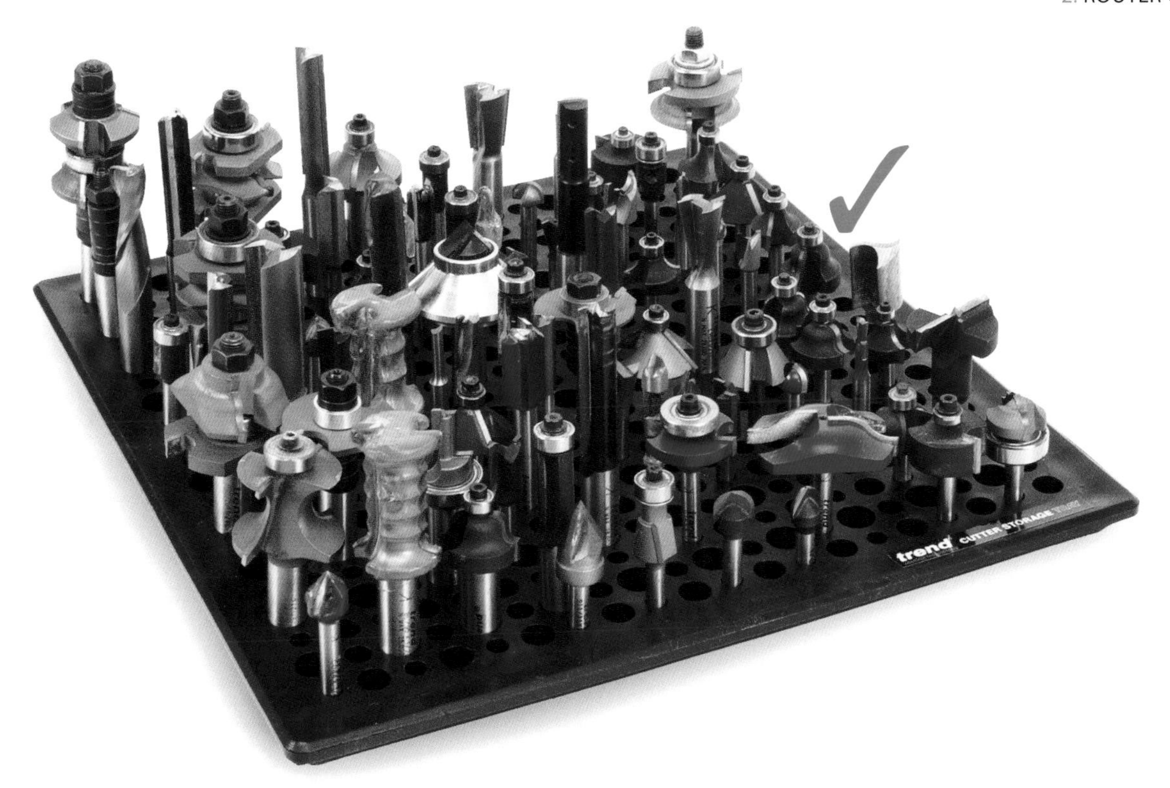

or in a suitable rack. In its simplest form this can be a block of wood with holes drilled in it, but make sure the bits can stand upright without touching each other. Make the holes very slightly oversize so you don't have to force the cutters in and out and risk cutting yourself in the process.

Another option is dedicated cutter racks which are available in a variety of styles and are well worth the investment. For the ultimate in storage you can buy cases with foam inserts and spare storage compartments.

If they are not likely to be used for some time spray the cutters with thin oil or rust preventing fluid. This is particularly important if you are working in a humid shed or workshop.

Secondly, keep your cutters clean. Resin soon builds up around the cutting edges and reduces the clearance angles leading to overheating. You can buy proprietary cleaning kits, which include resin cleaner, but oven cleaner is an excellent alternative.

Use an old toothbrush to clear away the softened deposits, never scrape at them with a knife or you will damage the cutting edges. Really stubborn deposits can be removed carefully with very fine wire wool or a fine wire brush. Once they are clean again, apply a coating of dry spray lubricant to help reduce friction and minimise further resin build-up.

Check the shank for any score marks that

might suggest that it has been slipping in the collet. This could be a sign of the collet wearing, or incorrect shank tolerance leading to poor grip and slippage. Worn or damaged collets will cause the cutter to run out of true and will more importantly damage the shanks of all your other cutters.

On bearing guided cutters, check that the bearing rotates freely with minimal side play. These bearings work very hard with the cutter spinning at 28,000 rpm and therefore have a limited life, so buy a few spares and replace them regularly. Be careful to keep any resin cleaners away from the bearings or you will dissolve their internal greasing.

Sharpening cutters

You can keep your cutters sharp with regular light honing, the trick is to do it when the edge is just dull rather than blunt. After repeated honing the cutter will require professional regrinding either by a local saw doctor or by the original manufacturer, as the better ones will offer a sharpening service.

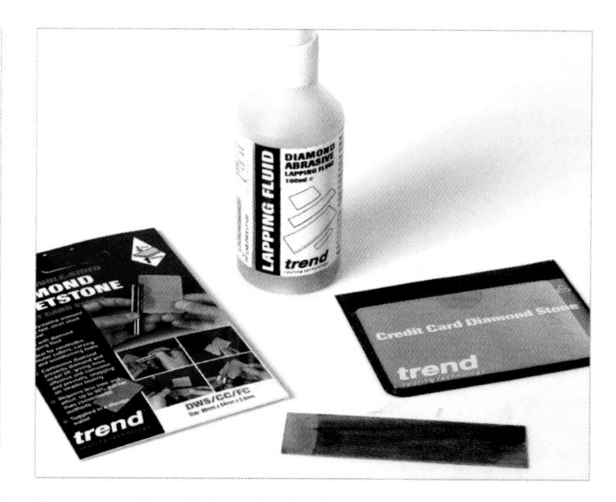

Cutters should only be honed on the flat faces of the cutting blade, as this will not alter the shape or the relief and clearance angles. For HSS cutters you can use conventional oilstones, but for TCT cutters you will need a diamond stone. These are readily available in a variety of shapes, sizes and grades. The fine grade is ideal for router cutters, although they may benefit from a further polish on an extra fine version. Do clean the cutters before you start though, or you will clog the sharpening stone with resin.

Diamond stones should be lubricated with a little water, but always dry both them and the cutter after use to prevent rusting. Some people prefer to use thin oil as a lubricant on diamond stones, but there is now a specially formulated diamond stone lubricant.

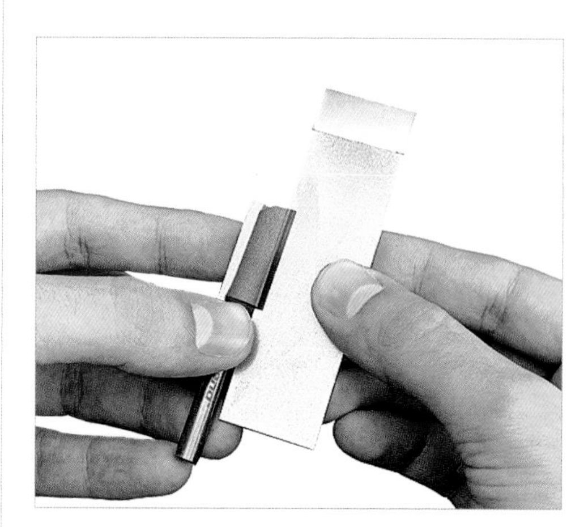

To hone the face of the cutting edge, press it firmly onto the face of the stone and draw it backwards and forwards a few times, making sure it is kept flat at all times. A few strokes should be enough as the diamond stones cut quickly, but remember to take the same amount off either side. Never try and hone the grinding angles.

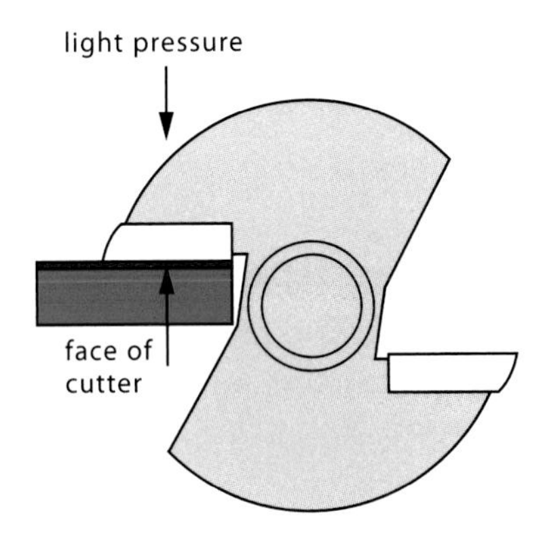

For bearing guided cutters, remove the bearing first but take care not to run the locating pin against the stone or you will damage it. Similarly, take care with pin-guided cutters, as even very slight scoring on the pin will cause it to mark the timber.

Regrinding

Badly chipped edges cannot be restored by honing; the only answer is to have them professionally reground. This is usually successful if the damage is not too severe, though on small or inexpensive cutters it is better to replace them rather than try a rescue job. Cheap cutters in particular, are often not strong enough to regrind and their thin carbide chips may shatter.

You should be able to regrind professional quality cutters up to four times if they are well maintained, but after that the cutting geometry starts to alter significantly enough to affect the cut and replacement is the only answer.

Regrinding will inevitably alter the profile of the cutter slightly, which may not be important unless it is part of a matched jointing set. In this case, both cutters must be reground by the same amount at the same time. Shims are usually provided with arbor mounted cutters to compensate for the thickness of tungsten removed during grinding.

Cutter damage and breakage

Although quality cutters are designed and made to withstand the forces of continuous professional use, damage can occur for a number of reasons and for future reference, it is always worth trying to find the cause. Very rarely is it due to some form of manufacturing fault or flaw in the cutter. Usually it is caused by the operator either selecting the wrong type of bit for the job, or applying it incorrectly.

Many newcomers to routing try to cut too deeply in one pass, or to feed incorrectly, both of which will damage cutters, particularly narrow ones.

Deep cuts should always be made in a series of shallow passes to avoid placing too much side pressure on the cutter and to allow the waste to clear. If you feed the router too fast the cutter cannot clear the waste quickly enough and will start to overheat and vibrate.

The waste may also pack in behind the cutter and start forcing it off line. Smaller cutters have narrower flutes and should therefore be fed more slowly.
Conversely, feeding too slowly is a common cause of overheating. You do not obtain a better finish by going slowly; all that happens is that the surface burns and the cutting edge is dulled. Determining the correct feed speed is covered in detail later in the Routing Techniques chapter.

Cutter damage and causes

1. Cutter tip chipped

The most common cause of chipping is contact with a foreign object of some sort. This may be a nail or screw in reclaimed timber, or even a dead knot. These knots are extremely hard and often contain ingrown mineral crystals that easily damage a brittle carbide tip. Damage can also occur if the router is left on the bench with the cutter exposed, so always retract it back into the base, or stand it on a block if you don't want to disturb the setting.

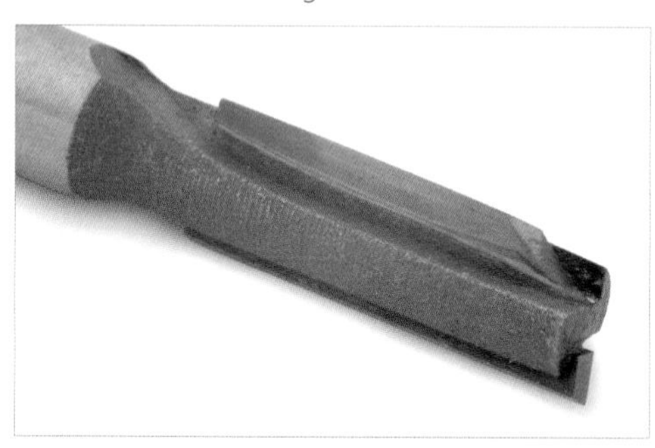

2. Tip breakage

This can be caused in the same way as tip chipping but severe cases are caused by excessive side pressure on the cutter, or feeding too fast. The cheaper the quality of cutter, the more likely this is to happen, as poor brazing or inadequate support for the cutting edges are characteristic of cheap cutters.

3. Bent shank

This is usually caused by a combination of not putting the cutter far enough into the collet and then using too much feed pressure with a dull cutter set too deep.

The general rule is to have a minimum of two thirds of the shank into the collet for maximum support. Good quality cutters will have an insertion point marked on the shank. The shank can also be bent if you get a kickback by applying the cutter to the work before it has reached full cutting speed.

4. Broken shanks

Shanks can be broken by excessive side loads and/or a faulty collet. Side load increases dramatically as you take a deep cut, so never exceed a cutting depth equal to the diameter of the bit in one pass. Over-tightening the collet may score the shank and form a point of weakness, as may a damaged collet, or vibration from worn motor bearings. Violent or sudden changes of feed direction will cause deflection beyond the normal limits, so always work smoothly and steadily.

5. Burnt cutting edges

These are usually the result of feeding too slowly, though forcing a blunt cutter or cutting too deep may have the same effect. Using HSS on very hard and abrasive materials will also quickly burn the edges. Once damaged in this way, the cutter is effectively ruined.

6. Bearing failure

Premature bearing failure is usually caused when they clog with swarf and dust. They are packed with grease and sealed for life so do not try and lubricate them, especially with thin oil, as this will just dissolve the grease. However, they should be regarded as consumable and replaced immediately they are found to be overheating.

7. Resin build-up

Resin from natural timbers, especially softwoods and plywood will stick to the back of the cutter and affect the clearance angle. Take care not to scratch the cutter by cleaning roughly with wire brushes or scraping hard with a knife, as this will leave scratches that accumulate resin.

8. Repeated re-sharpening

Repeated re-sharpening will reduce all the clearance angles and weaken the cutting edges to such an extent that waste becomes trapped and the cutter rubs on the work. Cutters only have limited re-grinding life particularly if they are small.

Cutter types

There are hundreds of different profiles and sizes of router bits, many of which have more than one function. It is therefore difficult to categorise them precisely, but the following guide will provide an introduction to the most popular forms.

Straight cutters

These are primarily used for cutting grooves, slots, recesses and dados, but straight or parallel flute cutters can also be used for mortising, edge trimming and, in conjunction with guide bearings and bushes, for template work.

They are the most basic cutters and vary enormously in size from tiny 1.5mm diameter ones for delicate work up to massive 50mm diameter versions. Cutter lengths vary from 5mm to 65 mm so the range is enormous.

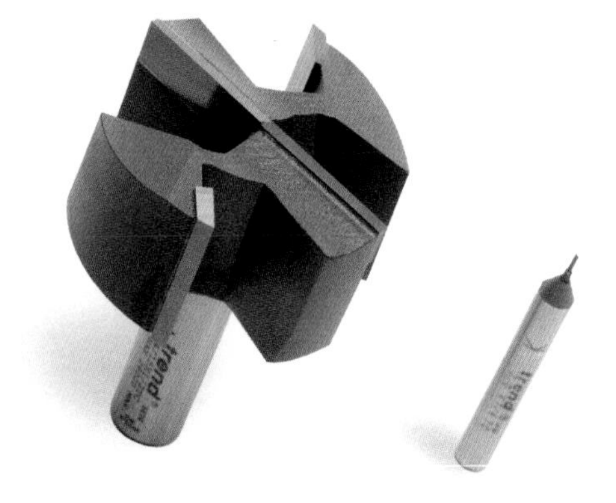

Single flute straight cutters are used for applications where fast cutting is of more concern than the standard of the finish. As they only have one cutting flute they allow waste material to clear easily and have good plunge cutting characteristics, making them ideal for rough cutting operations and for cutting out prior to edge trimming or profiling.

Two flute straight cutters are used for most routing operations, including edge trimming, grooving and rebating. Although they produce a superior surface finish to single flute cutters, waste clearance is far slower necessitating a slower feed speed. Cutters without 'bottom cut' should only be fed horizontally into the material, from the edge of the work or from a pre-drilled pilot hole.

Down-cut shear flute cutters have a slicing action that leaves the top edge free of breakout. They are fast cutting and are therefore ideal for grooving and trimming veneered and laminate faced surfaces.

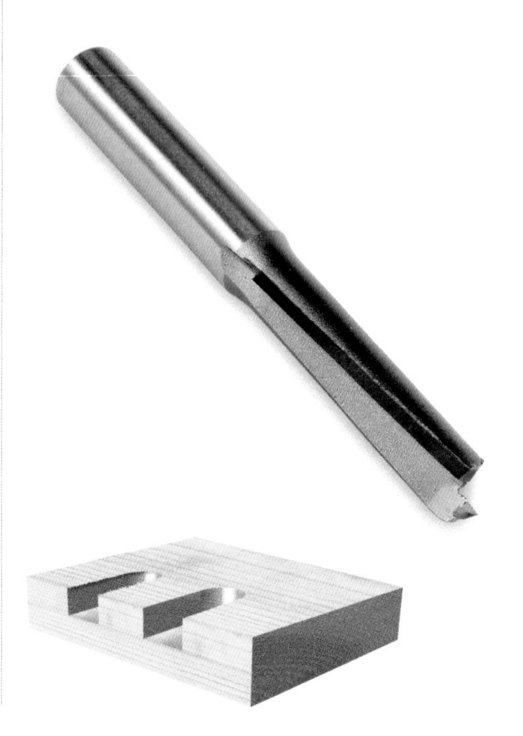

Up/Down-cut shear flute cutters have opposing top and bottom cutting edges that prevent breakout on both the top and bottom edges, making them ideal for cutting and trimming veneer and double faced laminate boards. All sheer flute bits can be honed by hand, because the flute sides are still flat.

Spiral cutters are suitable for small mortising and pocket cutting operations on timber. Available as either up-cutting or down-cutting, their action is to either draw the shavings up out of the cut, or push them down through the workpiece. The slicing action of spirals leaves a neat clean edge that is even better than the shear cutters because they make a single continuous uninterrupted cut with each revolution. Their disadvantage is that they are difficult to hone correctly by hand.

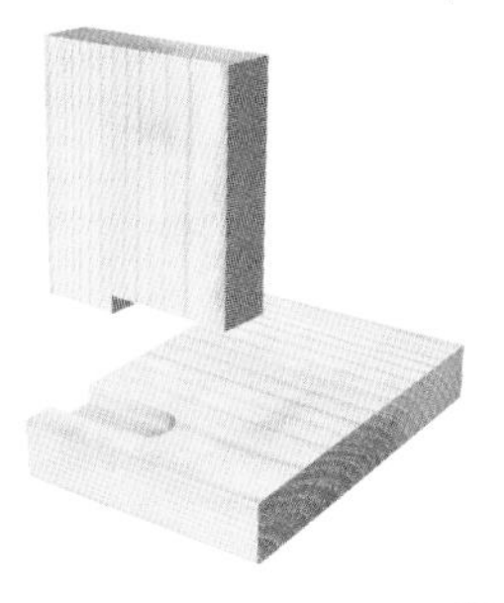

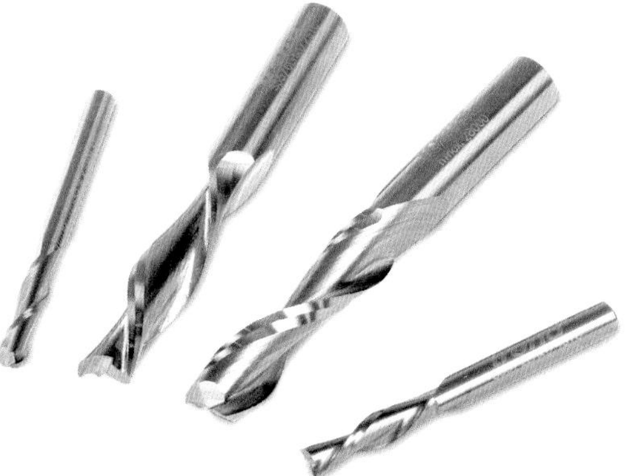

They are also used extensively for slotting and cutting aluminium alloy extrusions in the window industries, but in these situations cutting lubricant is required to prevent the material melting and sticking to the flutes.

Stagger tooth cutters are used for heavier morticing work, or when cutting deep pockets for locks and other door and joinery fittings, the extra clearance ability and rigidity of a staggered tooth cutter is helpful. However, you still have to make several passes to get the required depth and larger sizes can make the router more difficult to hold steady due to the amount of vibration they produce.

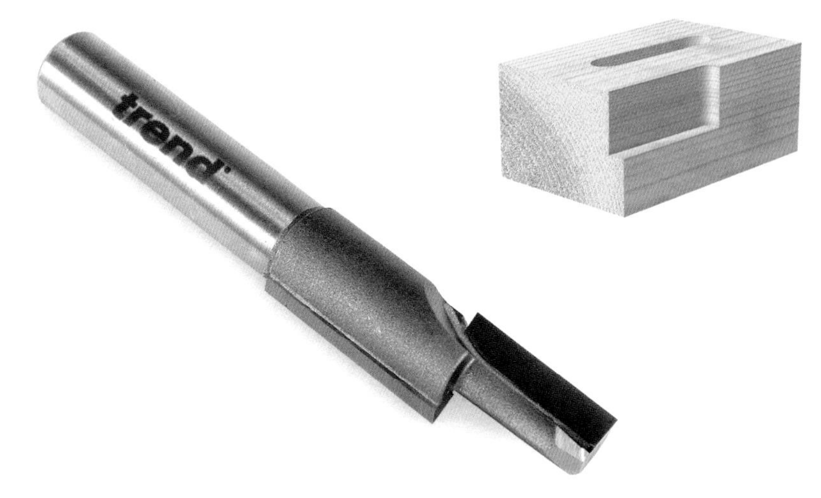

Plastics and acrylics. Although standard straight, spiral and shear two flute cutters can be used for machining rigid plastic and acrylic materials, specially ground cutters are available for this purpose. Always use a PTFE spray to prevent 'weld back' when routing soft plastics that are inclined to melt during cutting, applying it both behind the cut and to the cutter itself. Select a suitable cutting speed to keep the edge temperature low and minimise chattering along the edges of the cut.

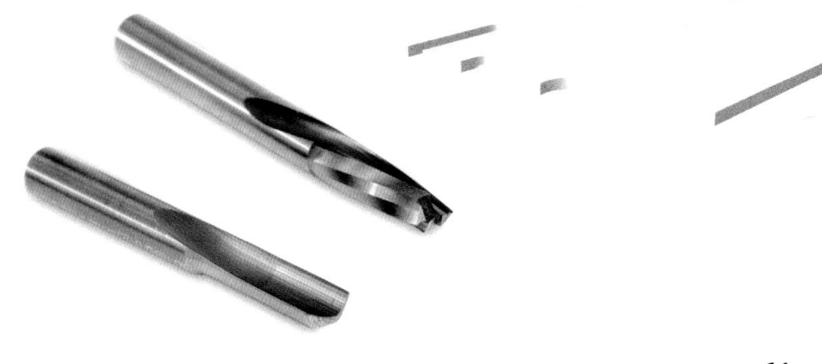

Round over and ovolo cutters

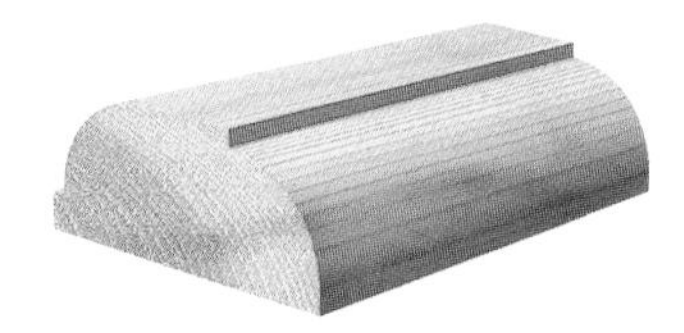

These are one of the most useful edge moulding cutters, as you can produce both profiles with the same cutter. The round over is self-explanatory, whilst the ovolo has two small shoulders at the extremes of the radius.

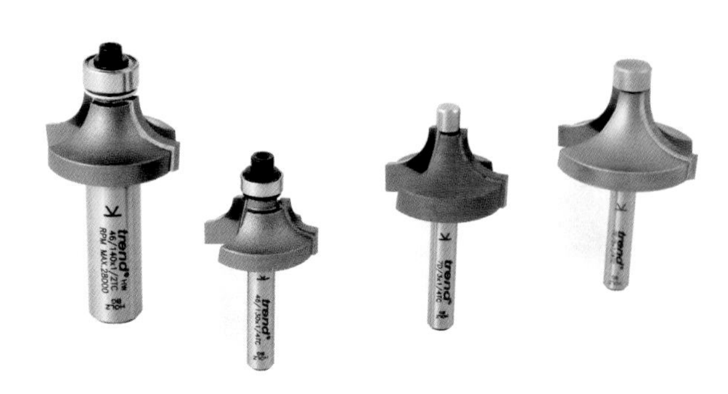

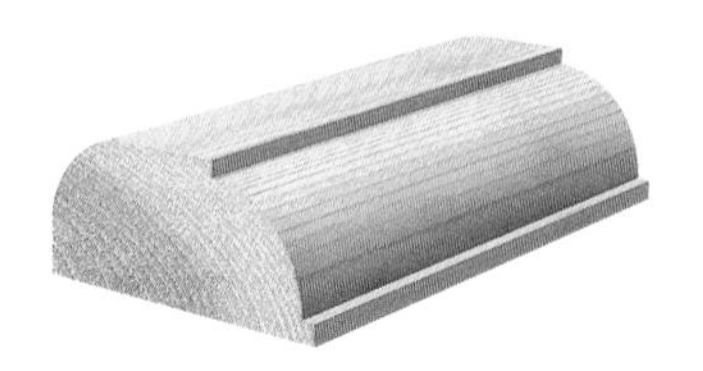

To use the same cutter for both profiles, you have to vary both the depth of cut and the size of the bottom bearing, or you can combine the two and have a round over with just a single shoulder. Rounding over the arris of a frame using a tiny radius bit makes an enormous difference to the finished effect, particularly if it is done after assembly.

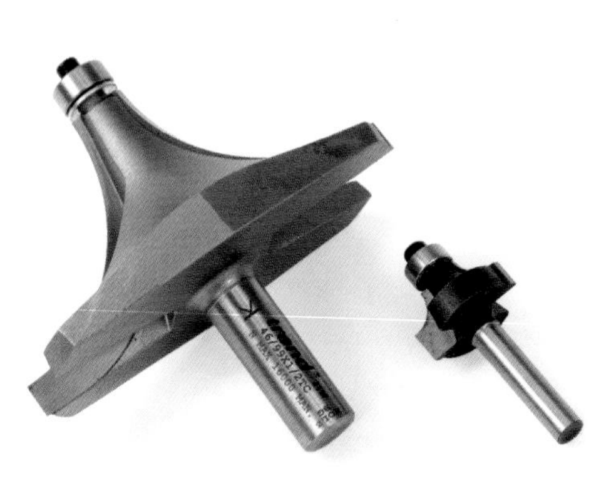

Available in a huge range of sizes up to the biggest 38mm radius, these cutters are an essential profile for your cutter kit.

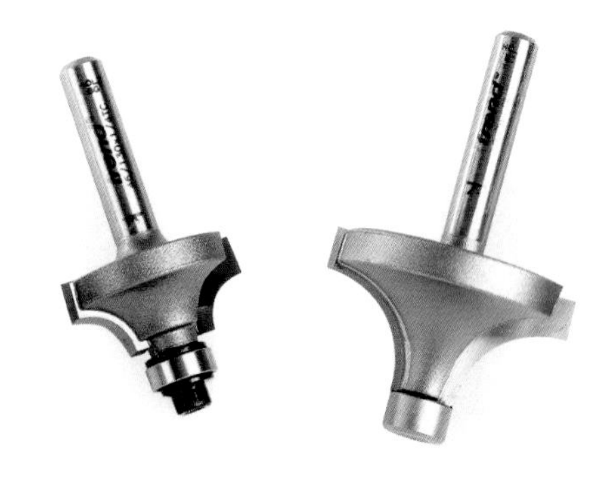

They are also made with guide pins rather than bearings, but these are obviously not as versatile as they are not interchangeable, but they will get into tighter corners.

Variations with bottom cut, with or without a guide bearing are used for panel cutting.

Cove and corebox cutters

These cutters produce the opposite effect to round over and are sometimes used in combination with them to produce the rule joint. Small diameter corebox cutters are also called fluting bits.

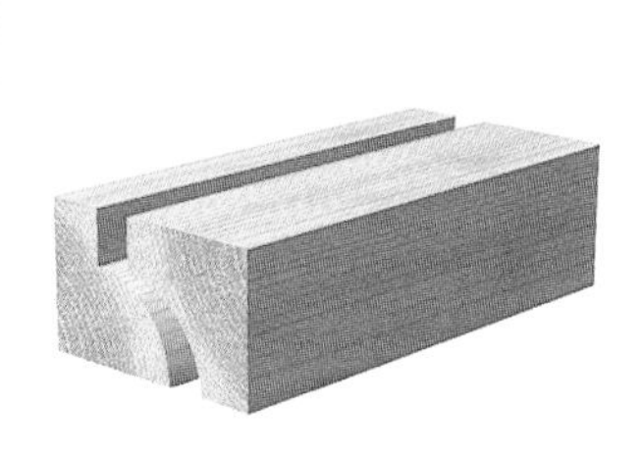

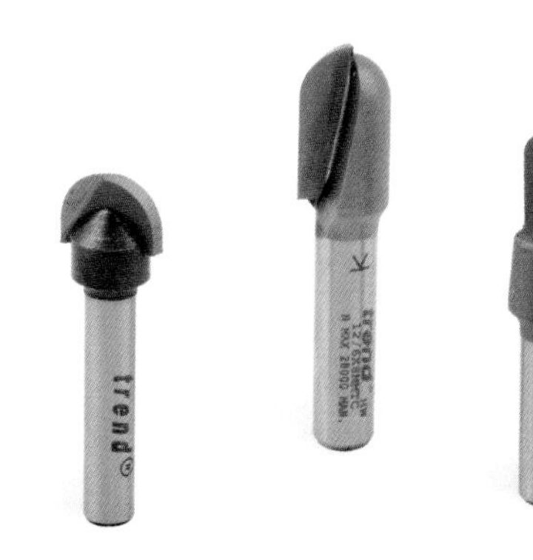

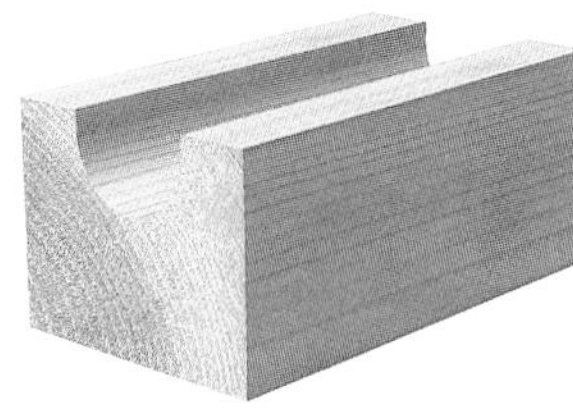

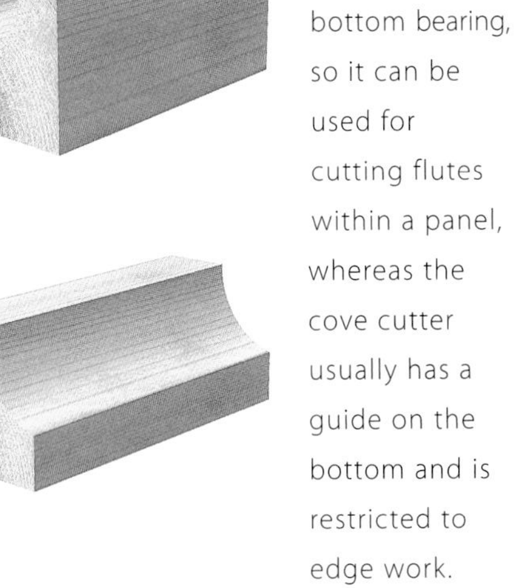

The corebox cutter has no bottom bearing, so it can be used for cutting flutes within a panel, whereas the cove cutter usually has a guide on the bottom and is restricted to edge work.

These cutters actually remove considerably more material than the ovolo cutter, so they should be used with care and always in a series of shallow steps to avoid overloading both the cutter and the router.

Stopped cuts with a corebox cutter are inclined to burn the timber very easily if you dwell in one place too long, so take care and reduce the speed if necessary.

Rebate cutters

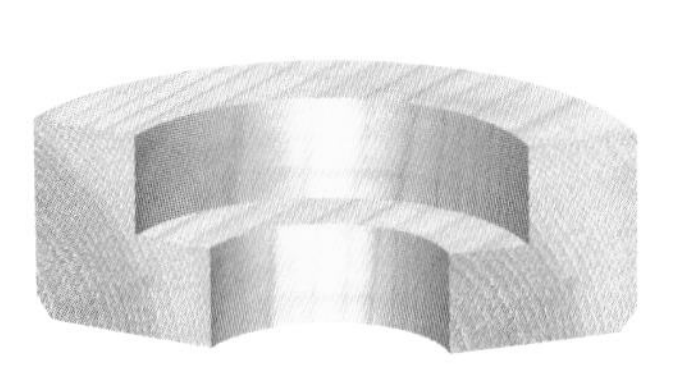

Rebating is a common application and you will need at least one cutter in your collection. The good news though, is that you can buy complete sets with a series of interchangeable bearings that produce a range of rebates with just the one cutter. You vary the width of the cut by changing the bearing diameter. Although you can cut rebates with a straight cutter and the router side-fence, the use of bearing guided cutters is easier and allows you to form a rebate round a curved edge, or within an already assembled frame.

Like many of the other profile cutters they are also available with guide pins as well as bearings, but these do tend to mark the work.

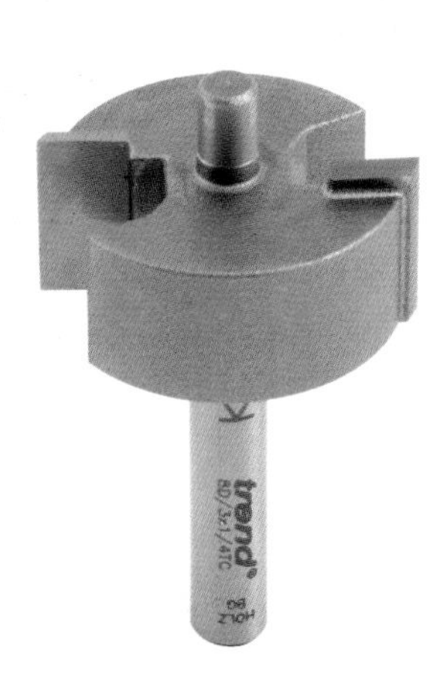

Trimming cutters

These are used to trim one surface back to match another, e.g. when facing boards with laminate or veneer. It is much easier to cut the laminate oversize and then trim it back flush to the workpiece after it has been stuck down. The router will leave a square or shaped edge depending on the cutter you use. Although there are some trimmers that require the use of the side-fence, most are self guided with bearings. When the bearing is the same diameter as the cutter it is called a flush trimmer and is available in various configurations that allow you to trim either one or two faces at once. They are particularly useful for template work.

Pierce and trim cutters are used to form internal cutouts for sinks, hobs and other inset fittings. For this purpose, the opening is first cut in the worktop core prior to the application of the face laminate or veneer. The laminate area within the opening is then pierced through with the drill point of the cutter, allowing the pin guide to be run around the internal edge of the opening, trimming the laminate back perfectly.

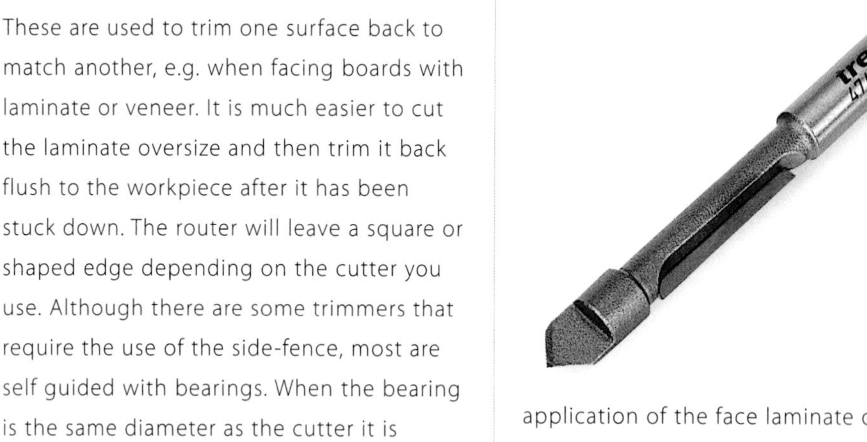

Before using bearing guided trimming cutters, make sure that the adhesive used to apply the laminate or veneer is thoroughly dry. If not, it is likely to clog the bearing and prevent it from turning. Also, remove any glue deposits from the edge of the base material and the overhanging edge of the laminate, as this will cause the bearing or side-fence to be lifted away, leaving an uneven edge to the finished work.

Edge and decorative moulds

There is an extensive range of decorative moulding cutters, including both classical and contemporary styles, and includes some of the cutters already covered. They allow you to reproduce many traditional shapes and profiles for furniture and joinery work and offer many possibilities in the design of attractive and innovative woodwork.

They can be used either as pure decoration, or to alter proportion, or maybe to mask or accentuate specific details. Mouldings are used extensively in both furniture and joinery construction. Some large elaborate profiles need a router with 1/2" collet, but you can often build up more complex profiles by making several passes with different shaped cutters.

You can also vary the profile of a bearing guided moulding cutter simply by changing the bearing diameter.

Matched pairs of moulding cutters can be used for cutting both the moulding and its reverse profile, as for instance when forming the joint between rails and stiles in doors, or the rule joint on a table. Another example is in window making where a glazing bar cutter and its opposite scribing cutter makes short work of stiles and sash bars for window frames.

As the range of decorative profiles is so vast it is best to build up your collection as you need it, but a few basics like a Roman Ogee are essential.

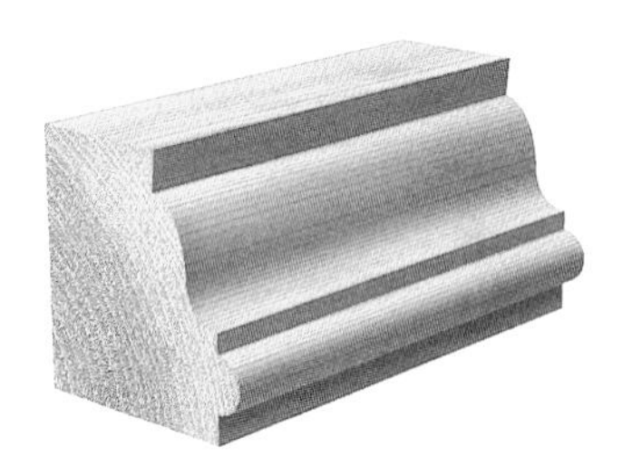

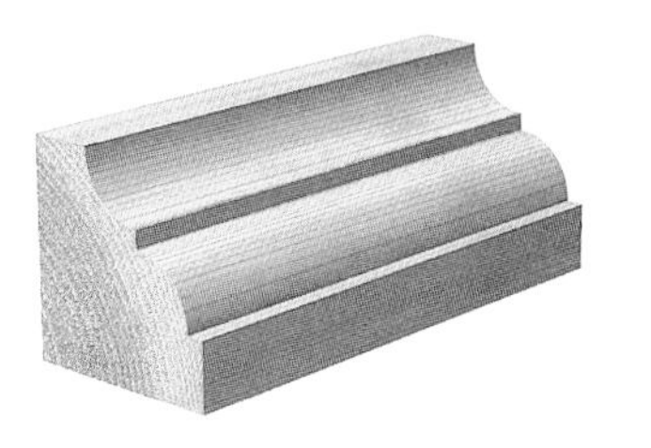

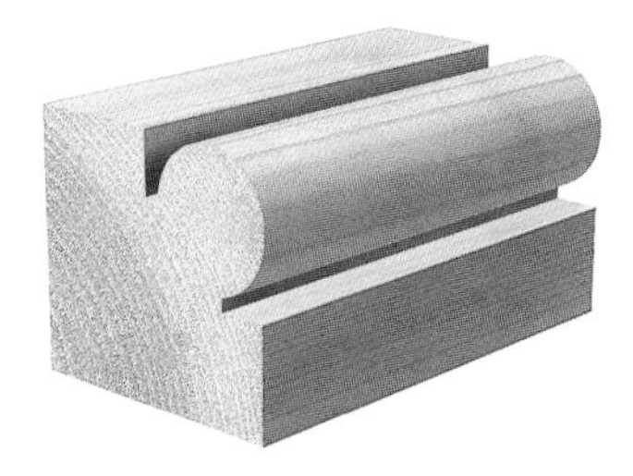

Beads and reeds

Although these are another form of decorative mould they deserve a separate description, as they are particularly versatile. The bead is a single semi-circular profile usually run down the corner of a frame and is often used to disguise a join between two components.

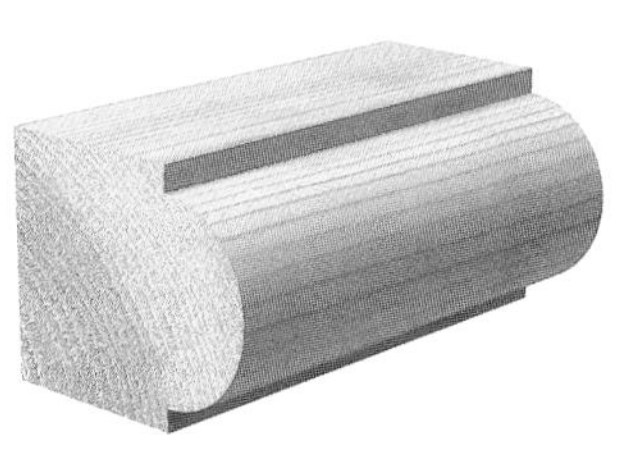

Used singly, as a decorative edge moulding with shoulders either side, it is called a staff bead, one of the classic profiles from the past.

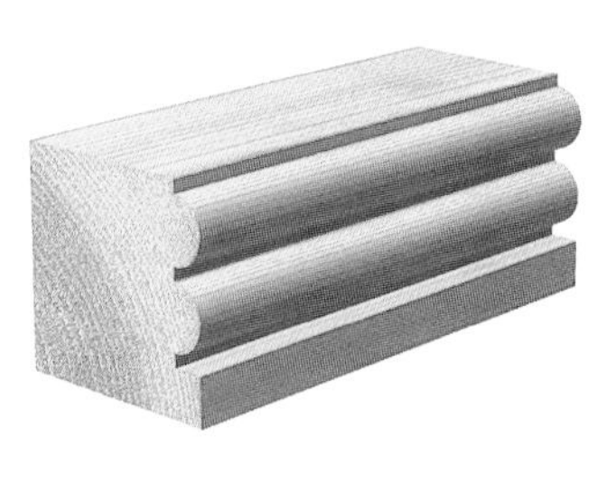

Sometimes several beads are combined on a flat face, an effect called a reed, which is useful for adding detail to otherwise plain edges.

Chamfer, bevel and V grooves

Chamfer and bevel cutters are usually self guided and allow you to very quickly add shape to an otherwise plain corner of the work.

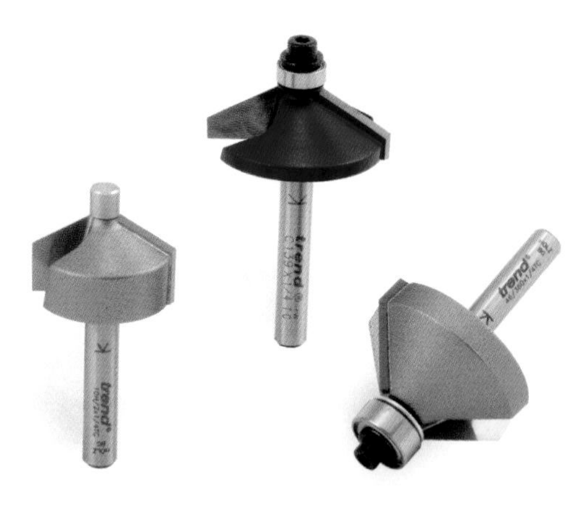

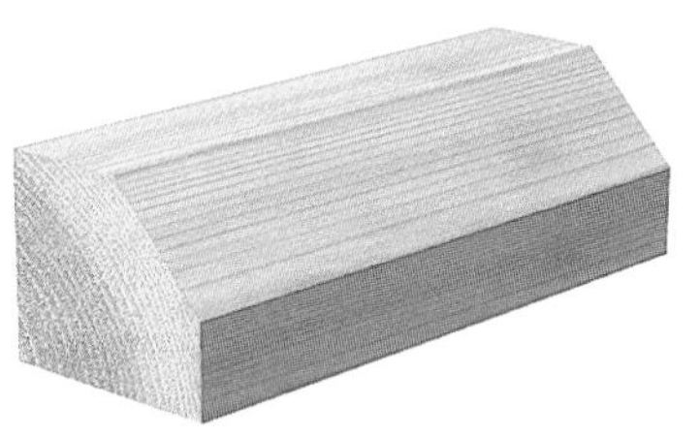

The stopped chamfer in particular is a very effective and practical detail. Bevels are not always 45°, though this is the most popular angle.

Using the other angles you can cut deeper or shallower tapers, or even the accurate angles needed for coopering or laminated work.

V groove cutters are mostly unguided and vary in angle from 25 to 60°. They are used for a variety of purposes from decorative grooving through to relief carving and letter engraving, either freehand or using templates. Small V bits are often referred to as veiners.

Dovetail cutters

Dovetail cutters are primarily used in special jigs that allow you to cut this otherwise time consuming joint very quickly.

But there is now such a huge variety of sizes and angles available that you can also use them to cut slides, housings and stair trenchings.

Jointing cutters

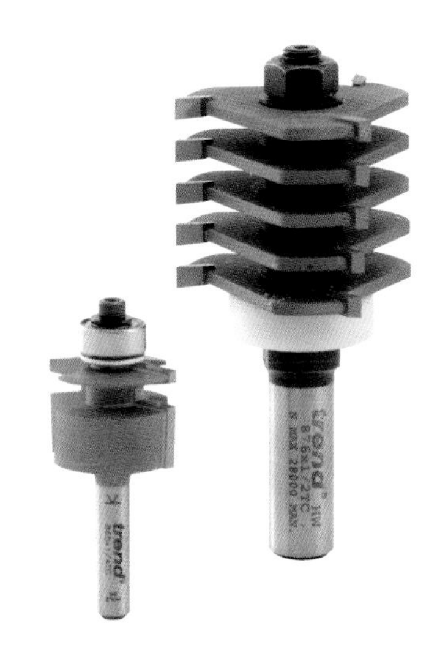

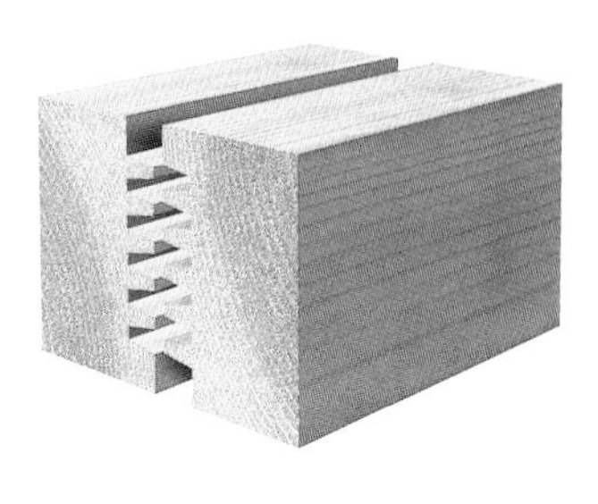

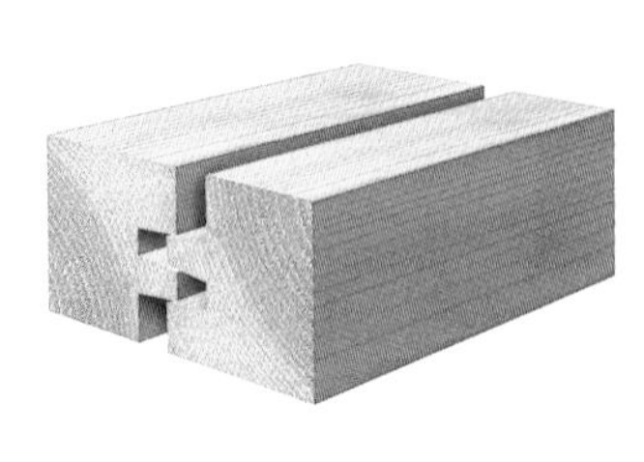

With suitable cutters you can use the router to join timber in various orientations. The idea of all these cutters is to increase the gluing area to add strength. For strengthening butt joints in flat timber, the finger joint is the classic option and this is available in single or multi finger variations. Ideally, for accurate work these cutters need to be used in a router table, but the timber should also be prepared very accurately.

For joining pieces at right angles, as for instance in drawer making, there are specialised sets available for making very strong and precise corner.

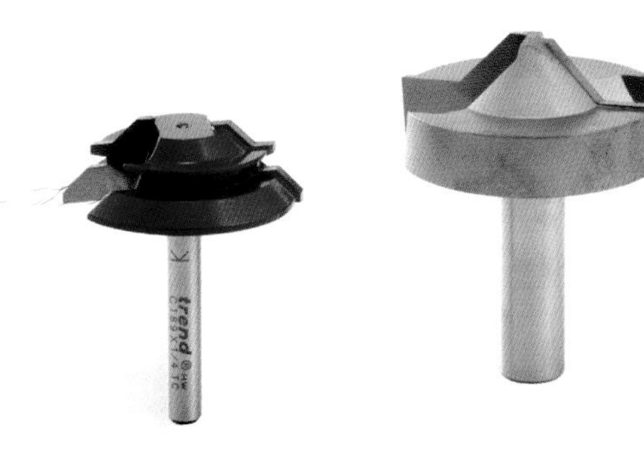

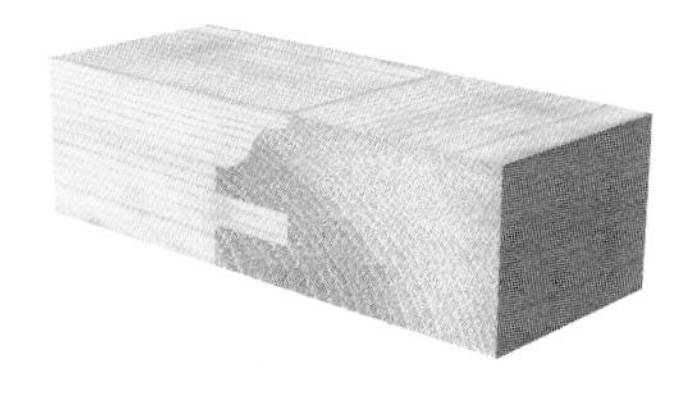

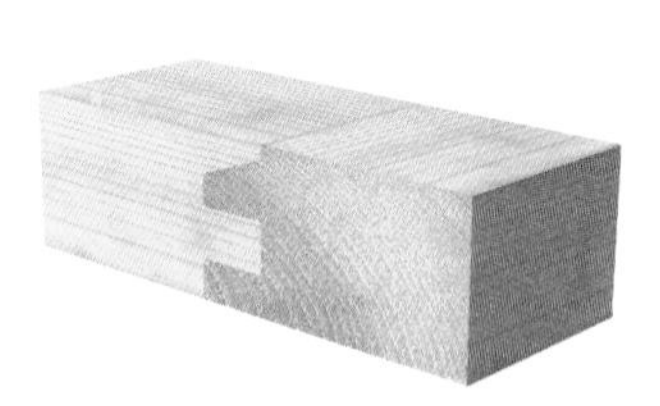

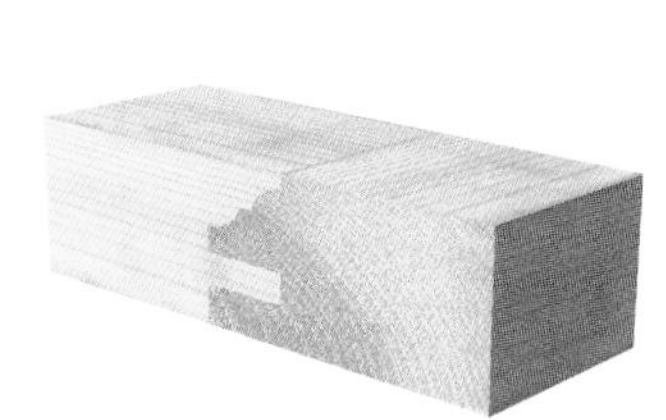

Profile and scribe

There are now single profile cutters with the advantage that they cut the whole joint in one.

They are perfect for light cabinet doors that have an internal panel and are available with a range of different profiles. The cutters were originally produced in pairs; one cutter forms the mould round the edge of all the components and the other cuts a matching scribe that forms the joint. However, newer cutters incorporate both of the required profiles in one; you just vary the cutter height to get the correct one. An alternative is to use a single arbor and re-arrange the cutters on it to suit either the profile or scribe operation. These are all large cutters and are normally only available with 8mm and 1/2" diameter shanks.

Panel raising cutters

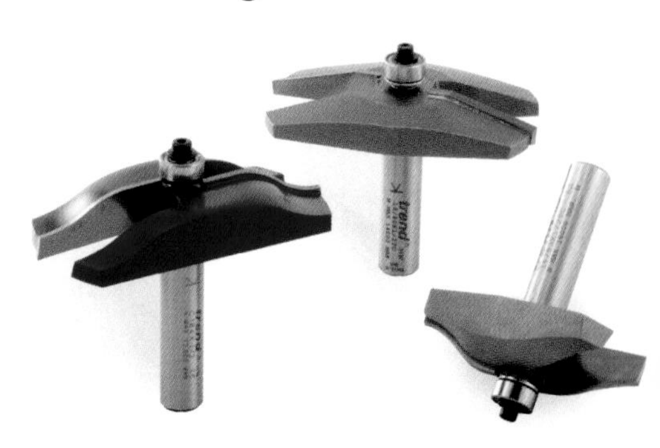

These are used to produce traditional raised and fielded panels, usually in conjunction with the profile scribe cutters.

Available in two forms, they can be either of very large diameter that requires the panel to be worked horizontally, or smaller diameter ones that are used with the panel held vertically. Being so large, it is essential that they are used with a powerful variable speed router that can reduce speed to about 10,000 rpm. Most of the horizontal cutters are bearing guided, so they can field curved or arch topped panels.

Panel mould cutters

These are different from the panel raising cutters in that they are used to cut decorative profiles into an existing plain surface. They are ideal as a means of quickly adding a panel effect detail to a flat door or drawer fronts, but as the cuts are all internal, the corners are necessarily rounded.

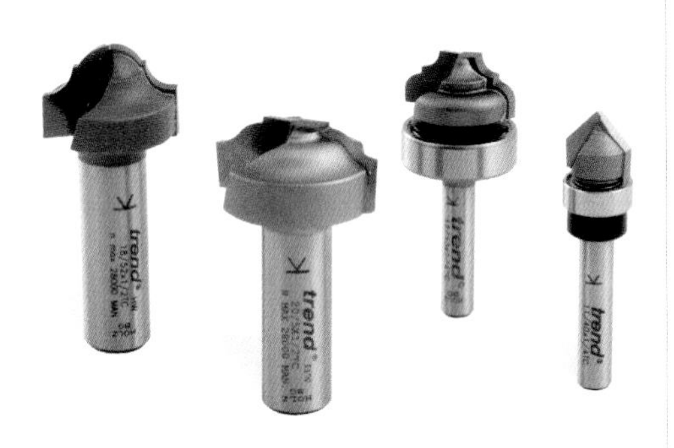

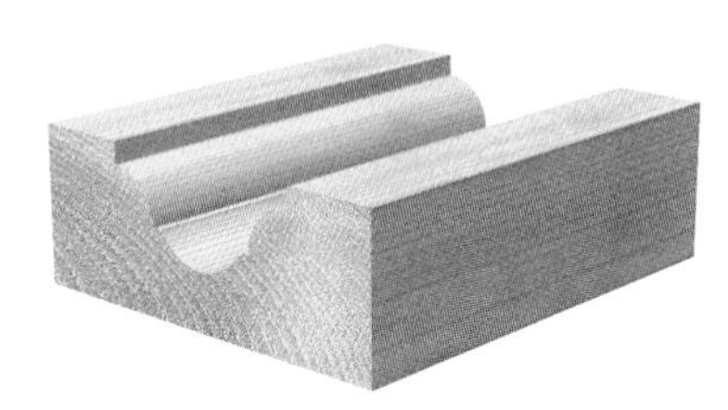

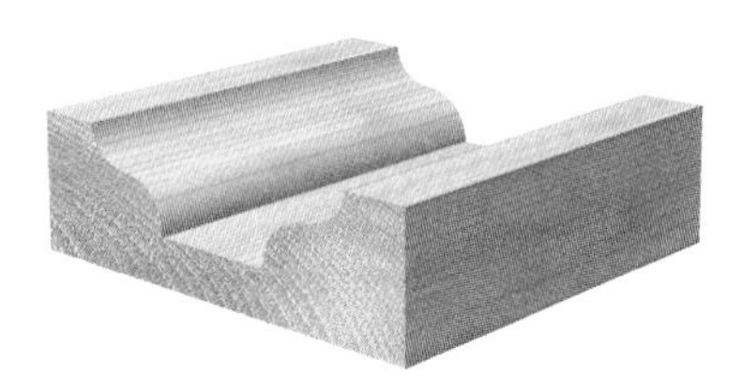

Normally, they are used in conjunction with a template and guide bush follower, though some have a top mounted bearing as a guide.

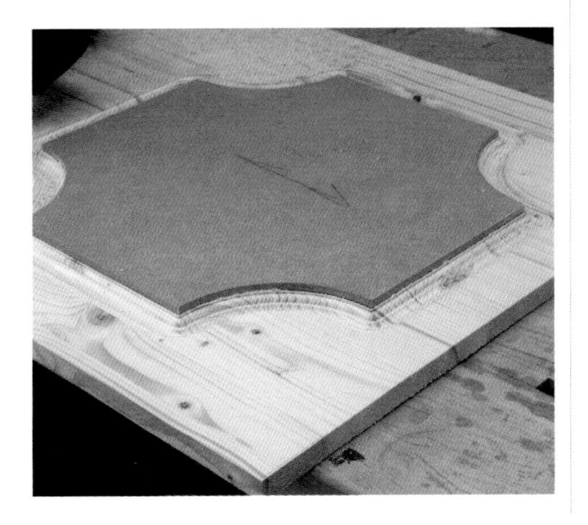

Slotting and grooving cutters

These are primarily functional rather than decorative and usually consist of a standard arbor onto which you mount a selection of different blades to cut very precise slots or grooves. These cutters can be used singly or stacked up in various combinations to produce specific customised profiles. You can intersperse bearings, shims and spacers to control both the depth and the width of the finished cut.

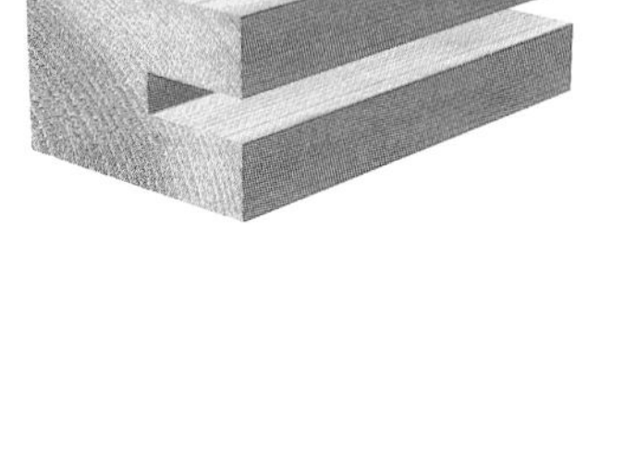

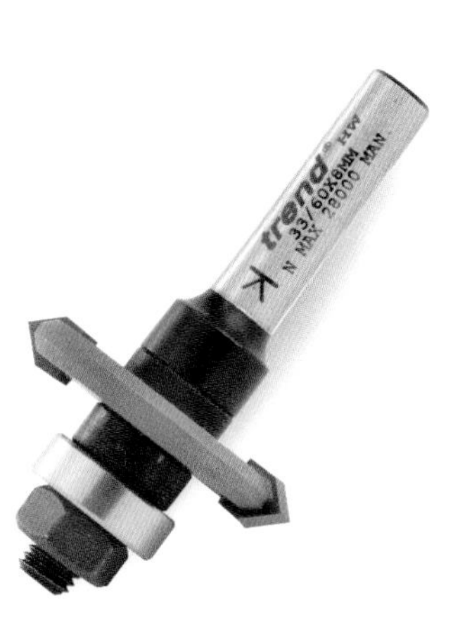

The slotting cutters consist of a flat steel blade which varies in thickness from 1.5 mm up to 20 mm in thickness, with diameters up to 50mm. The usual arrangement is for the disc to have at least two TCT teeth, each ground for precise cutting and clearance angles to ensure that waste clears quickly and freely.

Specialised versions allow you to cut different width grooves with the same cutter.

Other versions make decorative cuts in panels and frames to disguise glue lines, or to produce fluting effects. You can also use them to cut traditional tongue and grooving profiles. There are some threaded cutters that screw onto the arbor leaving no projection, which can then be used to cut flush to the inside of a frame, if for instance you are trying to deepen a recess to take double glazing units.

Dedicated groovers do not use an arbor but are specifically shaped to cut slots for pipes, slat walls and drawer pulls, or for inserting intumescent strips or weatherseal.

One very useful variation of the groover allows you to cut simple biscuit joints without having to go to the expense of a dedicated biscuit jointer machine.

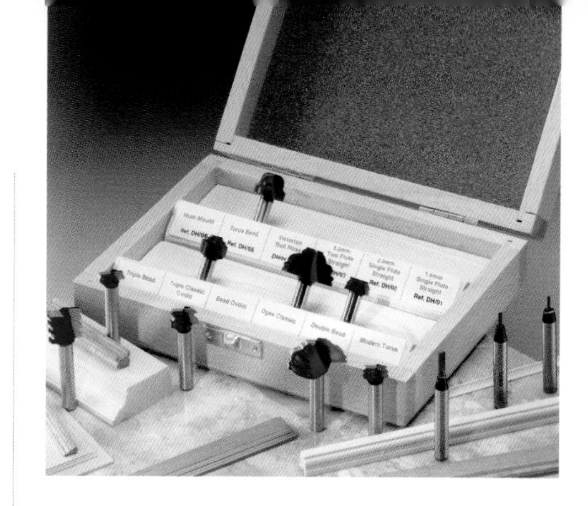

Miniatures

For dolls house work there is now a full range of cutters, all accurately scaled to produce miniature mouldings on skirtings, dados and cornices. These have standard 1/4" shanks and can be used in a conventional router, though a smaller one is easier to handle for this delicate work.

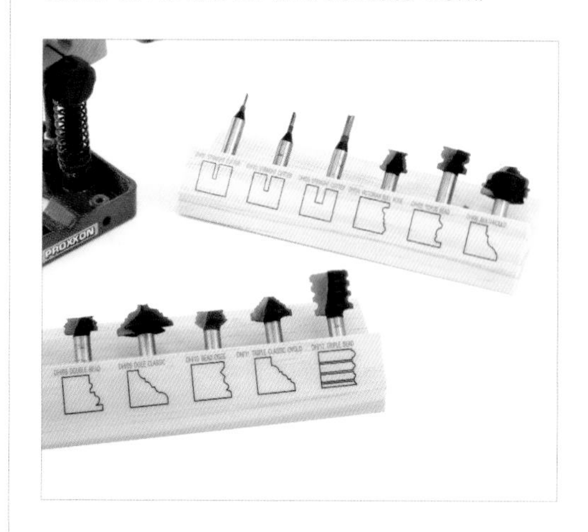

Cornice cutters

Although it is possible to build up a cornice mould with a series of different cuts on separate pieces of timber, it is much easier to use a dedicated cutter. This rather large tooling allows you to form the profile in one pass and then cut the back chamfer with a separate 45° cutter.

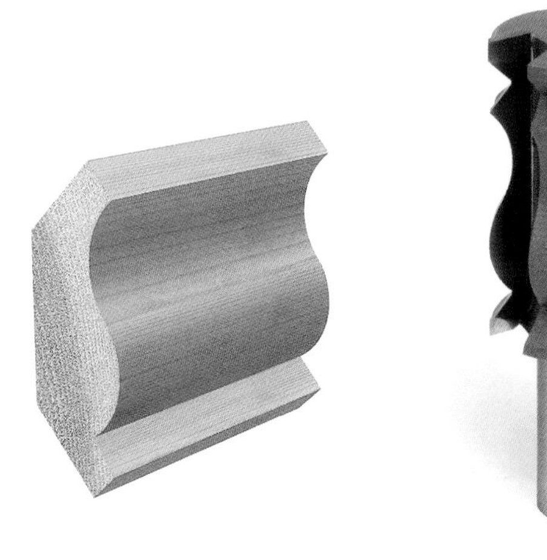

Corian® cutters

Many new kitchens feature Corian®, a resin composite material for making worktops and splashbacks. Although you can work it with standard cutters, there is a whole range of special profiles that have been developed just for this material. As well as having more efficient clearance angles, the cutters have plastic coated bearings to stop any marking of the surface.

Plastic and aluminium cutters

Again there is a specialised range designed to plunge and mill slots in both plastic and non-ferrous metals but particularly aluminium. Made from HSSE, these cutters should only be used with a coolant and also with the workpiece firmly clamped to prevent kickback. A lower speed range is also recommended.

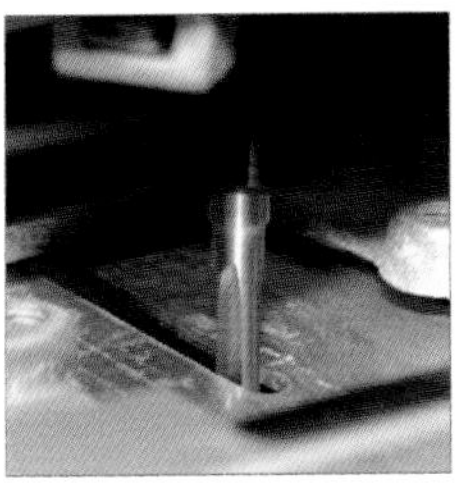

Drills and hinge sinking

Many users overlook the use of the plunge router for drilling, which is a shame because they do it superbly. They have plenty of power and allow straight cutters to be plunged into the work perfectly square, with minimal spelching or breakout. Special drills are available for the accurate sized holes needed for dowelling.

One of the best uses of the router is for drilling recesses for hinges using a dedicated hinge sinker. With all the fences and stops on the router, a hinge hole can be positioned and drilled with perfect accuracy.

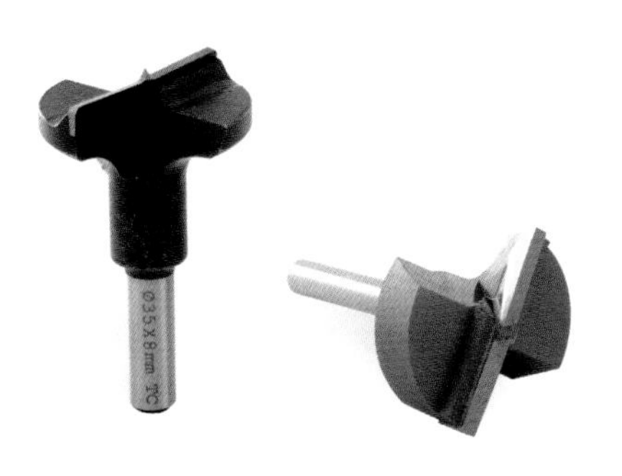

Burrs and rasps

Materials like GRP, metal, plastic and wood can all be ground with special burrs and rasps that are available for use in the router.

Made from either TC or STC, these cutters are often used freehand with the router motor removed from the base. Running at full rpm, they are largely used for de-burring metal, but the coarser rasps are popular for carving wood in the craft trades.

3. SAFETY

Using basic common sense, rather than rigidly following formal regulations, is at the heart of all safe woodworking practices. However, with routing you need to couple this realistic approach to an understanding of the obvious physical dangers from the machine, its cutters and the workpiece, as well as the less apparent risks to health, such as noise and dust.

Although we all tend to take safety for granted, with routers many of the dangers are more exaggerated because the cutting tool is hand-held and very much closer to you. It produces a lot of noise and dust and there are often exposed cutters spinning so fast you can hardly see them.

However, protecting yourself from potential danger is simple and when used correctly, the router is quite safe. Most accidents are down to operator error rather than equipment failure, but you must stay alert and be prepared for any eventuality. At 28,000 rpm accidents can happen fast!

Safety issues can be divided into a number of categories, some of which affect you directly like noise and dust. Others are less clearly defined such as safe workholding, feed direction and router maintenance.

Only key safety issues will be covered in detail in this section, the others are discussed in their relevant chapters elsewhere in this book.

Personal protection and health

Many of these dangers are obvious and quickly countered by even the least safety conscious router user. Nevertheless, it is worth considering them in some detail so you can decide on your own strategy to minimise any health dangers.

Eye protection

Eyes, your most precious asset, must be protected at all times. Normally the risk is minimal, just from flying chips or dust but there is potential for a cutter to break. Sometimes one of the router screws can vibrate loose and fall into the cutter, this has happened to me on a number of occasions and you are then presented with a situation where impact protection is vital as well. Loose knots in the wood are another potential danger as they can be scooped up and thrown out violently by the spinning cutter.

The options for eye protection are goggles, safety glasses or a face shield. Safety glasses are most comfortable and if you already wear glasses you can have a safety version made up to your existing prescription by your optician.

Goggles are a bit more cumbersome and can impair all-round vision, but they can be used over existing glasses if need be. Visors are another alternative as they give better general head protection and sit well off your face.

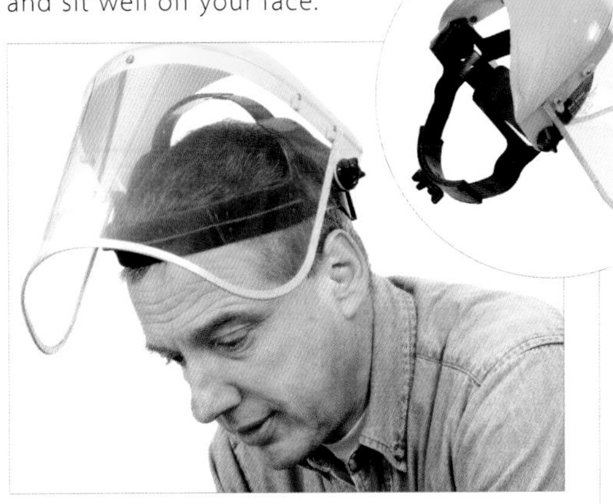

The type which flip up are best as you can lift them out of the way when you are not actually routing or if you need to take a closer look at something.

Hearing protection

It is generally recognised that exposure to noise above 80 decibels can cause permanent damage to your hearing. As most routers operate at over 100 decibels it is essential that some form of ear defenders are used, usually in the form of spring loaded muffs or conventional earplugs.

As neither of these is particularly comfortable to wear you have to be really disciplined about using them and always keep them handy. Remember, that hearing damage happens gradually and usually only becomes apparent when it is too late.

Respiratory protection

Dust is another danger that is cumulative and doesn't display any major symptoms until the damage has been done. We are just becoming aware of the whole health picture regarding dust, and fortunately manufacturers are responding by bringing out a range of masks, shields and powered extraction helmets that offer varying levels of protection.

The action of the router tends to generate clouds of dust as well as the more obvious chippings, but it is this really fine dust that does the damage to your health. It builds up in your lungs and the introduction of more toxic materials like MDF has exacerbated the problem.

The Health and Safety Executive classifies all wood dusts as toxic and possibly harmful, particularly with prolonged exposure. It is therefore essential to protect against these dangers, even when dust extraction is fitted to the router itself.

Unfortunately in the case of dust, the level of protection is reflected in the amount you are prepared to spend on protection. It is tempting to penny pinch, but remember that continued good health has no price.

At the very least you must always wear a simple dust mask of some sort. The cheap ones are effective to a degree, so you don't have to spend a fortune to get something that will at least provide basic protection.

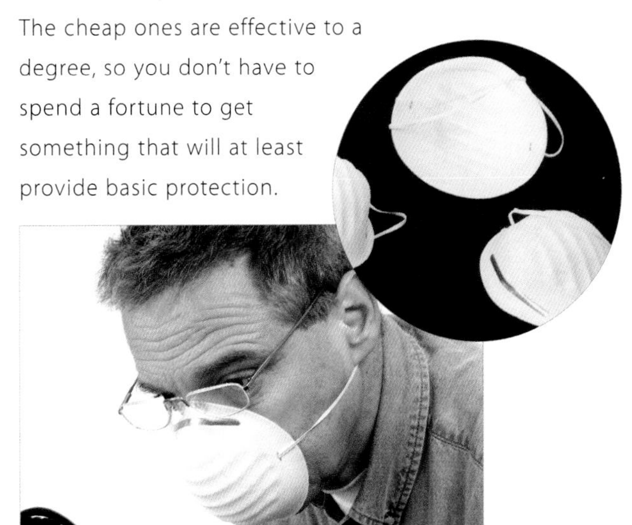

The cheapest paper and cloth type will need replacing after only a few hours, as they rapidly becoming soggy and uncomfortable. They don't necessarily fit the contours of you face either and some types of mask will also cause your glasses to steam up as you work, so check this out.

Remember that the dust doesn't stop when the router does. It will hang in the air for a considerable time, so unlike hearing protection you may need to keep the mask on for some time.

A better alternative is the respirator mask that provides very efficient filtration and you can even change the filter to suit different nuisance dusts or odours.

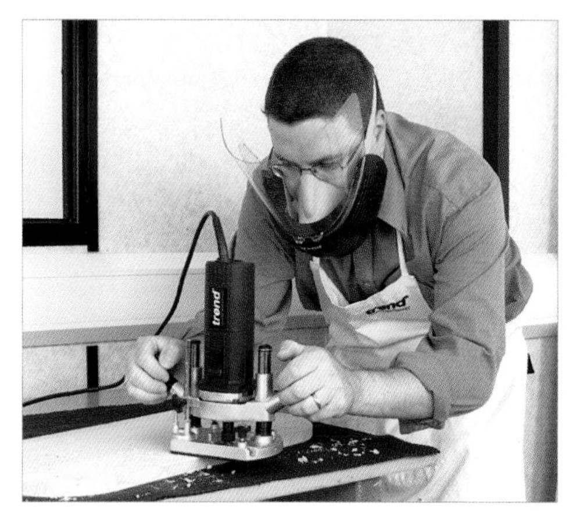

Although effective, these can become uncomfortable to wear particularly for extended periods, though the better ones have special valves to minimise uncomfortable moisture build-up and may even have an optional visor.

The best dust protection is provided by an air fed helmet. These battery operated masks feed a stream of clean filtered air down over your face, giving almost total dust protection.

They are very close fitting, even if you wear glasses or have a beard and the visor is impact resistant as well, so there is no need for additional goggles or safety glasses.

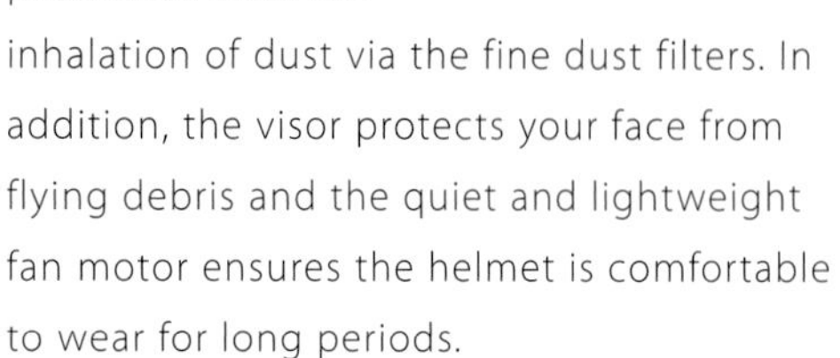

It is claimed that particles down to 1 micron are filtered out by these helmets. They provide excellent protection from the inhalation of dust via the fine dust filters. In addition, the visor protects your face from flying debris and the quiet and lightweight fan motor ensures the helmet is comfortable to wear for long periods.

Clothing

It is also important to wear the right sort of clothing in the workshop and proper footwear is a good starting point. It is very easy to drop a piece of material on your foot particularly when both hands are holding the router. Fine dust on the floor can also make it slippery so non-skid shoes or work boots with built-in toe protection are always recommended.

The rest of your clothing should be of the close fitting type preferably with no pockets, as these soon fill up with sawdust. A zip front smock with a rear pocket is ideal as there are no loose bits flapping about that can get caught in either the machine or the work.

Remember that your sleeves are very close to both, so elasticated cuffs are better, otherwise roll up your sleeves.

Being able to take off you overall before leaving the workshop is the best way to confine all the mess to one place.

Workshop safety

As well as protecting yourself personally, you also need to take some precautions with regard to workshop safety. Often, the area where you have to work is not a dedicated workshop. It may have to be shared with the washing machine or the kid's bikes, so it is even more important to observe some basic safety precautions.

For a start you need the work area to be well lit and preferably by daylight. If it is not, a mixture of tungsten and fluorescent lights is usually sufficient provided there is plenty of it. You need to be able to see clearly what you are doing.

You also need a good power supply and the more sockets you have the better, so you can then plug in where the cable is least likely to cause a trip hazard. Avoid overloading sockets by using lots of multiple adaptors.

If you can arrange it, some overhead sockets are excellent for minimising trailing cables.

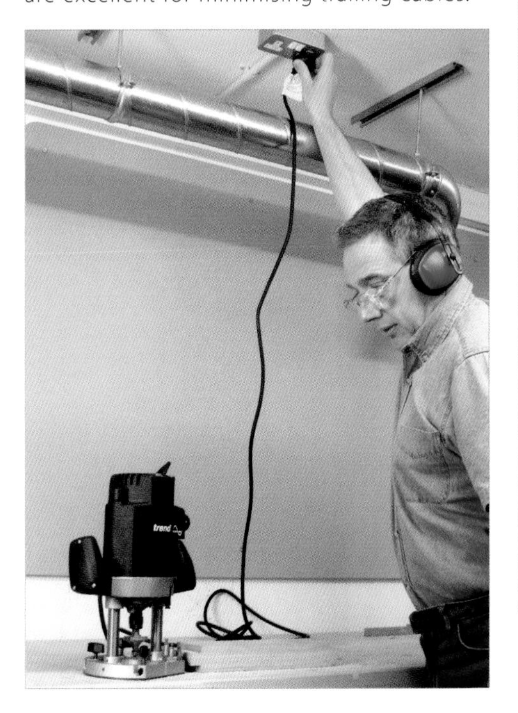

This works even better if you can install a few hooks in the ceiling to loop the cable over and keep it well out of the way.

To avoid getting tangled up if you are making circular cuts around a workpiece, make a dummy run first before you actually switch on. This will also show if you can make the cut in one easy pass. If you have to keep stopping to change your stance or position, the cut will show small burn marks, so if possible find a working position that allows one smooth movement.

Check that plugs are fitted with the right sized fuse. Most power tools are adequately protected by a 5 or 13 amp fuse, which is usually fitted in the moulded plug supplied on the tool.

If for any reason you need to change this plug, fit a fuse that is correctly rated to suit the power of the tool.

Always make sure you unplug the router before changing cutters. Switches can easily be knocked on accidentally and the consequences don't bear thinking about when you are handling the cutter. This happened to me once, but I only suffered a ruined overall, so don't think it will never happen. Also make sure the switch is 'off' before you plug in again.

Even in a small workshop you may have a dozen or more power tools, often with several plugged in at once, so it is important to label each plug to make sure you pull out the right one. Never unplug by pulling on the lead.

Whatever the type of electrical installation in the workshop, do make sure it is routed through an RCD circuit breaker to provide protection in the event of a fault, or if you accidentally cut the cable.

The workspace area also needs to be as clear as possible, as it is so easy to stumble over offcuts of timber or half finished work. Tidy up on a regular basis removing waste and debris.

Piles of shavings and chippings are also a fire hazard and removing this debris will also minimise the time spent searching for cutters or tools that might end up in the accumulated rubbish.

Give any routing job your full concentration at all times, particularly as you come to the end of a cut and automatically tend to relax.

Make sure you are not going to be interrupted and try to prevent other people distracting you.

Allow plenty of time to finish the job. Many accidents are caused by rushing or taking short cuts and certainly don't use a router if you are tired or ill.

Always check that the workpiece is held really firmly and work on a suitable bench at a comfortable height.

Although you can protect yourself from the noise, remember that others around you probably can't, so give some consideration to your neighbours if you have lots of routing to do, particularly if you have to do it outside. Proper insulation to the workshop is a good investment as it will minimise noise transmission as well as keeping you warm.

Keep a well stocked first aid kit handy to deal with minor cuts and bruises, and if you work alone always ensure you have a phone to summon help in the unlikely event of a more serious injury.

Dust management

Much has already been said about protecting yourself from the effects of dust, but you can do a lot by trying to catch the dust at source and preventing it spreading out into the workshop.

Most router manufacturers have started to address the problem and have developed clip-on dust spouts or shields designed to be used in conjunction with a vacuum extractor.

The problem with many of these spouts is that they can restrict both the visibility and access to the cutter. Some are better than others but there is a trade off here between effectiveness and ease of use. The worst ones are so inconvenient that you end up dispensing with them; not what was intended. Similarly, if you have to remove the spout every time you change the cutter it becomes very tedious.

Also bear in mind that acrylic hoods may be fine when they are new, but with only a little use the static build up is such that fine dust sticks all over it and you cannot then see what you are doing.

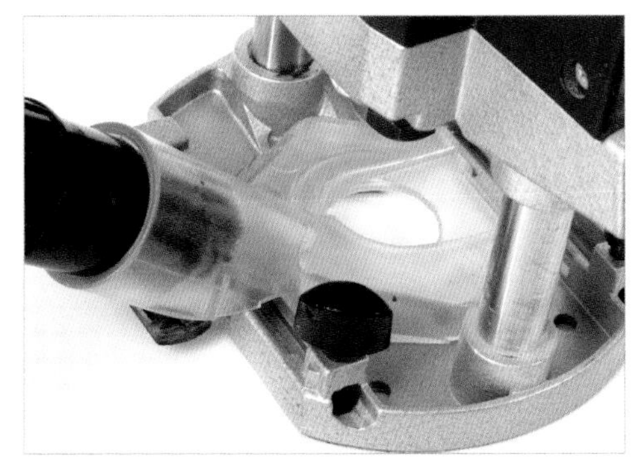

The other problem with 'on board extraction' is that the addition of the hose from the extractor can make the router cumbersome and more difficult to balance.

Extraction spouts that exit vertically rather than horizontally are a far better option, particularly if you can rig up an overhead support for the hose.

To collect the dust, you need a vacuum unit and the choice is quite extensive.

The answer for connecting to power tools is a high pressure low volume collector, HPLV, which works on the same principle as a domestic vacuum cleaner.

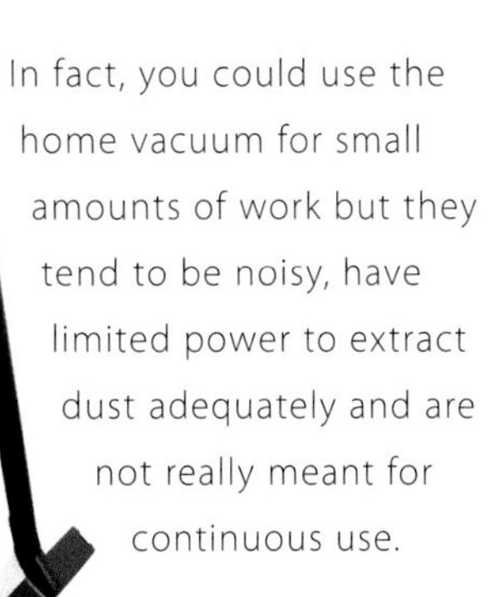

In fact, you could use the home vacuum for small amounts of work but they tend to be noisy, have limited power to extract dust adequately and are not really meant for continuous use.

The other type of extractor is the high volume low pressure type commonly used for machines that generate large amounts of waste such as planers and sawbenches.

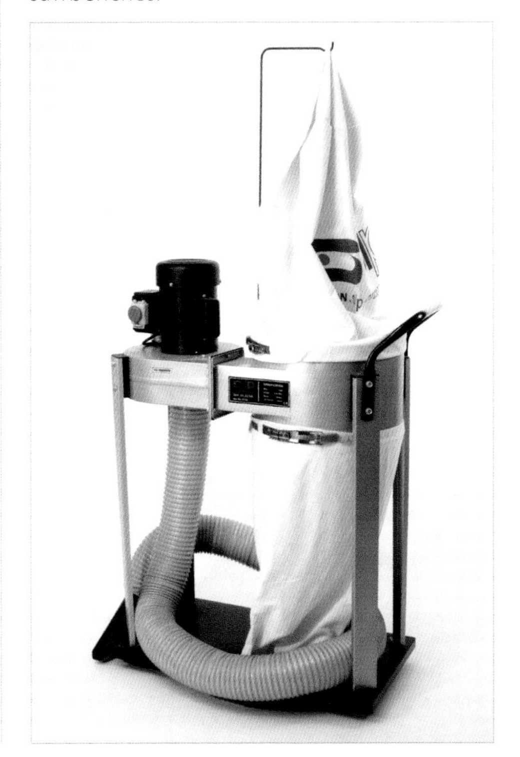

These work on a different principle and are not actually good at dealing with fine dust, as they tend to just blow it back out into the workshop through the top filter bag. They also have big diameter hoses, but don't be tempted to try and reduce their outlets to connect up to power tools. This does not increase the suction as you would think, but actually greatly reduces it.

The answer is to buy a dedicated workshop vacuum extractor that is designed for just this purpose. They usually come with a collection of connectors that allow you to hook up to a variety of different tools, as well as using them for conventional cleaning up.

They are totally enclosed and incorporate multi stage filtration that is effective down to a particle size of less than one micron.

Although such a system is very effective, you have to remember to switch the extractor on every time you use the router, which can get tedious if there are lots of cuts.

To overcome this snag the better ones feature 'auto start', which allows you to plug the tool directly into the vacuum. With these the vacuum then kicks in automatically when you switch on the tool and switches off again when you switch off the tool, but they have a time delay that will keep it running for a few seconds after you have switched off to clear the spout and hose.

These extractors are generally more powerful and quieter than their domestic equivalents, and the hose is longer and more flexible making it easier to handle.

A few of the more expensive routers feature built-in extraction hoods, which are obviously far less intrusive. Although these still need to be connected to an extractor, the waste is taken up through the body of the machine.

Remember that the effectiveness of the extraction may be compromised by fitting attachments like the side-fence or guide bushes. These may block the suction path, though some manufacturers have tried to minimise the effects by making guide bushes skeletal rather than solid.

There are some extraction hoods that mount on the fence bars and these are a good solution for straight forward edging work, but they are not suitable for any other cuts, as the hood gets in the way.

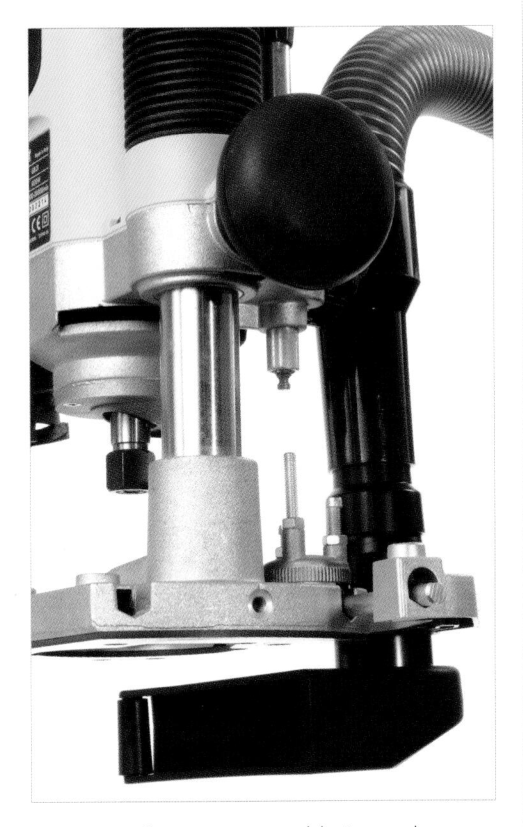

Extraction from a router table is much more straight forward. The fence assembly usually incorporates an outlet spout which does not need to move so you can make a really positive connection to it.

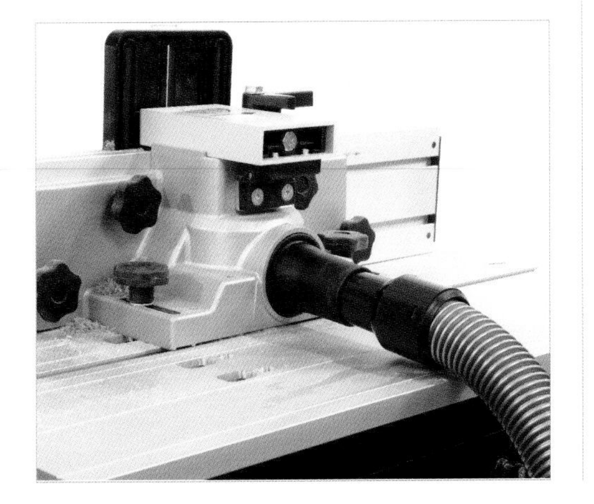

Although this will remove a lot of the waste, there is always some that drops down into the router casing, so spend a few minutes sucking it all out occasionally. Unfortunately, no matter what form of extraction is adopted, it will never be totally effective and should be used in addition to the personal protection strategies already described.

As a final measure, you might like to consider installing an ambient air filter. These self-contained units usually hang up on the ceiling, cleaning the whole workshop environment.

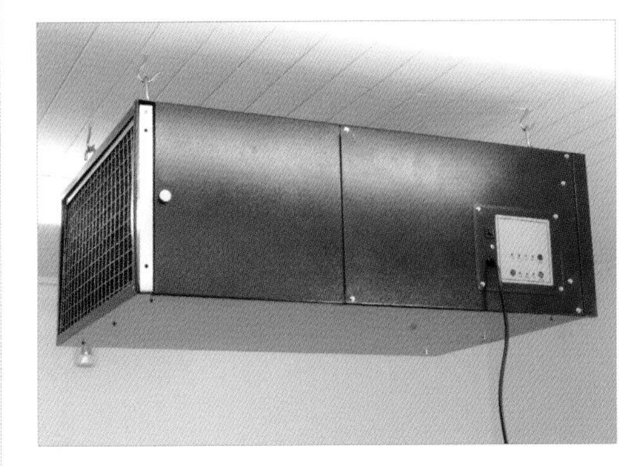

They make an amazing difference to the air quality and minimise that layer of fine and dangerous dust that accumulates on all the workshop shelves. They are cheap to run and maintain, working silently in the background, a must for the serious woodworker.

Safety checklist

Although many of the following precautions have already been discussed, or are explored in more detail in other chapters, it is as well to reiterate a basic safety checklist. The features are in no particular order and the list is not exhaustive, but it should help you maintain a safe routing environment

1. Remember that a router is a power tool and should be treated with respect so read the user manual, stay alert and don't work if you are tired.
2. Take all the necessary personal protection precautions.
3. Always unplug the router when changing cutters or accessories and make sure it is switched off before plugging back in.
4. Only use good quality bits that are kept sharp and clean and properly fitted into the collet.
5. Make sure the work is securely clamped in place before you approach it with the router.
6. Never try to rout small pieces unless they are clamped or held in a suitable jig.
7. Always make deep cuts in a series of shallower passes.
8. As you prepare the timber cut some spare stock for making test cuts to check cutter settings.
9. Remember that some electric tools spark, so don't use them near flammable solvents.
10. Don't use the router in wet conditions.
11. Don't contact the wood until the router has reached full speed and always feed in the correct direction.
12. Tighten up all locking knobs before you start and make sure that their anti-vibration springs are in place.
13. Leave bits to cool down before removing them from the collet. Check the collet regularly for dirt and wear.
14. Don't overload low powered routers with heavy cuts or with large diameter bits and match the rotation speed accordingly if the router has variable speed.
15. Where possible, use an extractor to minimise swarf build up that can affect the cut.
16. Cutters are sharp and may require handling with gloves if they become stuck in the collet or when removing them from the manufacturer's protective wax covering.
17. Use only quality cutters and ideally those conforming to Holz BG or the new EN standard. This guarantees that they have been thoroughly tested and have appropriate chip limiting features.
18. Always select the shortest possible length of cutter that will do the job and if there is a choice pick the largest shank diameter. Make sure the collet capacity matches the bit diameter perfectly.
19. If you are not retracting the cutter after a cut, wait until it stops before you put it down and ideally place the router on a block to protect both you and the cutter.
20. When the router is not in use put it away on a shelf or preferably in a cupboard to prevent shavings and dust falling into the top motor grille.

4. GETTING STARTED

If you are a nervous newcomer to routing and particularly if this is your first machine, it is important to spend a little time familiarising yourself with the controls, features and accessories.

It may all look a bit intimidating at first so you need to build up some confidence in its handling and thoroughly understand what it all does. Take it out of the box, read the instruction book and then have a play with the various components. You will soon realise that there is nothing at all complicated about a router.

Getting to know your router

With any new machine, even a brand new one, it is worth making a few basic checks before you get started. Inexpensive models are not always assembled with the care you would expect and are often covered with a thick layer of protective grease, so you need to get all this cleaned up before you start.

Initial checks

1. Check the machine thoroughly for any transit damage and compare the list of parts in the manual to what you have in reality. This will help familiarise you with some of the terminology as well.

2. Remove the collet and lock nut. Clean off any protective grease and apply a little light machine oil.

3. Make sure the plunge columns are really clean, and then apply a light coating of dry spray lubricant.

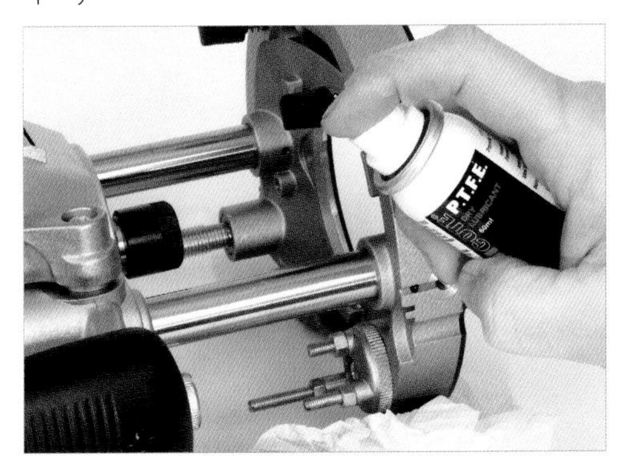

4. Release the plunge lock and check that the action operates smoothly by bringing the carriage up and down a few times. The lock should grip positively without having to apply excessive pressure.

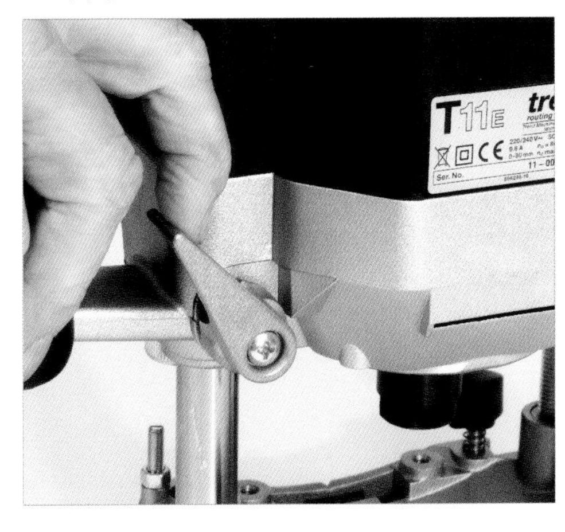

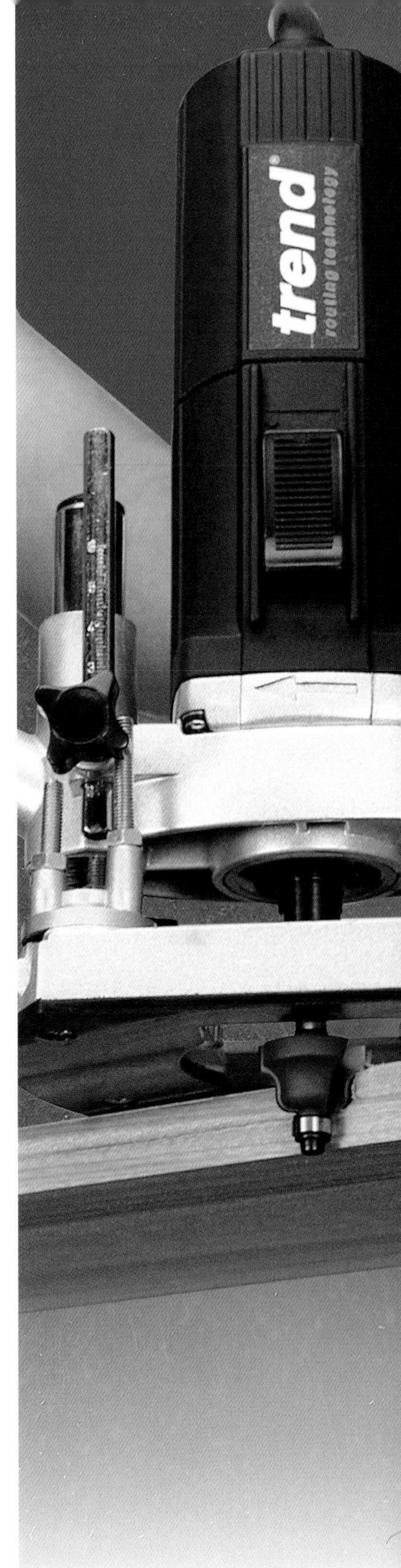

5. Check that all screw threads are clear of swarf and that the clamping screws and other threaded parts operate without binding or cross threading.

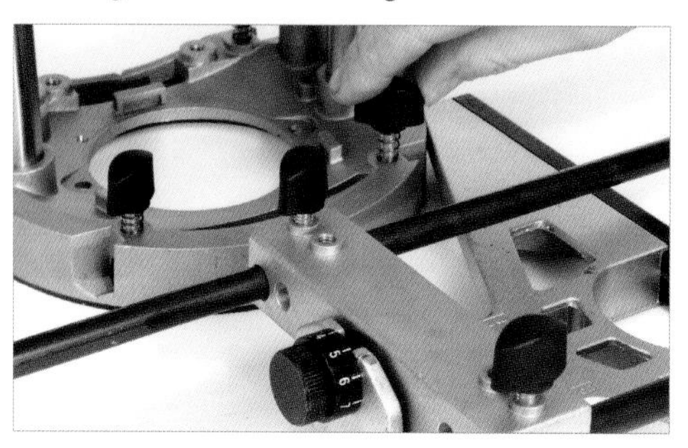

6. With the aid of the instruction book, try fitting all the other loose parts and accessories together. The fine adjusters and other controls should work easily.

7. Plug the machine in and see how the motor runs. It should feel smooth and not vibrate excessively. There may be some initial sparking as the new brushes bed in, but this should settle down after a few minutes running.

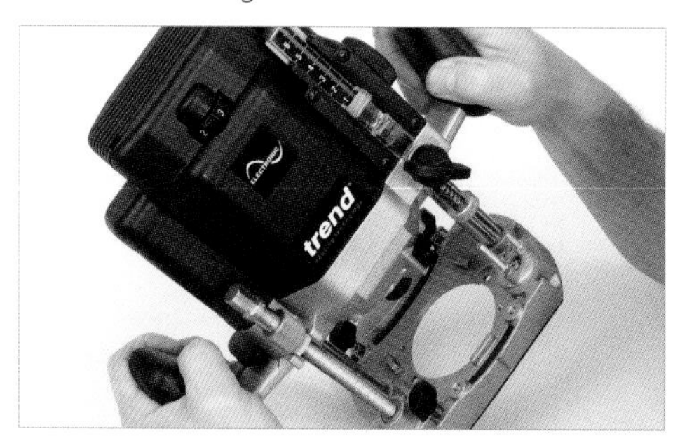

8. If it has variable speed, check that this control operates correctly with a smooth, stepless speed transition.

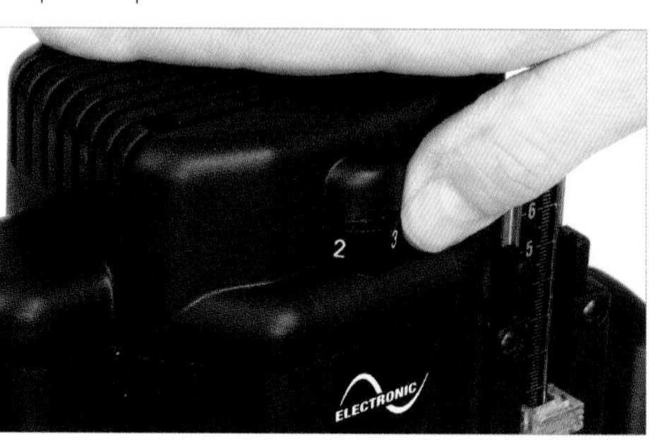

If all is well, you are now ready to put your new router to work, so let's make a start and fit a cutter.

Fitting a cutter

Before you start making any adjustments, make sure the router is unplugged from the mains and get into the habit of doing this every time you change cutters.

Remember, "keep your fingers out until the plug is out!"

Some routers are supplied with several different sized collets so make sure you fit the correct one for the cutters you are using. Better quality ones should be clearly labelled. Remember that the difference between metric and imperial collets is often minute, but enough to damage both the collet and cutter if you mismatch them.

Where appropriate, fit the collet into the locknut before you insert it into the spindle.

Take care not to cross-thread the nut as the thread is very fine and easy to fit incorrectly. If you are struggling with this, try turning it anti-clockwise a few times first just to line it up and then screw it on clockwise a few turns with your fingers.

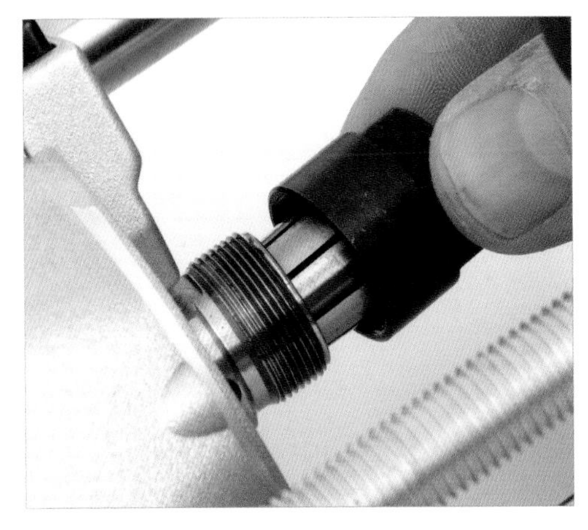

Fit the cutter by pushing at least three quarters of the shank length into the collet, or up to the insertion point if it is marked. This amount is essential for a secure grip that won't cause the cutter to vibrate or damage the shank.

Don't insert the shank in completely in the mistaken belief that it will be even more secure. In this situation, the collet tries to tighten up on the irregular web at the

bottom, but can then only grip unevenly, if at all. Also, the shank can bottom onto the actual router spindle which leads to excessive vibration and may damage the motor. There are similar problems if you don't push the shank in far enough and you should resist the temptation to gain extra depth of cut by hanging the cutter a long way out of the collet.

There is a real danger here of the cutter coming out and/or damaging the collet.

Tighten up the nut as far as you can by hand and then lock it using the spanner provided with the machine. Modern routers have a spindle lock so you only need to use one spanner, but make sure it is the right size or you will round over the nut.
Don't over tighten the nut. Remember that the spanner gives huge leverage and there is no need to lean on it with tremendous force. If the cutter shank and collet are both in good condition you should be able to get it secure with moderate pressure only. If you cannot, something is wrong somewhere, so check the condition of the nut and collet.

Setting the depth of cut

No matter what type of cut you are making, it is essential to preset the final depth using the stop built into the router. These stops vary from a simple rod and clamping knob to a more sophisticated geared slide.

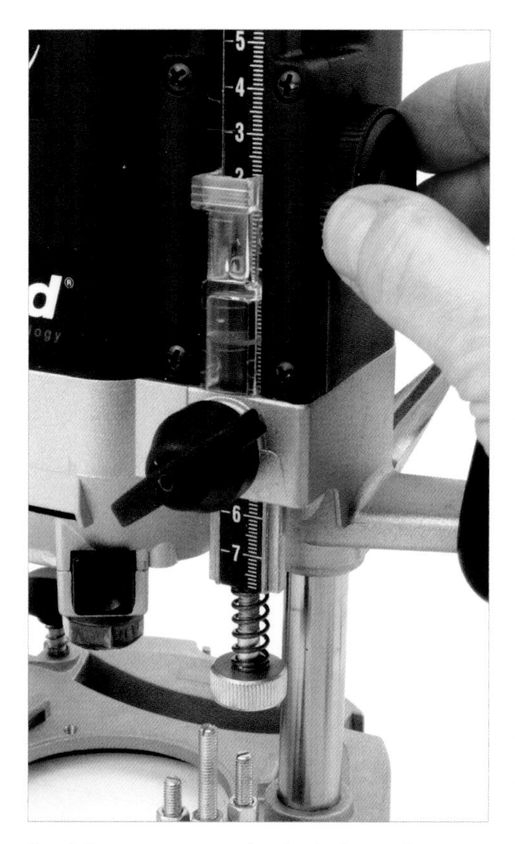

Precision stops may also include a micro adjustment or dial gauge. The stops allow you to cut grooves, housings and recesses to a consistent depth, particularly if you are making multiple passes. Remember, that to avoid overloading the router and tooling, make deep cuts by taking a series of shallower passes to reach full depth.

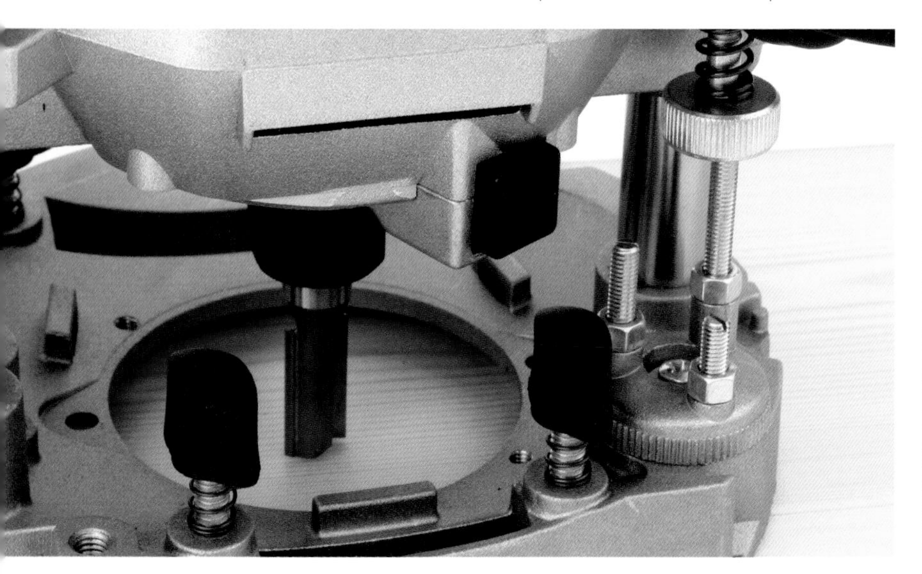

There are several ways to set the depth stop, depending on what you are doing.

The simplest way is to stand the router on a flat surface and plunge down until the cutter just touches the surface, then lock the plunge mechanism. Now lower the depth stop rod until it touches one of the spindles of the turret stop, ideally the lowest one. Refer to the scale on the router body prior to raising the rod by the required depth of cut and locking it in place with the knob. Release the plunge lock and let the router resume its normal resting position.

Whilst this method is quick and easy for most situations, it isn't over precise and there are alternatives where the depth setting is more critical, for instance, when inlaying something like a hinge. In this case, use a piece of the actual inlay material itself as the spacer between the rod and turret.

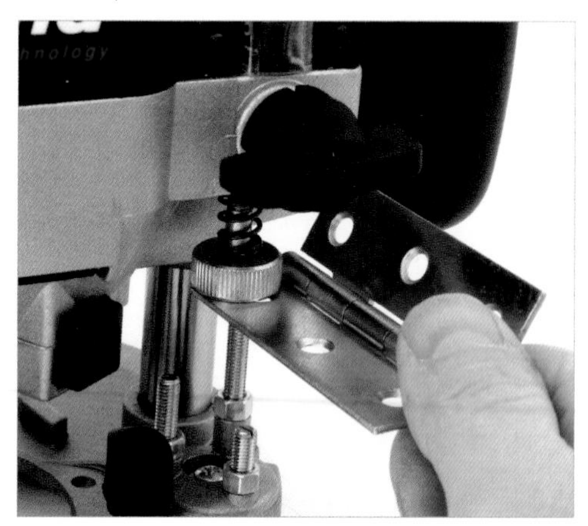

Alternatively, turn the router upside down and use a rule or gauge to set how far the cutter protrudes, adjusting it with the plunge action. Lock up at the required depth and then fix the depth stop rod at this setting.

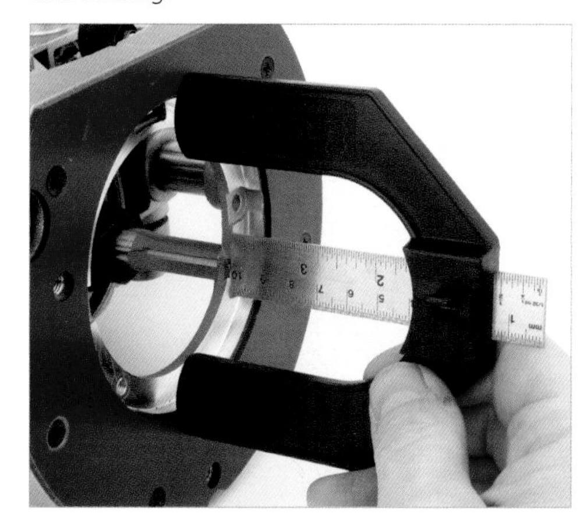

Always make a trial cut in a piece of scrap if the setting is critical, or consider fitting a fine adjuster which will allow very precise depth control by over-riding the plunge action and effectively giving you all the precision of a fixed base router. Usually, sold as an accessory, the majority of these fine adjusters replace the depth stop rod and screw directly into one of the turret spindles, though some are built into the plunge column.

With the plunge lock released, they allow you to screw the body down in a very controlled way, but remember to lock it up when you reach the required setting as vibration during a cut can cause the adjuster to unscrew.

A fine adjuster like this is vital if you are working with the router inverted under a table, or with many of the jigs like a dovetailer where the fit of the joint relies on minute adjustments to the cut depth.

The turret stop is provided so that you can make a series of cuts at preset depths. This is particularly useful if you have a very deep cut to make and want to divide it up into a series of intermediate shallower passes.

Using a three position turret stop

Once the turret stops are set up, the procedure for using them is as follows:

Step 1
Set the turret stops to equal steps (i.e. 3mm or as required). Lower the tip of cutter onto workface and set the depth rod to equal a distance of 3mm above highest stop.

Graduated scale on router
Cutter
Router depth rod
Turret stop
Router base
Workpiece

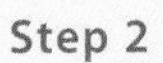

Step 2
Plunge cut to the first stop (3mm) and rout to complete cut to that depth.

3mm

Step 3
Rotate turret to the centre stop and cut the work to that depth (i.e. 6mm total depth of cut.

6mm

Step 4
Rotate turret to the lowest stop and cut the work to that depth (i.e. 9mm total depth of cut).

9mm

Step 5
To cut a further depth, set the cutter to the bottom of the cut, and retract the depth stop rod. Rotate the turret back to highest stop and set the rod to the required depth (i.e. 3mm). Repeat steps 2 to 4 until required depth of cut is reached.

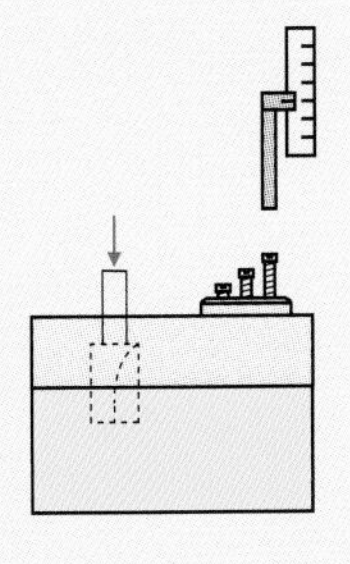

The cutter turret rotates on 'click stops' to line up under the stop rod for each pass. However, each turret is independently adjustable relative to the others. To adjust, simply slacken off the lock nut, then wind the screw in or out with a screwdriver and then re-secure it with the locknut.

Sometimes you don't always want to retract the cutter back into the router base, particularly if it is at a fixed setting with a fine adjuster. But avoid putting the router down on the bench with the cutter exposed as this is potentially dangerous and damaging to both you and the cutter, especially if you don't wait for the cutter to come to a stop first.

Therefore your first job should be to make a safety block which allows you to put the router down, no matter how much cutter is exposed. This is just a block of 50mm timber with a large hole drilled in the centre.

Use this to ensure that both you and the cutter are always protected, it will soon become one of your most useful router accessories!

Using the side-fence

All routers come with a side-fence, which is essential for machining grooves and mouldings in a straight line, either on an edge or parallel to it.

It fits onto the router with two guide rods, though some smaller machines may rely on just one. Coarse adjustment to the width is made by sliding it along the rods then locking it in place with the knobs.

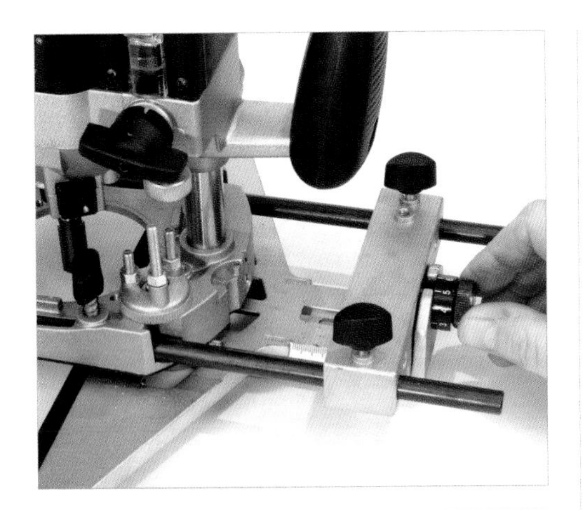

As with the depth control, you can also add a fine adjuster for more precise setting, measuring the fence to cutter distance with a steel rule.

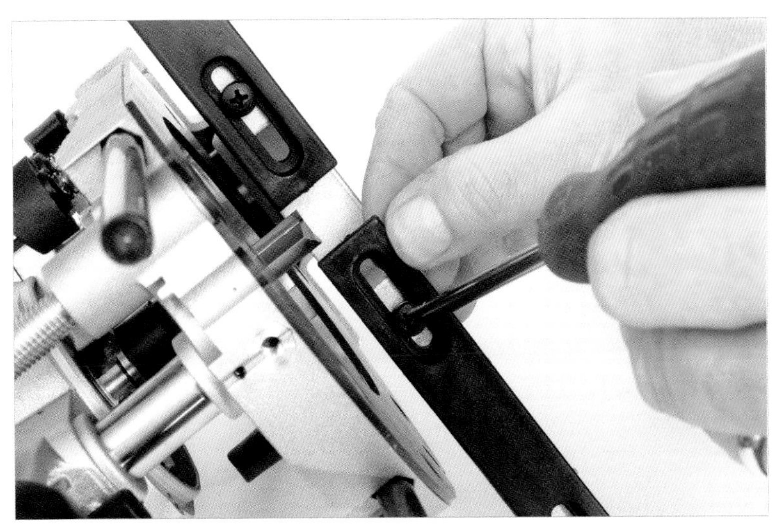

Side-fences are generally fitted with plastic facings that are slotted to allow you to close the gap between their ends and the cutter. Making this gap as narrow as possible reduces any risk of the fence pulling in at either end of the cut, but do leave at least 3mm clearance to allow shavings to clear freely from around the cutter. Whilst it is not essential, try and make the effort to adjust the gap to suit each cutter, particularly if you are working with extreme sizes.

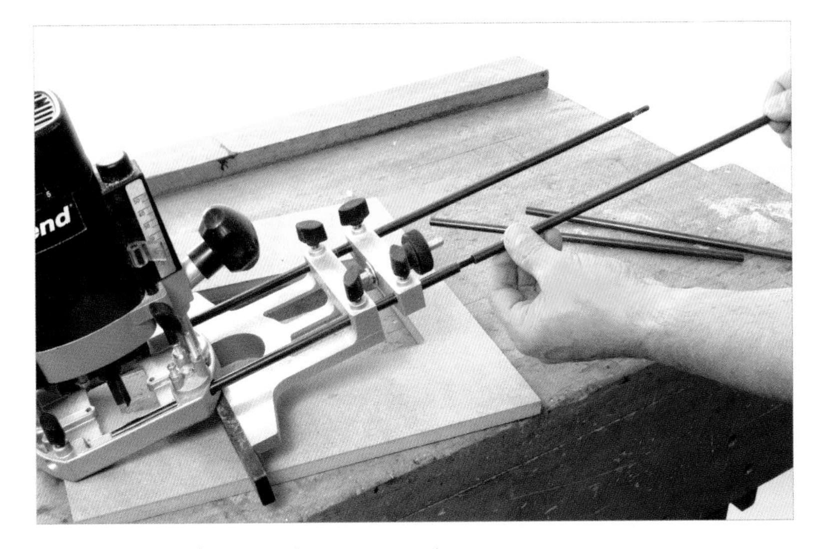

The maximum distance that a cut can be made from the edge of a workpiece is determined by the length of the fence rods. This distance can be increased by substituting longer rods and some manufacturers offer this as an option. However, if the length gets excessive they tend to flex unduly and the cutter starts deflecting off line.

Tip

Make sure you don't lose the springs that are fitted under all the locking knobs. These are an anti-vibration device, designed to stop the knobs unscrewing and falling out into the cutter. This can happen, especially if you are working without the fence and the knobs work loose.

Handling and feeding the router

Newcomers to routing have the understandable tendency to grip the tool tightly and press it down too hard onto the work. However, this tends to inhibit smooth movements and in fact the router is then more likely to snatch.

Instead, hold the router by the side handles in a firm but relaxed way and complete each pass in a steady continuous movement, keeping the same feed rate throughout.

Take care not to slow down at any corners or other changes of direction, as this always leaves burn marks that are difficult to remove later.

Most routers have their handles set fairly low on the base which gives better control. However, the lower you can hold it the better and there are some specially made sub-bases which you can bolt on for better balance and to reduce any tendency for the router to tip.

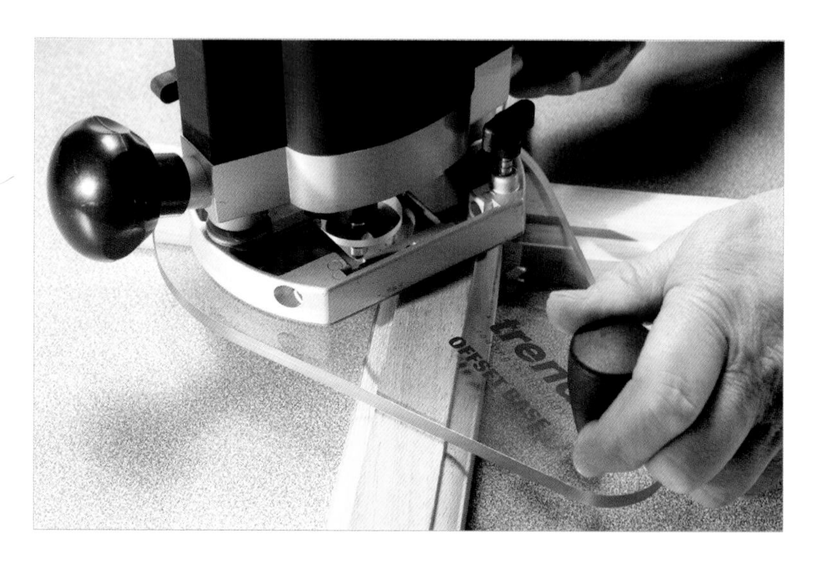

Plunge cutting

When you need to plunge cut into the face of a board, firstly preset the required depth using the turret stop, if you are going to make several passes. Adjust the side-fence and position the cutter carefully at the beginning of the cut. Switch on and allow the router to reach full speed, push down firmly on the handles until the depth stop engages and then lock the plunge.

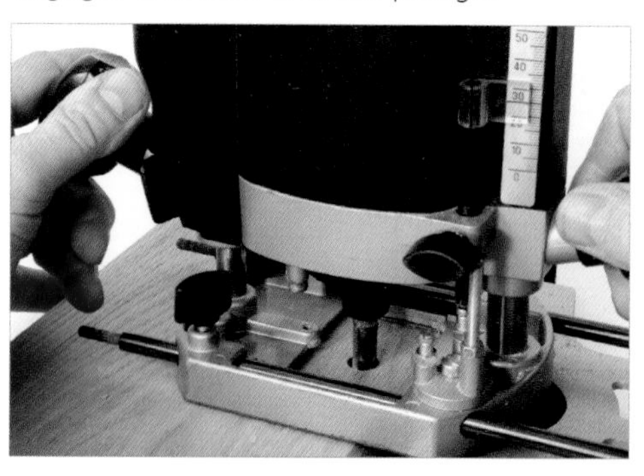

Make the required pass, release the plunge lock, allow the cutter to withdraw and then switch off. If you are making multiple passes for a deep cut and particularly when plunging right through the work, it is better to set a cut depth of only 1.5 mm for the final one to leave a perfect finish.

Portable folding benches with moveable jaws give a huge clamping area and you can hold workpieces both vertically and horizontally. You can also use dogs in the same way as the tail vice on a conventional bench, or even hold tapered work, as either end of the vice opens independently. The only snag is that they are rather low and therefore uncomfortable to work on for any length of time.

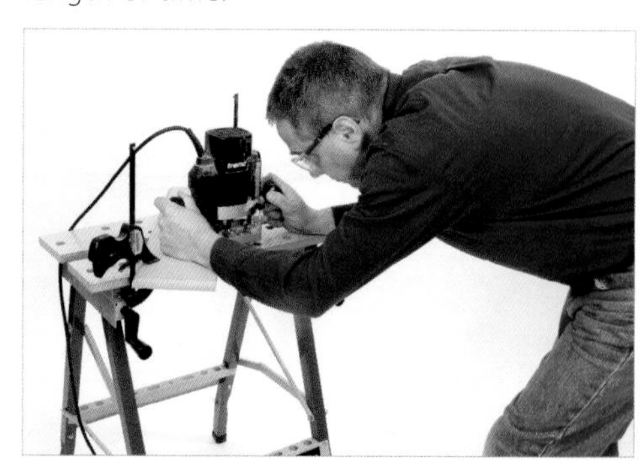

Try supplementing one of these benches with a false top that raises the height and increases the clamping options. Screw it to a block held in the vice jaws.

Repetitious jobs with thin work pieces may justify making a separate workboard that uses folding wedges for simple and speedy clamping. Use them in conjunction with battens or pegs screwed to the workboard.

Another way if you need access to all the edges, is to glue or screw the work to a backing board that in turn can be gripped in a vice. You can even use the straightedges of this board as a guide if you need to rout in a straight line across an irregularly shaped piece.

Hot melt glue guns allow very secure and rapid fixing without any form of obstruction. A pea-sized blob will hold a reasonably large piece of work, just use more for bigger pieces. Afterwards you can prise the two components apart with minimal damage.

However, by far the most useful way to get a temporary fixing in this situation is using double-sided tape. There are various types available, ranging from the thin variety sold in Stationery shops, to the really heavy cloth stuff used by carpet fitters. They work best on a clean, flat, dust free surface. A melamine-faced workboard is ideal, but you may need to seal porous substances to maximise the holding power. Even a small amount of tape gives tremendous grip, but apply plenty of pressure initially to get the adhesive to stick, and then the downward force of the router should be enough to hold everything in place as you work.

Sometimes it is necessary to cut right through the work which will obviously damage the bench surface. In this case use a piece of sacrificial material like hardboard or MDF pinned or glued to the bench, but check that any pins are punched well below the surface.

Tip

After use, double sided tape can usually be rolled off with your thumb, but check the effects of it on a piece of scrap if you are using veneered boards and make sure any invisible traces of adhesive are removed before staining and polishing.

Materials and their preparation

You can rout a range of materials including non-ferrous metals and most plastics, but with wood based materials some machine much better than others. Unfortunately, there are no hard and fast rules here, a lot depends on the type of cut you are trying to make and you also have to consider other factors like cutter condition, feed speed and grain direction. You cannot beat hard earned experience in assessing how a particular piece will work, so experiment with different cutter and feed speeds, as well as varying the depth and direction of cut.

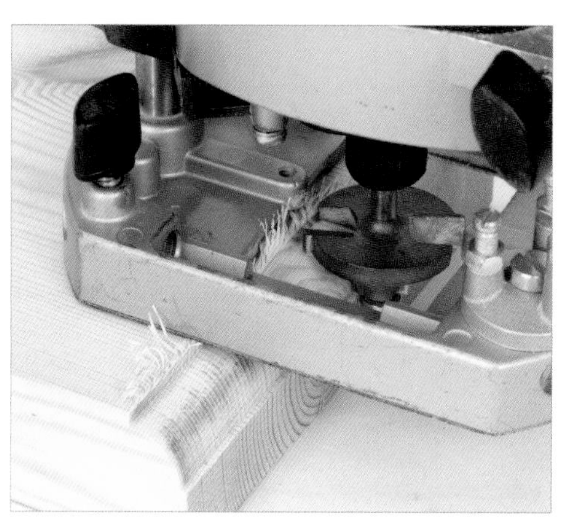

Surprisingly, softwoods tend to be more difficult to work with a router and require the cutters to be in tip top condition. Because these timbers are relatively soft, it is also tempting to feed the router too quickly which causes feathering, or leaves the edges of the cut fuzzy. What's more, softwood tends to be full of resin which can build up on the cutters and bearings, causing marking or burning.

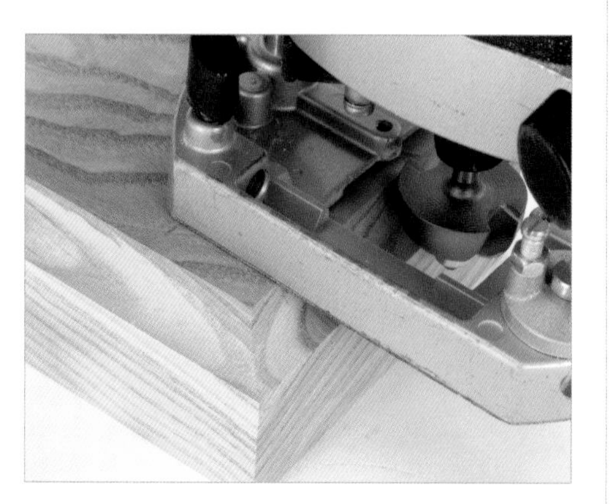

Hardwoods on the other hand tend to cut more cleanly even if the cutter is not as sharp as it should be. The moisture content of the timber has a bearing on cutting performance as well. You will get nice clean shavings off a piece of air-dried material, whereas kiln-dried stock will probably be more dusty. Some hardwoods contain ingrown deposits of gritty minerals that wreak havoc even on TCT cutters. However, on hardwoods the differences between side and end grain is less marked and you will probably get a more uniform finish with less scorching.

MDF is a wonderfully consistent material to rout provided you take suitable precautions with the dust. Sharp TCT cutters will leave a really clean finish but they will need much more frequent re-sharpening than on timber as MDF is very abrasive.

Plywood has an even more destructive effect on cutters, particularly if you make long cuts when the alternating layers of side and end grain will actually wear grooves even on TCT cutters. So keep varying the depth of the cutter to spread the load if you have to use ply, but also be prepared for regular cutter replacement.

Chipboard is another easily routed material but it does have a similar blunting effect like MDF, as it often contains tiny particles of metal and soil which spark when you hit them. Routing intricate profiles in chipboard is virtually impossible and this material has more or less been superseded by MDF. Faced chipboard though, is still very popular and the thin laminates on this are very difficult to cut cleanly using a saw. However, cutting it to the final size using a router will leave a perfect finish on both faces.

Preparation

With any woodworking project it is essential that the material is first properly prepared, particularly if you are using timber rather than man-made boards. You will never be able to work accurately if the material is not finished true and square.

Although sawn timber in its rough state is much cheaper to buy than prepared stock, you must then have the capability to cut and plane each piece to its precise size. It may be possible to do this by hand for small sections, but you will get more consistent results by using powered machinery.

Even buying 'planed all round' (PAR) material from a timber merchant does not necessarily guarantee that what you get is perfect, and you may still need to cut or plane it to particular dimensions or true up the ends.

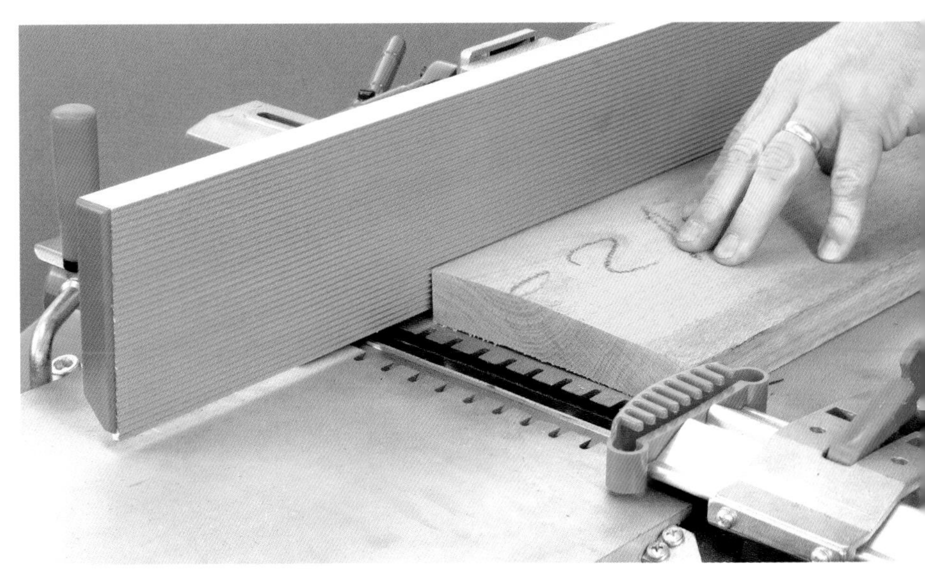

If you already have a small workshop, the most essential machines for this initial preparation work are a circular saw and planer thicknesser. Couple these with a good quality chop saw and you should be able to produce perfect stock for any routing project. However, the more time you spend at the preparation stage, the better the finished result will be.

If you are on a limited budget, or don't have the space for any machinery, some merchants offer a service preparing timber to cutting lists. However, this is a very labour intensive process and is therefore costly and they will not necessarily take the same sort of care in selecting suitable pieces that you would. The results are therefore often rather disappointing and your project gets off to a bad start.

For example, material that is planed too quickly will be left with pronounced ridges that will be faithfully reproduced by any form of bearing cutter. Edges that aren't properly square will register differently

When you fit them into a jig, joints just won't fit if the original timber preparation is not perfect. Don't try and blame any deficiencies here on the router, accuracy can only be achieved if the material is properly prepared in the first place.

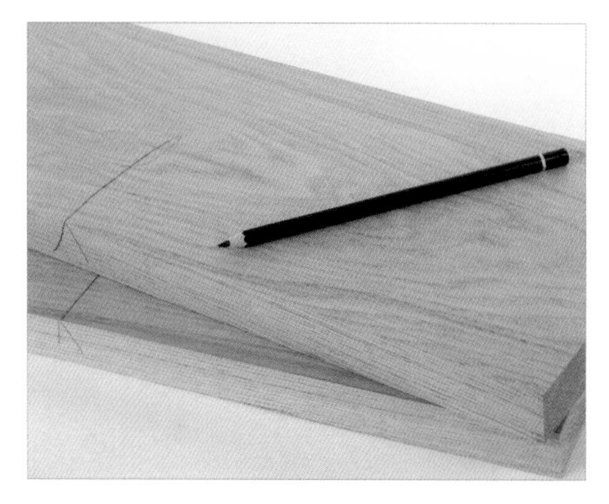

Without doubt, preparing your own material is the best answer, and whether you use hand tools or machinery it is essential to follow traditional woodworking practices. On solid timber, mark out the face side and edge and then work off these as reference surfaces for all subsequent operations.

Grain direction is one of the most important considerations when you are working with a revolving cutter in a router. So take both the grain direction and figure into account before starting any preparation. Most routing operations are carried in the same way, based on the principle that the feed direction is usually against the direction of rotation of the cutter.

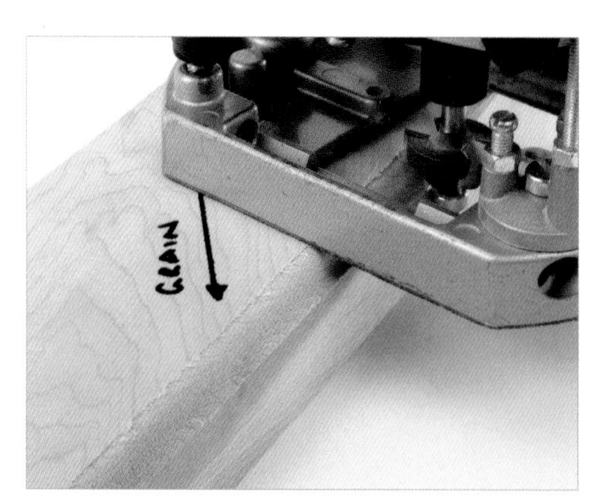

So if the grain is lying towards the direction of cut, the fibres will be bent back and broken off leaving a rough finish.

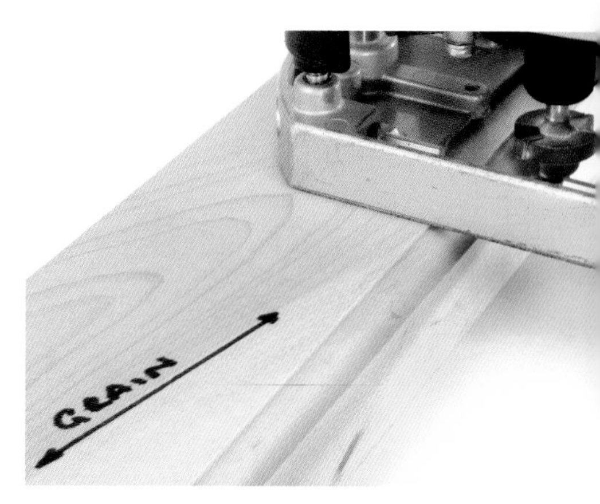

However, if they lie with the feed direction, the fibres will stay flat and cut cleanly. Think of the effect of brushing a dog's coat if you want an analogy. Brush it the wrong way and it all stands up on end, but it remains smooth if you work the other way.

This business of the grain direction is particularly relevant when you are working with curved surfaces, where changes in grain direction are inevitable and totally unavoidable. In these situations, you may be restricted to a damage limitation exercise, but refer to the section on 'backcutting' in 'Handling and feeding the router' later in this chapter.

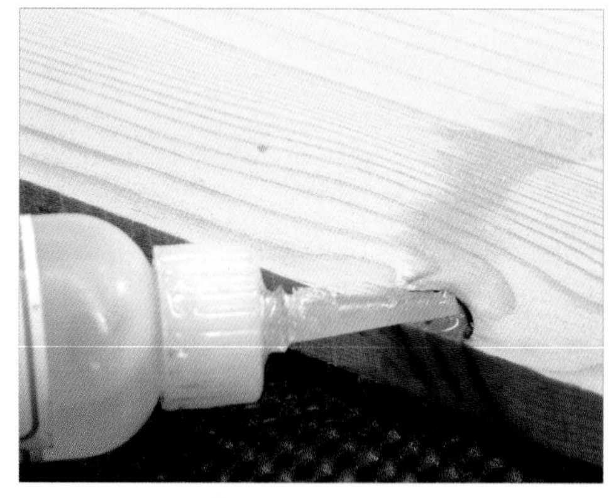

Where possible you should always avoid routing through knots, especially if they are dead or loose ones as they may be thrown out by the action of the cutter. If cutting through an obviously loose knot is unavoidable, run in a small amount of thin superglue to stabilise it before you make the cut

The grain direction may sometimes be dictated by the way you need to orientate the figuring for a particular effect, for example in creating handed panels or matching pieces. This visual orientation may not always be the best from a machining point of view and you sometimes have to strike a balance between the two. But if you think ahead a little you can build in some measures at the material preparation stage to overcome these potential problems.

For instance, it may help to leave a particular piece slightly over-length to give some infeed or outfeed run-on if you think the grain is such that it will tear at either end of the cut.

Similarly, if there are a lot of small components to machine, plan the cutting order so that you are always working with as bigger section as possible.

E.g. making narrow mouldings by routing the edge of a wide board and then ripping it off before repeating the process.

If you are making batches of components which all need several machining operations, make sure there is room for them to be stacked separately, so there is then no confusion about which cutter is used on each component.

Other tools required

Accuracy at all stages of the work is the key to using the router successfully. So even when your material is prepared properly you will still need a few simple measuring and marking tools in addition to the router and its basic accessories.

Any form of woodworking is limited by the dimensional stability of the material itself, as well as the ability to cut it accurately. Do not be over concerned about absolute precision though, as woodworking is different to engineering and a tolerance of plus or minus 1mm is normally acceptable for most jobs. It is usually more important to have matching components all exactly the same size, rather than having them a precise size.

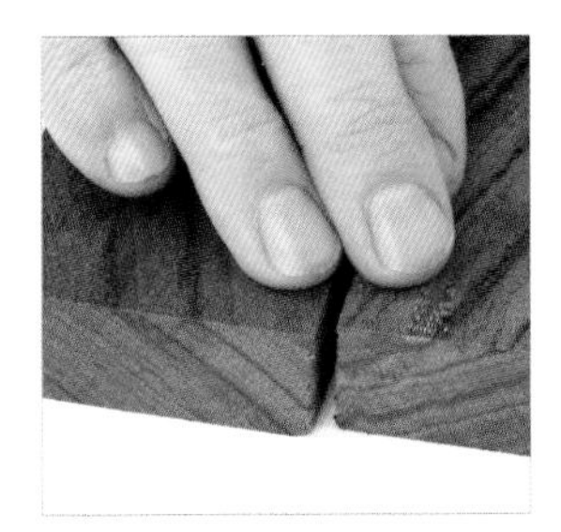

Although many discrepancies are visible to the naked eye it is sometimes more reliable to use your sense of feel to check for any errors. Your fingertips are incredibly sensitive and can detect differences of as little as .025 mm, so get in the habit of using them.

Pencils can be notoriously inaccurate as a means of marking and need to be kept really sharp or the line becomes imprecise. A good marking knife is more reliable, if the cut line is critical. Scribing a line with a knife will often help to minimise spelching on cross grain cuts as well.

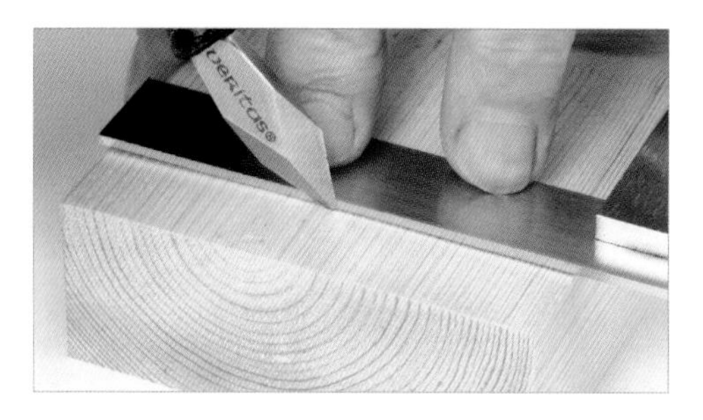

A long steel tape measure may be fine for sizing up your pieces of wood, but it is useless for really accurate measuring.

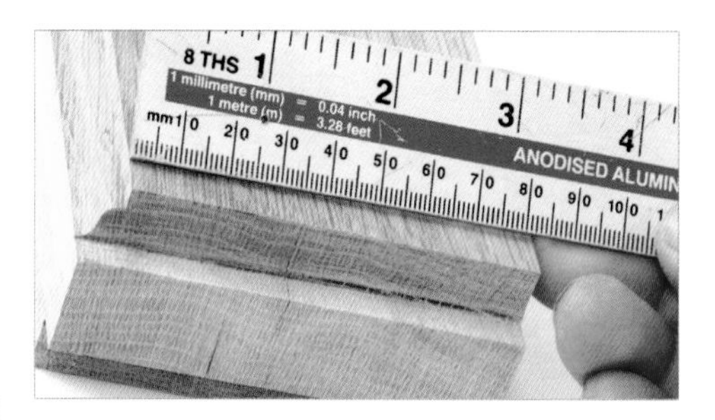

For this, you will need a short steel rule with clear graduations. Although this can be used for jobs like measuring the projection of the cutter, it is often more accurate to measure the result of the cut, as they are not necessarily the same thing. A slight buckle or twist in the timber or router baseplate can introduce inaccuracies that are not clear until you actually make the cut.

A good quality square is essential, the steel machinist's pattern being better than the bulky woodworker's type, but a combination square is another alternative as this will give you 45° angles as well. This is one tool that does need to be of really good quality, as a less than perfect square is useless, so buy a good one and look after it.

A sliding bevel and protractor is needed for all the intermediate angles. These are often combined into a single tool, which again doesn't have to be superbly accurate; you just cannot work wood to fractions of a degree.

A straightedge is required not only for marking out and checking flatness, but also as a guide for straight cuts.

A 1m length provides the best compromise between convenience and function. Supplement this with a good quality Tee square and you should have all the basic marking out operations covered.

Lastly, do consider buying a cranked spanner to replace the one provided with your machine. These cranked versions are very cheap, but make cutter changes so much easier, particularly if you are working under a table where access is restricted.

Tip

You will find a dial caliper another invaluable aid for checking both inside and outside measurements. The dial type are not prone to subjective interpretation, you just read off the measurement. An expensive engineers type is not necessary, as you often only use comparative measurements rather than high precision ones.

Holding the workpiece

It is essential that the work is held securely before you start any routing operation, otherwise you will have great difficulty controlling the path of the cutter and risk damaging the work. At worst, it may be spun off violently with potentially disastrous consequences for you, the work, the cutter or the router itself.

There are literally dozens of ways of clamping the work, using a variety of strategies depending on the type of work and the cut you are trying to perform. You can use many of the traditional methods like G-cramps, bench dogs and vices, but also add to these a wide range of homemade devices such as folding wedges, cams and pegs or even a purpose made workboard. Sometimes you may have to combine several clamping methods for particularly awkward jobs.

The aim is to get secure clamping but at the same time minimising any interference with the path of the router or side-fence, which is not always an easy compromise. You also want to be able to clamp quickly, particularly if there are lots of components to machine, so over-complicated set-ups are best avoided.

Whatever method of clamping you choose, remember that you need to protect the work from any damage. Use pads of MDF or cardboard underneath any metal jaws, though many specialist cramps are now fitted with plastic shoes for this very purpose.

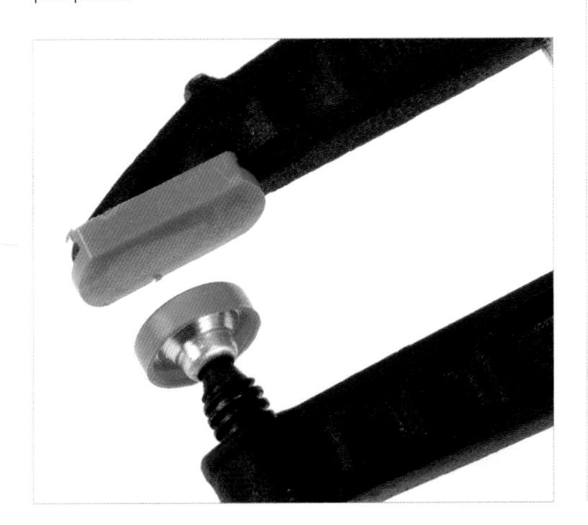

Wherever you work you need a stable and rigid working surface, preferably quite high up, so you don't need to stoop too much to see what is going on.

In the workshop this can be your normal workbench, or if space allows, you can make a dedicated router bench with that all-important extra height and built-in provision for a range of different holding devices.

Tip

In many situations, the use of a special router mat will provide all the support you need. This has a specially designed rubbery consistency that resists slipping. Just lay it on the bench, drop on your work and away you go. Being so simple and effective, a router mat is always my first choice for holding small components, but it maybe less effective on bigger pieces.

Traditional bench vices are only suitable for holding pieces that can project clear of the jaws, but they are useful for edge work on large boards if you can provide some additional support to stop them pivoting.

The metal jaws must be covered with wooden facings to protect the work and prevent damage to the cutter if you are careless when guiding the router.

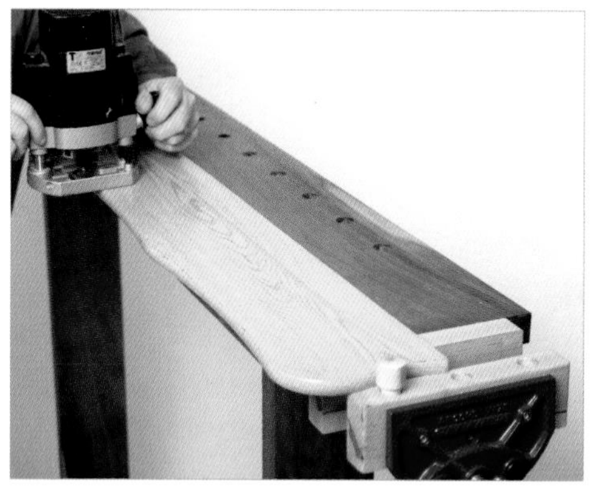

A tail vice is the most versatile as you can use it in conjunction with a variety of bench dogs to hold flat work.

One very handy trick is to use a sash cramp gripped in a bench vice for holding a workpiece by its ends, but make up a couple of wooden saddles to support the work and stop it twisting over.

A standard G-cramp will often suffice if the wood has to be held flat on the bench, but you will need plenty of overhang on the bench top so you can locate it well clear of the routers path.

Although you can exert great pressure with a G-cramp, they are slow to use as their screw action takes some time to adjust to different openings.

Quick action clamps are probably a better option as you can adjust the clamping width in just a few seconds. They are also available in a huge range of sizes, up to really big ones for clamping doors and the like. I particularly favour the type that you can operate one handed, enabling the user to secure a guide batten onto the work at the same time.

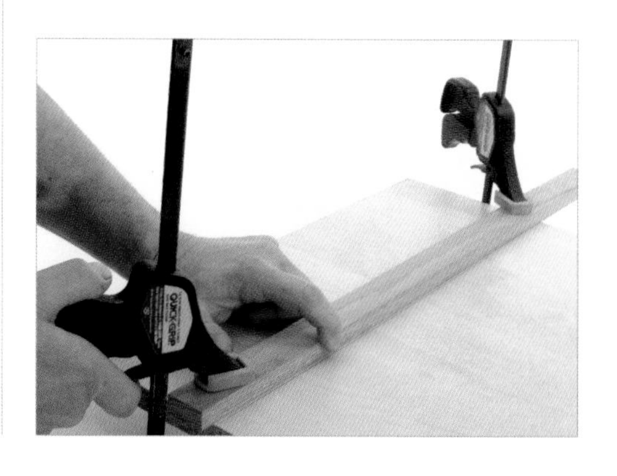

End socket cramps are a great way to secure fences and stops but leaving the surface free of any obstruction. However, you need to drill a 9mm hole to locate them and the minimum recommended material thickness is 18mm.

Toggle clamps are available for either top or side clamping. They can be screwed directly to the bench or to a special workboard and are particularly useful for repetition jobs as they allow the work to be positioned quickly and then secured.

They will accommodate work up to 60 mm in thickness and their low profile means minimal interference. Quick release mounting plates for use with toggle clamps allow rapid repositioning of the clamp and often reduce the number of clamps required.

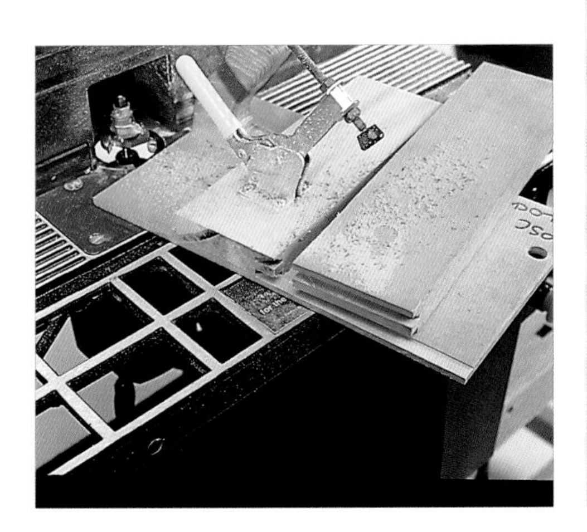

Workboards are the most convenient way of holding small pieces, and you can design one to take a range of different fences, stops and holding devices. They are easily made from pieces of MDF or laminate covered board and are secured by screwing a batten to the underside which can then be gripped in the vice. For extra versatility, drill holes in the board to take pegs or cams, or cut tee slots and fit toggle clamps. Cams or eccentric clamps are made up from scraps of timber and are best used in pairs.

Having created a vacuum beneath the workpiece, the external air pressure is sufficient to hold it firmly in place. Some vacuum clamping devices have multiple cell chucks, which are divided into several chambers that are shut off independently with automatic ball valves. This allows various sized workpieces to be held, as unused cells remain completely airtight.

Vacuum clamping

Vacuum clamping provides a very effective method for holding and releasing the workpiece and is therefore ideally suited for repetitious batch work. It is generally used only in professional workshops where speed is vital, as it can prove an expensive option for the occasional user. However you can rig up suitable homemade devices that offer a very reliable method of holding while avoiding the need for separate clamps that can obstruct the routing operation or spoil the workpiece. Vacuum chucks are made using flat self-adhesive foam sealing material or round neoprene strip formed into individual cells. The workpiece itself then completes the sealed chamber from which the air is removed through an exhausts port built into the chuck.

To get the necessary suction you need to buy a dedicated vacuum pump or couple up to a domestic vacuum cleaner. This latter option is obviously more cost efficient for the home user, but only short periods of clamping are recommended as continuous restriction to the airflow will overheat and damage the unit.

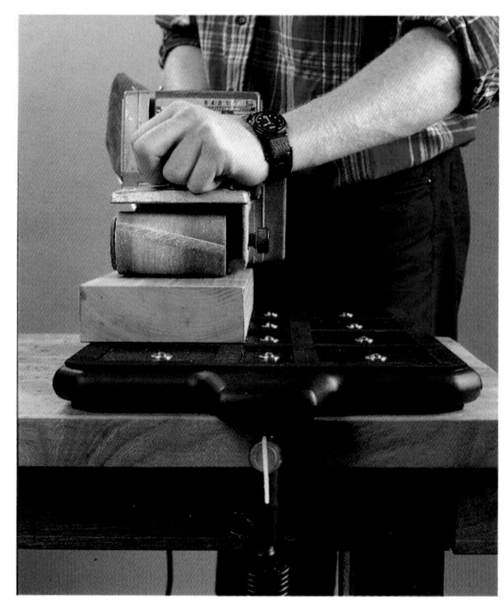

Proprietary multiple cell chucks for use with a vacuum cleaner are readily available in a variety of sizes and these are ideal for the amateur user who is dealing with lots of small components. They can also be used for other jobs like holding work for sanding, etc.

However, for the chucks to work properly, it is essential that contact is made all round the seal, so bowed or warped pieces won't normally hold. You can even make your own specially curved chucks contoured to a specific shape.

With any vacuum holding system, always check that the work is held down securely before you start cutting.

How does it work?

The top surface has a rubber gasket with a matrix of cells in two sizes which when used in combination provide maximum holding area for small or awkward shaped workpieces. The lower surface has a rubber gasket with one large vacuum cell which is used to clamp it to the workbench.

The timber is pushed down to activate the air valves in the cells to engage the vacuum. The vacuum suction then holds the workpiece securely onto the bed. A red handle is used to release the vacuum.

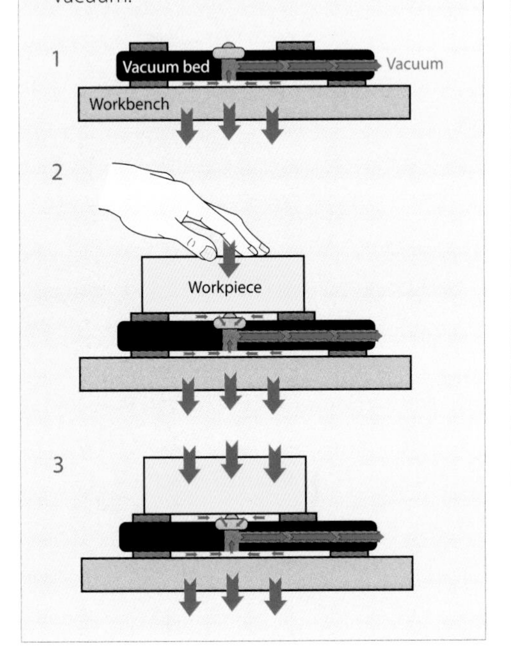

Cutting depth

To avoid overheating or snapping the cutter, it is important not to overload it by cutting too deep in a single pass. Determining the optimum depth is largely a matter of experience and depends on several factors such as cutter shank size, power of the router, hardness of the material being cut, and the router feed speed. As a rough guide the depth of cut should not exceed the diameter of the cutter when you are using cutters up to 1/2" diameter, or the diameter of the cutter shank, whichever is smaller.

Pyramid chart to assess cutting depths

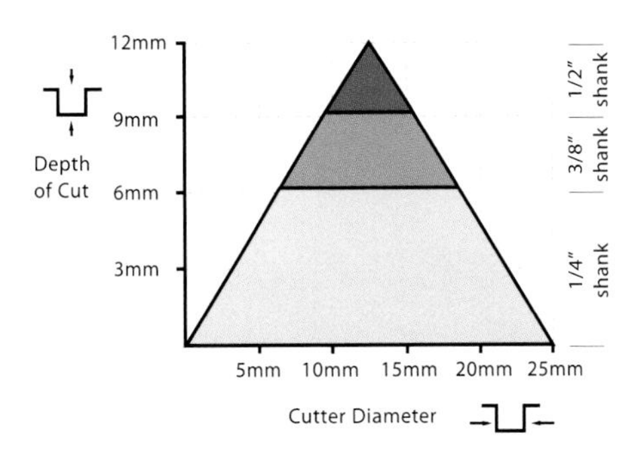

Example: Ref. 3/6 (10mm diameter cutter)
For 1/2" Shank maximum depth of cut = 10mm
For 1/4" Shank maximum depth of cut = 6mm

Guide to the chart

1. The cutter has a standard shank length.
2. The cutting length of the cutter is not excessive relative to the depth of cut.
3. The workpiece is of medium density timber.
4. A feed speed of 2-3 metres/minute is maintained.
5. The cutting edges are clean and sharp.
6. At least three quarters of the cutter shank is gripped in the collet.

If any of the above criteria cannot be met, take several shallower passes until the full depth of cut is reached. You will soon develop a feel for when the correct cutting depth is being used as factors such as noise, feed resistance and drop in router speed will indicate when a deep cut is attempted. Never force a cutter to rout too deep a cut in one pass, instead stop routing, re-adjust the cutting depth and try again.

Check you have reached the required depth by making a trial cut in a piece of scrap material. It is more reliable than trying to measure the cutter projection from the base of the router.

Feed speed

This is largely dependant on experience and a keen ear for what is happening to the noise from the motor. Feed rate varies with the composition of the material being cut, its hardness and the type of cutter being used. For instance, a single flute cutter will clear faster than a two flute one so you can feed it more quickly, although the resulting finish may not be so good.

If you feed too tentatively, heat is generated in the cutter and the friction causes the timber to burn and the cutter edges will overheat and suffer damage. On the other hand, if you try and go too quickly the waste material will not clear fast enough, the router will slow down and again the finish will be poor.

It is only with practice that you will get a feel for the proper feed rate. Close observation of both the type of waste you are producing and the resultant surface finish is a good guide as to whether you are feeding properly.

If the bit is sharp you should be producing

Tip

In most situations you can help by making bigger cuts in several passes as already described, but the enclosed shape of some cutters means that they have to be made in a single pass. In this case use a straight cutter to remove some initial waste that would have overloaded the profile cutter.

fine wispy shavings and leaving a clean, neatly severed finish on the work, particularly with natural timbers.

If you feed too slowly, the waste changes to powdery dust and there is some scorching along the cut surface.

Listen carefully to the sound of the motor. If you are feeding properly there will always be some slowing down, particularly with big cutters, but the sound must not become laboured. If it is slowing unduly, reduce the feed rate and/or the depth of cut in combination until the motor resumes a relatively free running sound.

All this assumes that the cutters are sharp in the first place. If they are not, then the feed rate has to be reduced further and the finish will never be of a high standard.

Most beginners tend to be overcautious and feed the tool far too slowly in the mistaken belief that the finish will be better. In fact, bits will stay cooler, keep sharp for longer and produce a better cut surface if you increase the feed rate moderately.

The feed rate also needs to be one continuous operation at constant speed. Even the slightest hesitation in the speed of feeding will leave a scorch mark that is very difficult to remove with abrasives.

This is why it is always better to take a final very shallow cut to clean up any burning or roughness as you can make this pass really quickly without slowing the cutter.

When you reach the end of the cut, always lift the router by releasing the plunge lock while the power is still on and then switch off when the bit is clear of the work. If you try and switch off while the cutter is still in the cut, it will burn, but more importantly, the slightest wobble will cause an even deeper mark and the slowing cutter may try to grab the work, kicking the cutter sideways.

Similarly, you should always start the router with the cutter clear of the work and not in place in an existing cut. The starting torque will inevitably twist the router and cause the cutter to snatch.

Feed direction

Newcomers to routing often don't realise that there is a right and a wrong way to feed the router. With certain exceptions the golden rule is that the feed direction should always be against the direction of rotation of the cutter. This ensures that the cutter is pulled into the work and whatever is guiding it is then pressed against the edge of the work. This way, the cutter will not wander off line and you will have no problem controlling it.

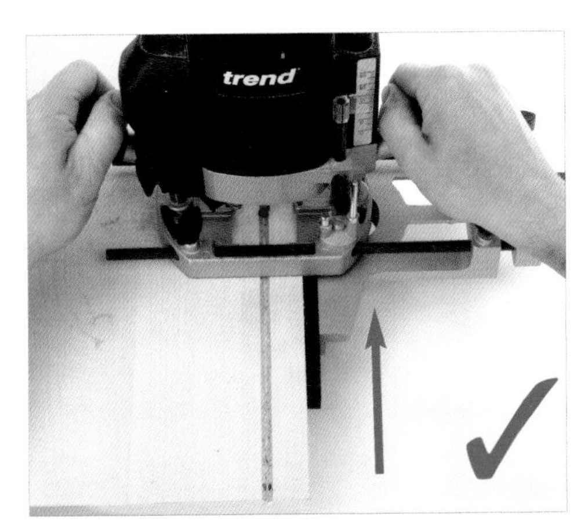

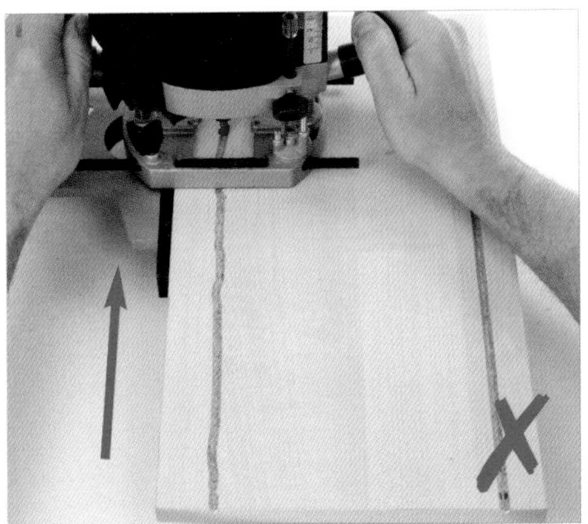

If you feed the wrong way, the fence or guide will try and veer off, the router may snatch and you will have great difficulty keeping it on line.

If you view your router from above, the cutter rotates clockwise and you need to feed against this, but the direction varies with the type of cut you are making.

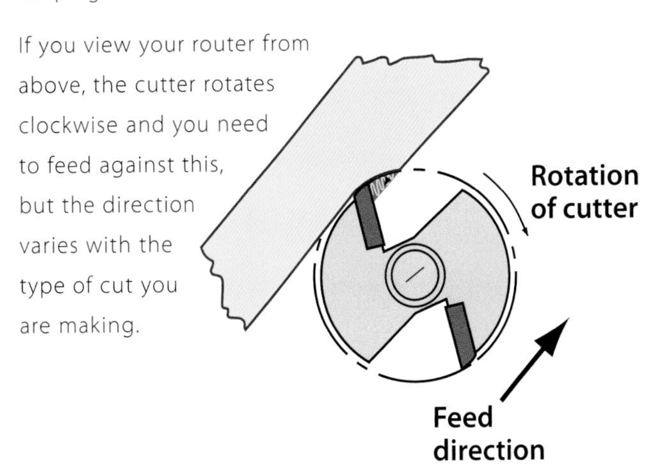

For edge moulding the router has to be fed from left to right. Similarly, if you are using a straightedge or fence as a guide for internal cuts, the feed direction should always remain against the direction of rotation of the cutter.

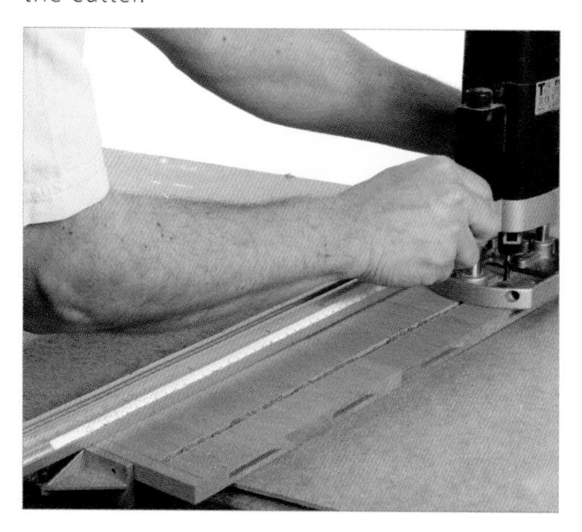

If you are moulding around the outside of a board, this means feeding the router anticlockwise when viewed from above.

If you are working round the inside of an opening, then the router has to be fed clockwise.

Similarly, if you are using templates, external ones will require the router to be fed anti-clockwise.

But internal ones need feeding clockwise.

Cutting circles with a trammel is a similar situation, so the router must be fed anticlockwise to keep the cutter pulling out against the centre point of the trammel.

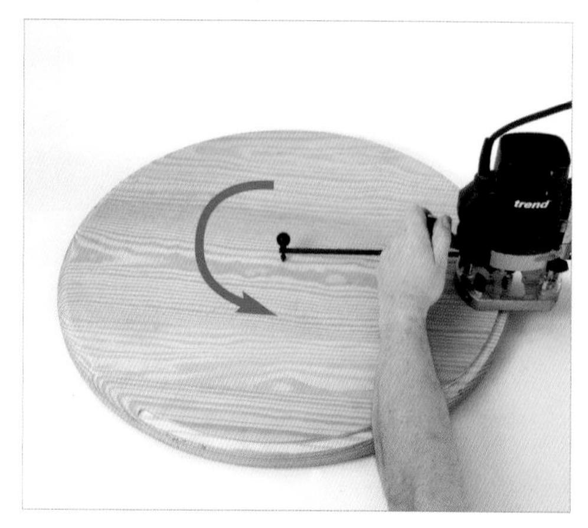

It doesn't matter if you push or pull the router as long as it travels in the right direction. Some cuts like rebates are often easier to make if you pull the router towards you but although the set-up may look different, it is actually the same as far as the router is concerned.

With solid timber, you also have to consider grain direction in conjunction with feed direction. As you make a cut across the grain it is likely that there will be some splintering or breakout as the cutter emerges from the edge.

If you are routing all the way around the board, make the end grain cuts first and then the break-out should hopefully be cut away when the side grain is cut.

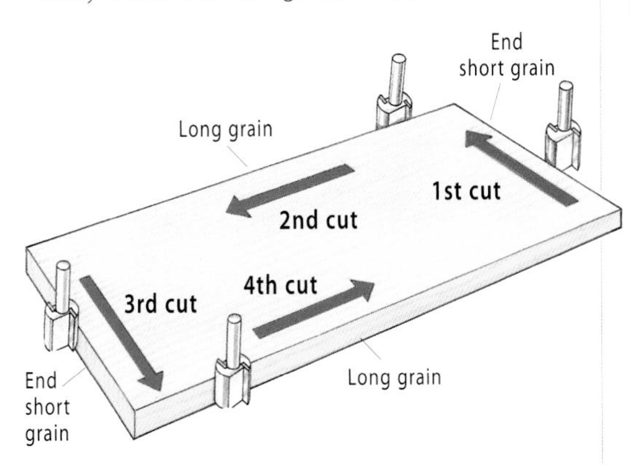

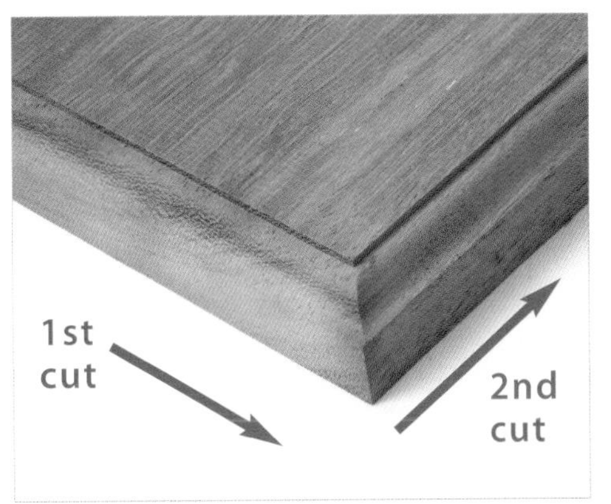

If you are only making end grain cuts, eliminate breakout by clamping on a sacrificial support strip and machining right through into it.

Alternatively, plunge the cutter down to full depth on the exit corner of the board before you make the cross cut.

If you are routing freehand in the centre of a board, as for instance removing some of the ground from a carving, it doesn't really matter which way you feed, but if you increase the cutting depth in progressive stages, then do keep working in the same direction.

Backcutting

As with any rule, there are some exceptions and always working with the cutter rotating against the direction of cut may not always be the best way if the grain orientation is difficult. Rebates in solid timber often show minor damage to the wood fibres along the bottom edge of the cut.

For a really clean cut across end grain, or where the grain is very swirly, it is permissible to use the backcutting technique as long as you exercise caution and remain vigilant to the potential problems of 'cutting the wrong way'!

Backcutting involves making a very shallow initial cut, but feeding the router with the direction of rotation of the cutter.

Then once the fibres have all been scribed neatly, you can make the rest of the cut to full depth, feeding the router in the conventional way as for instance when using the dovetail jig.

If you are edge moulding, some timbers may have diagonally orientated grain and there is then the possibility of it splitting out ahead of the cutter. This can be overcome by backcutting first before making the main cut. Or try making a couple of shallower passes by raising the cutter or fitting a bigger diameter bearing.

Circular work is another potential routing problem area as there are so many different grain surfaces exposed. You are bound to end up cutting against it somewhere. In this situation, you can make several successive, but very shallow passes cutting the 'wrong' way in the difficult areas.

A straight forward edge mould can sometimes look ok, but in reality it feels as if the surface is covered with a series of tiny ripples. This can usually be cleaned up by firmly pulling the router backwards at the same setting as you have just used to make the initial cut. Theoretically, it shouldn't remove any more timber, but the smoothing effect is often amazing.

If you are trimming edge lippings flush to the face of a board, the feed direction has to be opposite to normal so that the lippings are pressed back against the edges, rather than prised off.

Although backcutting will not damage the cutter, the fence or guide will try to wander away from the intended line and you need to be extra careful to stop it snatching.

Your first cut

Quick guide

You should now be thoroughly familiar with your new router and all its components, so it is time to put it all into practice and start building some confidence in its use. If you are a real first time user, try this simple exercise, cutting a 3/8" deep by 1/2" wide groove using the standard side-fence for guidance. A medium sized router should be able to make this cut in one pass, but if you have any doubts do it in two stages.

1. First check the router is unplugged from the power supply.

2. Fit a straight 1/2" diameter cutter into the collet making sure at least 3/4 of the shank length is engaged within the jaws.

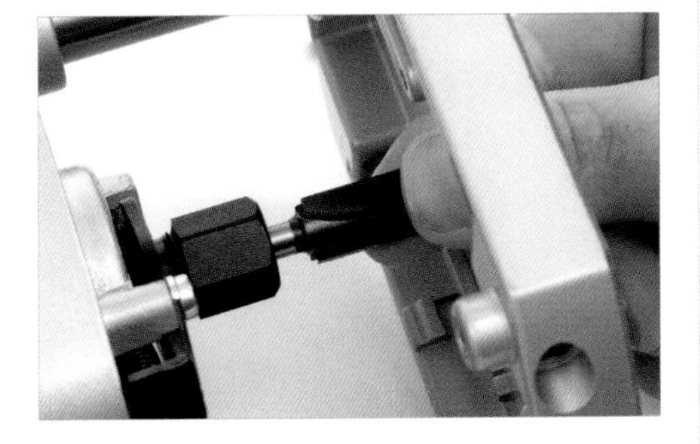

3. To set the depth of cut, release the locking lever or knob and plunge down until the cutter tip rests on the surface of the bench and lock it in that position.

4. Now set the depth of cut by adjusting the depth rod until there is a 3/8" space between it and the turret stop. Use either a rule or spacer blocks.

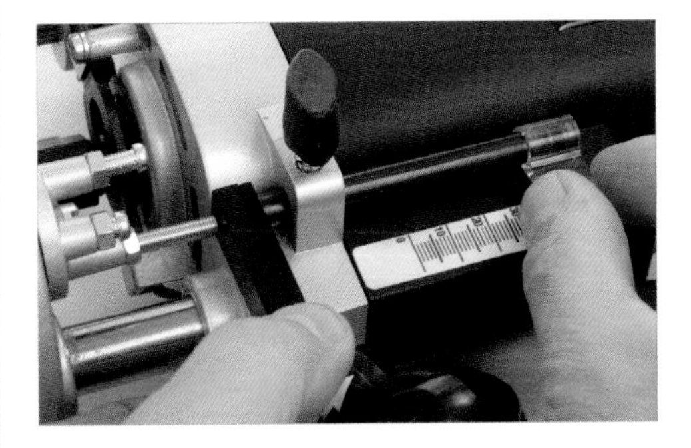

5. Release the plunge lock and allow the router to spring back to the resting position.

6. Fit the side-fence to suit the position of the intended groove and lock it up tight on the rods, making sure these are also held firmly in the router base.

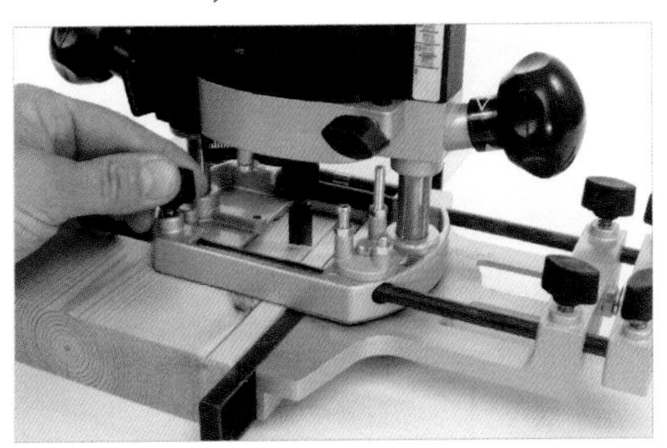

7. Clamp the workpiece firmly to the bench making sure the cramp will not impede the path of the router.

8. Check that the router switch is off and then plug in.

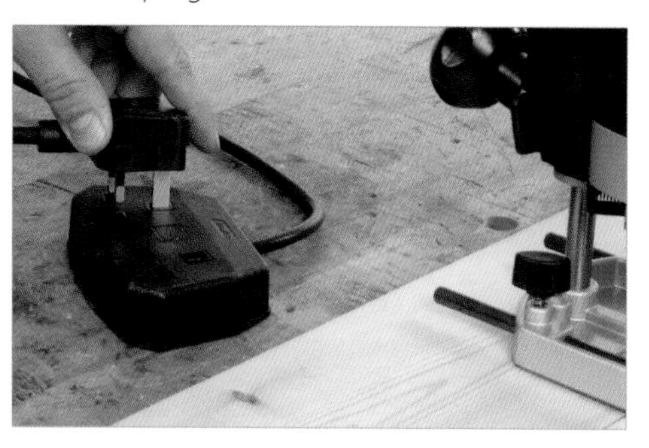

9. Switch on the router and let it reach full speed.

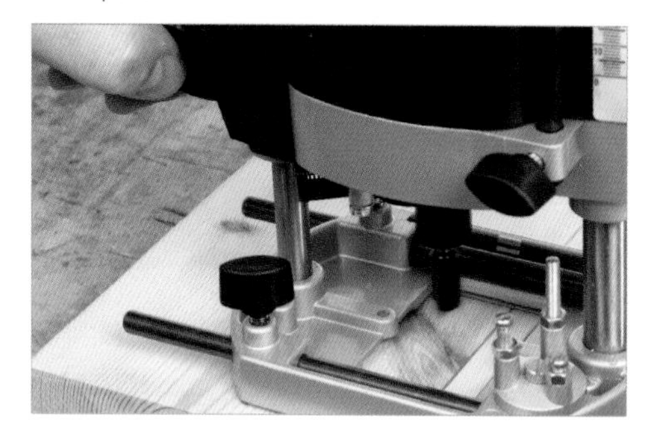

10. Position the cutter over the work and plunge down to the preset depth and lock.

11. Quickly start moving the router forward until it reaches the end of the cut, maintaining pressure on the side-fence to keep it against the edge of the timber.

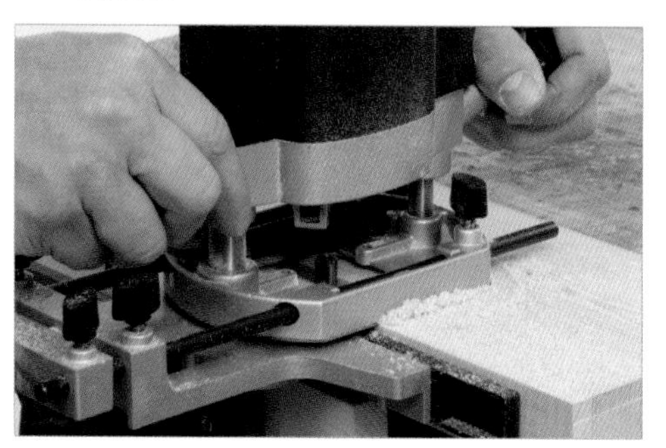

12. Release the plunge lock, turn off the router and allow the cutter to come to rest before putting it down.

Congratulations! You have just completed your first router cut, and it wasn't that difficult or scary was it? A whole new field of woodworking has just been opened up to you.

Welcome to the world of the router!

5. GUIDING THE ROUTER

The ability to guide the router the way you want it to go is essential and there are several accessories available to help you. Some are provided with the machine itself, whilst others have to be made or bought as extras, but they all contribute significantly to the productivity and versatility of the router.

Routing with the side-fence

The side-fence or edge guide is used when you are machining grooves or mouldings either along, or parallel to a straightedge of the workpiece.

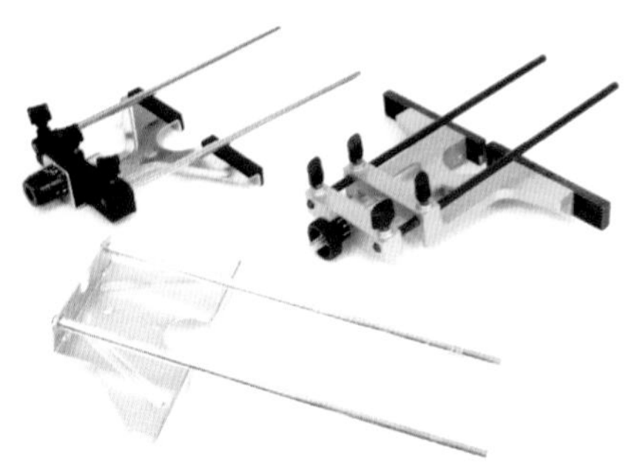

It is usually supplied with the router and varies in construction from being a simple piece of pressed steel to a more sophisticated aluminium casting with built-in micro-adjustments. As the side-fence is such an essential part of the router, it is important that you take a good look at this as well when you are choosing the router itself.

Although each side-fence is usually designed specifically for its own particular make or model of router there are third-party versions available designed to fit all popular routers, e.g. the Micro fence. These often represent a significant investment, but they can offer increased accuracy and versatility over the standard guide.

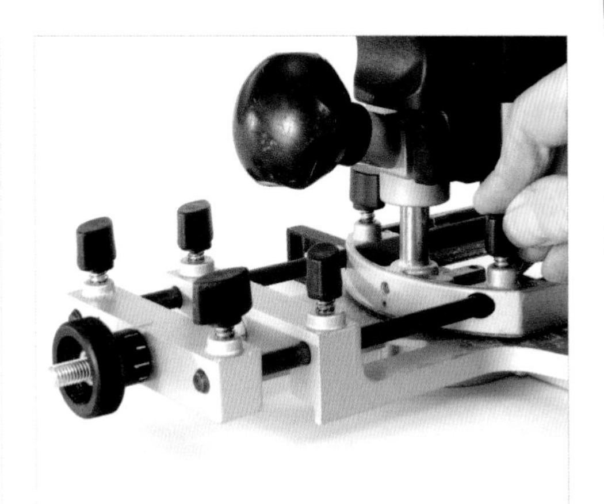

Typically, the side-fence is fitted to the router with a pair of parallel metal rods which slot into the base plate, and it can then be locked in place with clamping screws in both the fence and base castings.

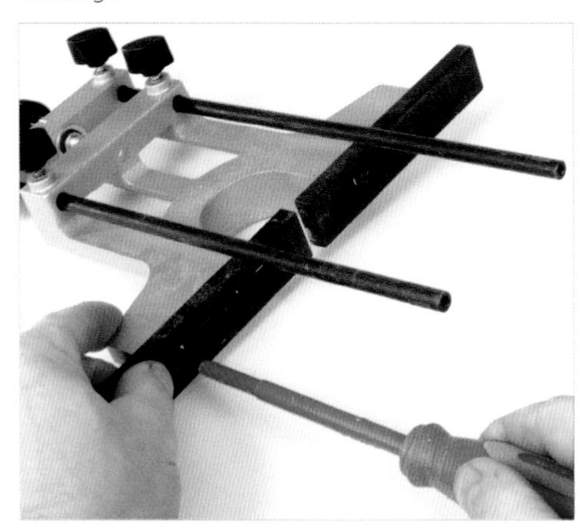

Better quality fences are fitted with false plastic facings held by recessed screws. Facings are slotted and adjustable so you can reduce the gap between their inner ends and the cutter. Closing the faces in this way reduces the risk of the fence pulling in at the start and finish of a cut. However, you must allow sufficient space for the waste to clear quickly and freely from around the cutter, 2 or 3 mm should be sufficient.

This arrangement also means that the standard facings can be removed and replaced by custom-made wooden versions for special applications.

The maximum distance that a cut can be made from the edge of the workpiece is determined by the length of the rods supplied.

This distance can be increased by substituting longer rods of the same diameter, or by using extending rods that screw together. However, if the length becomes excessive they tend to flex, causing the cutter to leave a distinctly rippled effect.

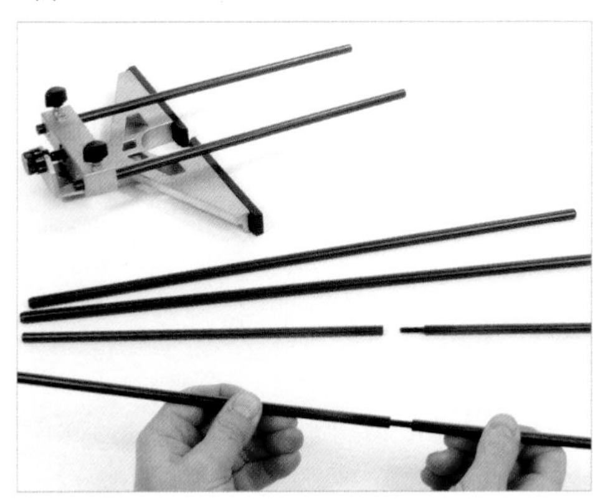

A side-fence can be somewhat clumsy to use and some practice is needed to apply it smoothly every time. The protruding ends of the fence rods and even the fence itself, need a significant amount of working room, so always do a dummy run with the router switched off to make sure there will be no obstructions when you come to make the actual cut.

Clamps are notorious for getting in the way and also check that the power cable is clear and cannot become trapped in the fence.

When you're using the side-fence, the feed direction of the router should always oppose the direction of cutter rotation to keep the fence pulled in hard against the work. However, it may sometimes be necessary to use the back cutting technique already described for some edge trimming or moulding operations. This is quite acceptable provided cuts are only light, but as the rotational action of the cutter is now trying to pull the fence off line, this technique should never be used when cutting grooves or panel moulding.

Positioning the side-fence for cutting grooves and housings

Mark out the position and width of the cut on the face of the first workpiece. Place the router on the face of the work and lower the cutter until it just touches the surface. Turn the cutter by hand until the cutting edges are aligned at right angles to the face of the fence.

Now position the cutting edge against the marked line, and slide the fence up tight against the edge of the workpiece. Tighten all the clamping screws on both fence and router, making sure that the cutter remains on the line as you do so.

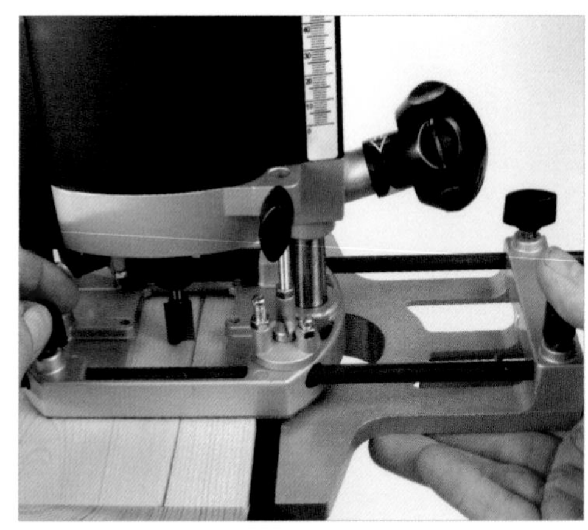

An alternative way is to measure the required distance between the fence and the nearest cutting edge, but always remember to measure to the actual cutting edge rather than the body of the cutter as these are not the same diameter.

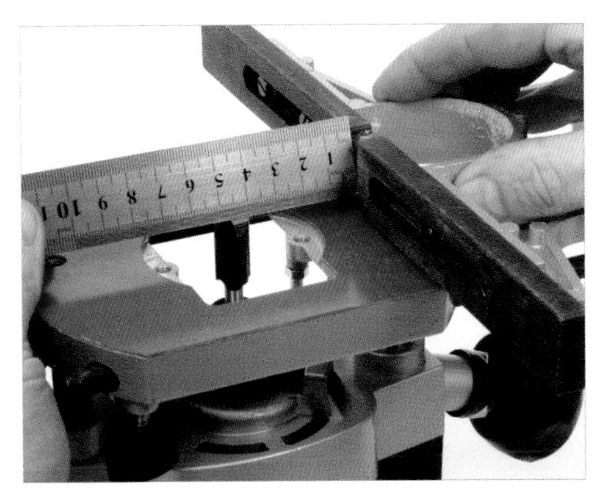

Check the setting by placing the router over the work and lowering the cutter onto the surface. If there are several identical pieces to be machined, it is only necessary to mark out the first piece, as the fence settings will reproduce the same cut on subsequent pieces.

For really fine adjustments of the fence some form of micro adjuster is essential. If this is not a standard feature of your fence it is usually available as an optional extra, so again check availability before you buy a particular model of router. Although the design of micro adjusters varies, they all work on the same principle and allow you to make minute adjustments that are difficult to achieve by manually sliding the fence along the rods. Sometimes just the act of tightening up the locking screws on the fence is enough to move it slightly out of position. A micro adjuster overcomes all of these problems.

Positioning the side-fence for machining the edge

First set the cutter against the marked line and then bring the fence up into position. Adjust the fence facings to allow sufficient clearance for waste material to clear from the cutter.

If you have to machine a deep profile that forms an undercut it is impossible to make several passes by adjusting the cutter vertically. Instead, the cut has to be worked in progressive horizontal steps resetting the side-fence to increase the width of the cut on each pass.

Maintaining contact between the side-fence and the work is not critical when you are edge moulding, as any deviation will not affect the finished profile, as it can be corrected by making a second pass. However, as we already seen, if you're cutting grooves or mouldings within a board but parallel to the edge, any deviation will deflect the cutter away from the line of the cut and spoil the work. Using the fence on the correct side of the router relative to the direction of rotation is obviously the main factor here but also ensure that the edge of the work is square and flat.

Drops of glue or resin, or even areas of raised hard grain are enough to cause both fence and cutter to deviate off line.

Always maintain an even and constant pressure on the side-fence, keeping it against the edge of the workpiece whilst making the cut.

No matter how careful you are in using the side-fence, it can still catch you out occasionally, usually at the beginning or end of the cut.

The usual tendency is for the router to turn in as there is relatively little support for the fence in these areas, but there are several strategies you can adopt to overcome the problem.

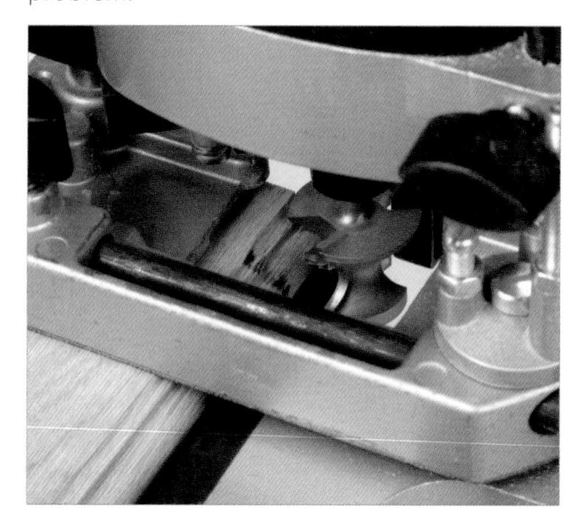

a. By leaving adequate waste at each end of the work that can be cut off after making the cut.

b. By temporarily clamping waste battens at either end of the work which also eliminates break out when you're working across the end grain.

c. By fitting longer wooden faces to the fence. If you're using a relatively large edge moulding cutter, replace the existing faces with two separate longer ones. However if you're making small mouldings that do not cut across the full depth of the workpiece, a one-piece fence can be fitted and the cutter plunged part way into it. This produces a continuous fence that minimises the possibility of the cutter turning in. However, there can sometimes be a problem clearing the waste with a one piece fence, so it may be necessary to cut an additional clearance slot.

The same problem can occur at the start and end of the cut in the vertical plane, as the cutter aperture in the base plate drops off the end of the work. This is usually a matter of technique and with a little practice you subconsciously adjust your grip to compensate.

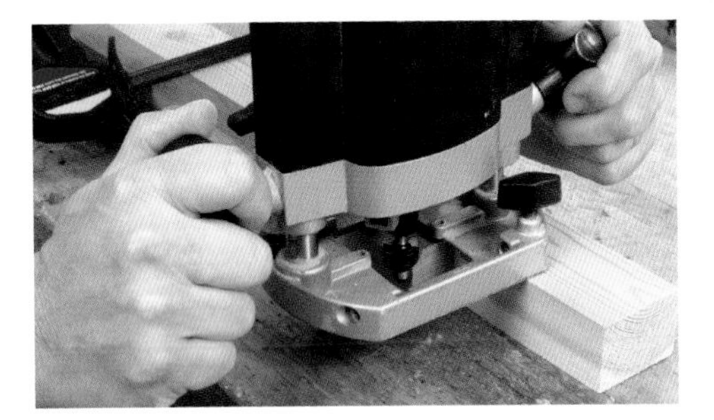

Tip

If you are struggling with the router tipping and a particular cut is critical, clamp a long batten alongside the work to support the router beyond the length of the cut edge. This is a particularly useful tip if you are trying to work on the edge of a very narrow workpiece.

Making the cut

1. Check that the edge of the workpiece is straight and free of any high spots and make sure it is clamped firmly to the bench. Any end, or waste battens must be flush with the top face.
2. Set the depth of cut to make the first shallow pass and then use the turret stop to set the final and intermediate cuts. Adjust the position of the side fences and make sure all clamping screws on both the router and fence are fully tightened.
3. With the cutter clear of the workpiece, apply gentle pressure against the front section of the fence. Switch on and allow the router to reach full speed. Start the cut, keeping the full face of the fence against the edge of the work and maintain a constant feed rate. At the end of the pass, reverse the pressure onto the rear section of the fence to prevent the cutter turning in at the end of the cut. Switch off only when the cutter has left the work and then allow the router to stop before lifting it clear.

Modifying the side-fence

Occasionally the edge profile you are producing may require the addition of an auxiliary face to the side-fence in order to maintain sufficient support.

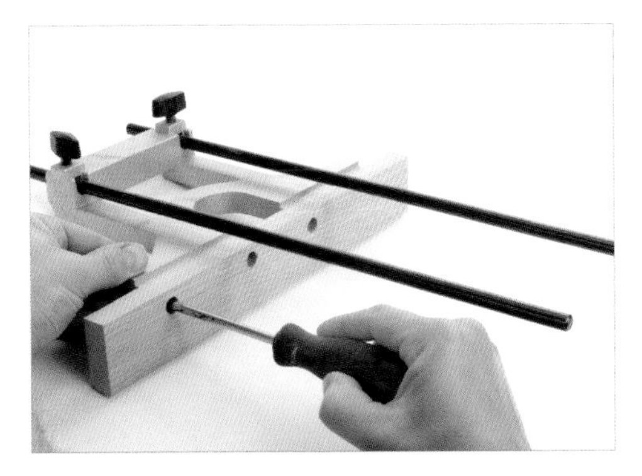

E.g. When cutting a deep profile that will leave an inadequate guiding edge that may not even be line with the fence itself. In this case, screw on a deep fence and run this against a secondary guide edge fitted below the workpiece.

Similarly, if the profile ends up cutting away the full face of the edge, for instance when you're rounding over or edge planing, you have to modify the fence by fitting a false cheek to the rear portion.

Ideally, this should be profiled to be an exact reverse of the moulding but if this is difficult it is usually possible to use a simpler profile to bridge over the detail.

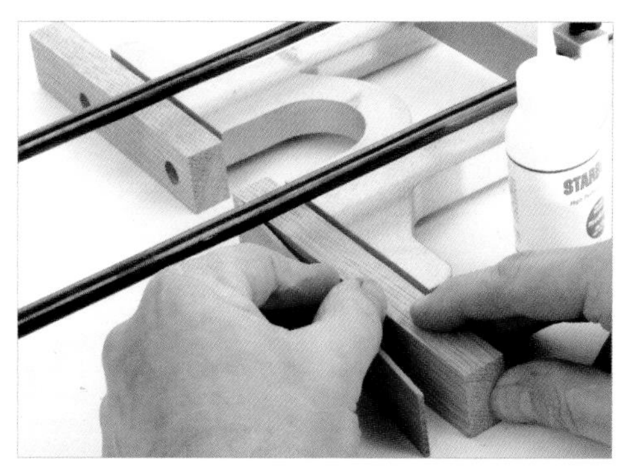

In the case of edge planing, the rear portion of the fence is fitted with a thin spacer to make it about 2mm thicker than the front fence. The cutting edges then need to be aligned perfectly flush with the face of the front fence to produce a cut the same thickness as the spacer.

For really accurate positioning of mortise, housings or grooves, the addition of a second side-fence positioned on the opposite side of the work, makes the job foolproof. You may be restricted in this by the length of the support rods, although you can replace the standard ones with longer ones. If you are using the double fence technique, do make sure that the faces of the workpiece are parallel and the

top surface is flat and be aware of the router tipping at the extremities of the cut.

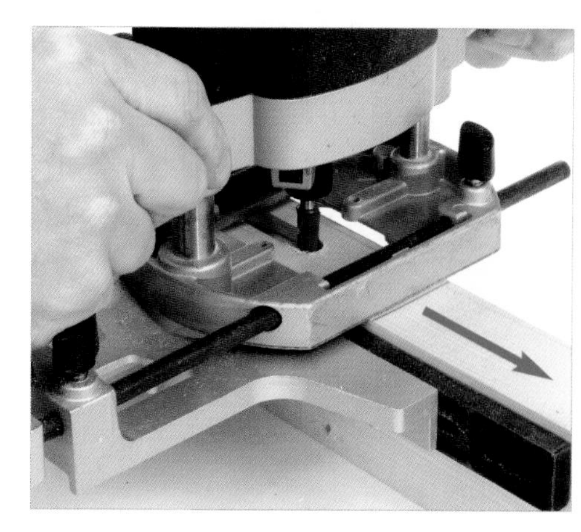

If a groove has to be perfectly centred across the width of the work, use a cutter slightly narrower than the required width and make the first pass. Then turn the router round and make a second pass in the opposite direction. Use the same principle for putting in a series of flutes or parallel grooves, working from either side of the work each time.

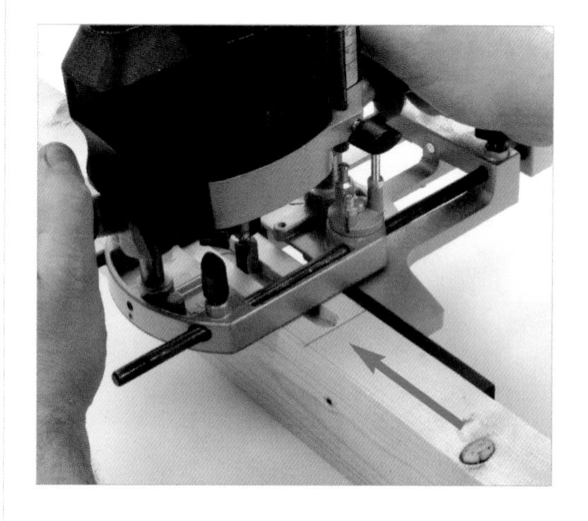

Tip

If you need to widen a groove and are just using a single fence, always make the second cut by moving the cutter away from the edge of the work, i.e. to the left, and then feed the router against the rotation of the cutter. Now any deflection of the cutter will be into the pre-cut waste area rather than into the edge and face of the work.

In certain cases, the side-fence can also be used to guide the router against a curved edge. For this, it is necessary to fit a shaped block to the fence, which is either cut to match the radius of the curve, or designed to support the fence against the guide edge at two points only.

Fence maintenance

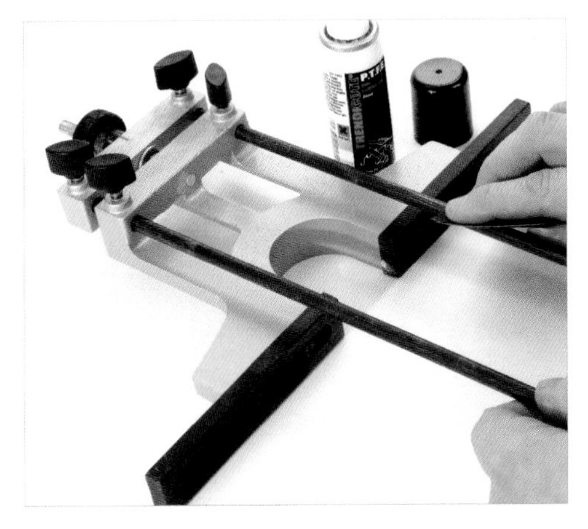

For accurate setting it is important that the fence slides smoothly on the rods so these need to be cleaned periodically to remove sticky resin deposits.

Another problem is that repeated use of the clamp screws can sometimes raise burrs on the surface of the support rods. These should be removed with a very fine file or fine abrasive paper. A quick spray over with a dry silicone lubricant will ensure the rods slide freely in both the fence and the router base plate. Check that all the clamping screws turn freely as they sometimes become jammed with fine dust and the fence then appears to be secure. It is also important that the anti-vibration springs remain in place.

Straight line routing

Sometimes it is just not convenient, or even possible, to use the side fence for straight cuts. For instance you may be routing a groove across the face of a very wide workpiece and the bars of the side fence are just not long enough and would certainly be very unstable even if they were.

In this case, the router can be guided by a simple straight fence, such as a timber batten or clamp guide.

All routers are made with the baseplate concentric to the cutter axis, although some may also have one or two flat sides to ensure that the router will run against a straightedge.

Straight guides should always be made from a rigid material that is at least 8 mm thick. This will prevent it from flexing along its length and also stop the router accidentally lifting up over the edge. Stable materials such as MDF, plywood, or Perspex are ideal, and the guide must be wide enough to allow it to be held securely in position with suitable clamps that are out of the path of the router. It must also be longer than the required length of cut to allow the router to be guided accurately at the entry and exit points of the cut and prevent it turning in.

To help you line up the straightedge accurately every time it can be fitted with a stock at one end, very much like a standard Tee square. You can buy ready made versions, but it is quite simple to make up your own. Make sure that the stock is long enough and fixed to form a perfect 90° angle.

Then, with the router running against the guide, machine a slot across the stock, (clamping it against a piece of scrap will help to minimise breakout.)

Finally, use a V cutter to put a centre line down the middle of the groove as an aid to positioning. Now all you have to do is align the groove in the stock with the centre line of the required cut.

Of course you can develop this idea further for cutting at an angle across the workpiece by attaching the stock to the straightedge at the necessary angle, either by screwing it in place for a permanent arrangement, or using a bolt and wing nuts for an adjustable guide.

No matter what sort of straight guide you choose, it is essential that it is clamped firmly in place. You can use standard G clamps, which are usually to hand in the workshop, but other clamps and holding devices are less likely to obstruct the path of the router and may offer a better solution. These include end socket and toggle clamps fitted to the ends or underside of the guide.

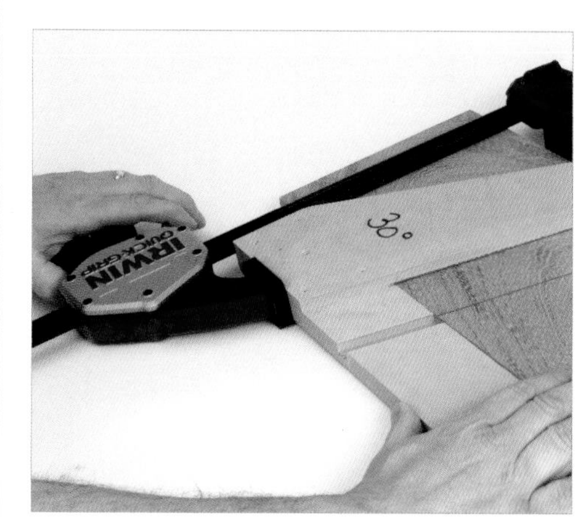

Ideally, use clamps that can be operated single handed, as you can then hold the guide in place with the other hand as you tighten up to stop it moving as the pressure comes to bear.

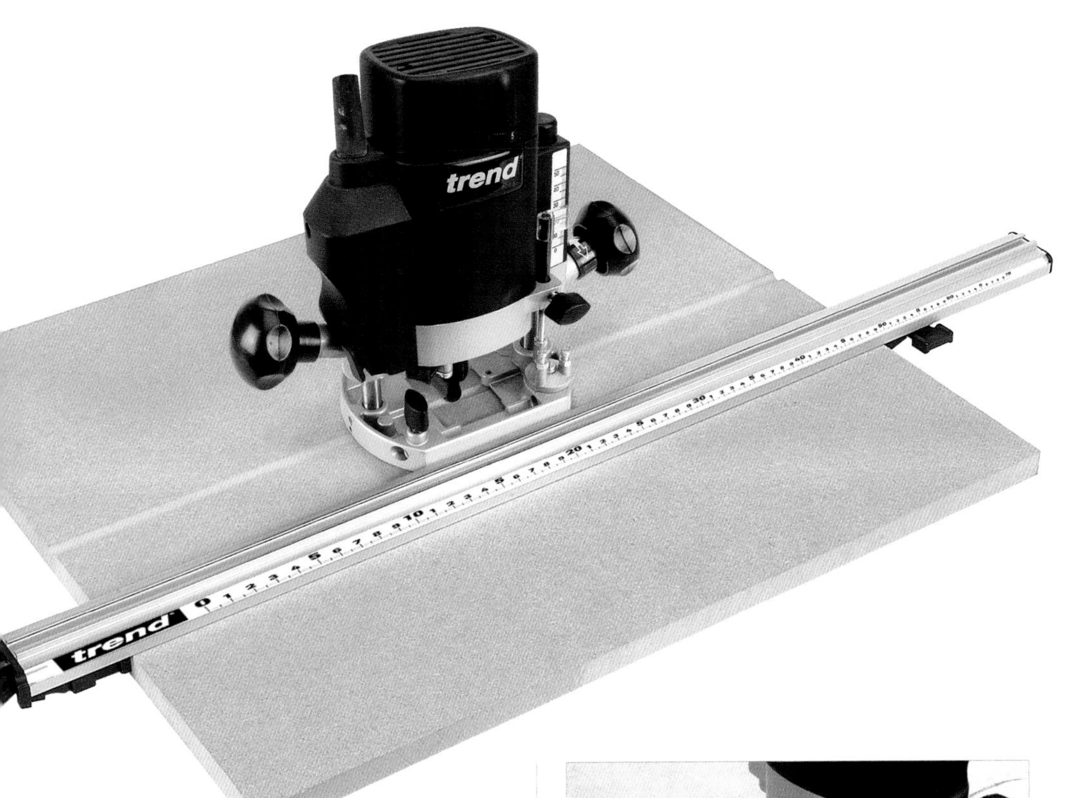

Clamp guides and tracks

Ready made clamp guides, consisting of low profile extruded aluminium straightedge with integral clamping systems, are one of the best options for guiding the router along straight cuts.

They are available in a variety of different lengths and the simple clamping action allows the guide to be fitted quickly, whilst the low profile presents little obstruction to the path of the router.

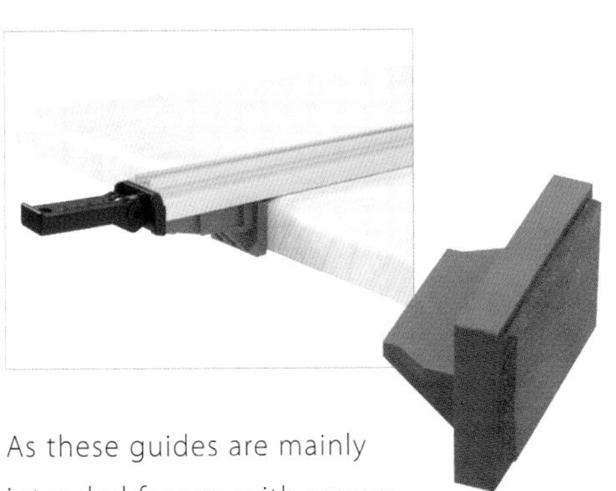

As these guides are mainly intended for use with square edged workpieces, they may not always be able to grip properly if the workpiece is very thin or is already moulded along the edge, as in a kitchen worktop. In this case, deeper detachable jaws are available as an optional accessory.

Similarly, you can also add a squaring attachment that clips to the fixed jaw and allows more accurate positioning for 90° cuts.

To use these guides, adjust the jaws to suit the width of the workpiece before positioning for the cut. Then apply light pressure by lowering the locking lever half way and check that the guide edge is still correctly positioned. You can tap it gently to make minute adjustments before applying final pressure by lowering the locking lever fully.

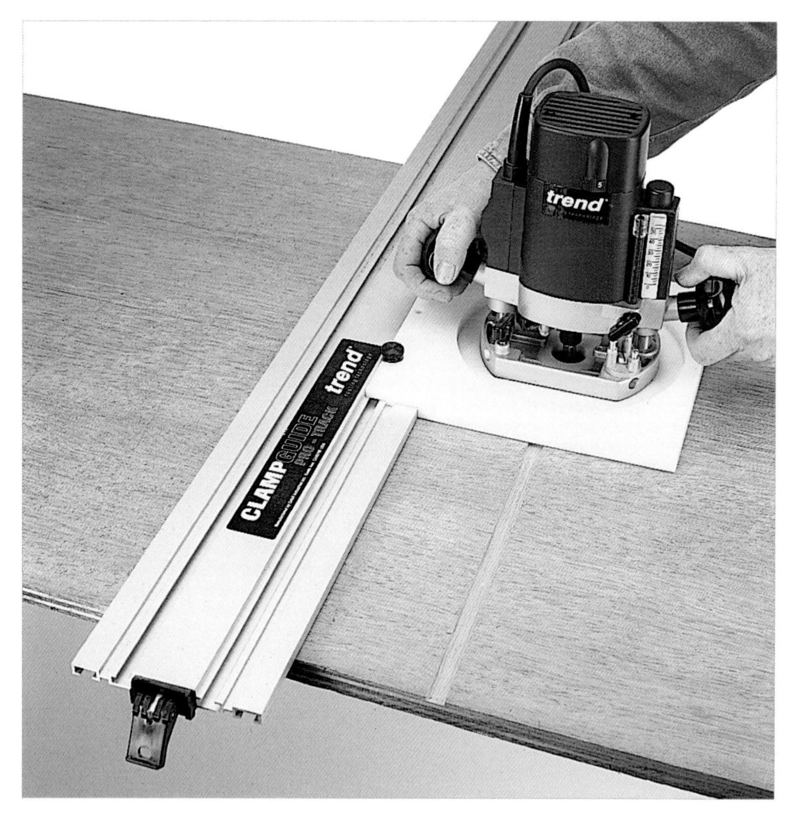

A more sophisticated version of this arrangement is the guide track system where the router is mounted on a sliding plate that fits into a Tee slot along the top of the track.

This is obviously a superbly accurate arrangement and the tracks are available in detachable sections of various lengths to suit virtually any application. They are particularly good when you are working with large sheets of material. The Trend Pro-track can also be fitted with stops to limit the router travel if you are cutting stopped housings, slots, etc.

Another variation, the Trend Back to Back Bench Clamp, incorporates bottom jaws which allow you to attach the guide directly to the bench and you can then use the top jaws to hold the work.

Positioning a straight guide

Start by marking out the position and width of the cut on the face of the work. If you are using a router with a flat sided base, turn the cutter so that the cutting edges are at right angles to the flat side.

Measure the distance from the cutting edge to the outside edge of the base.

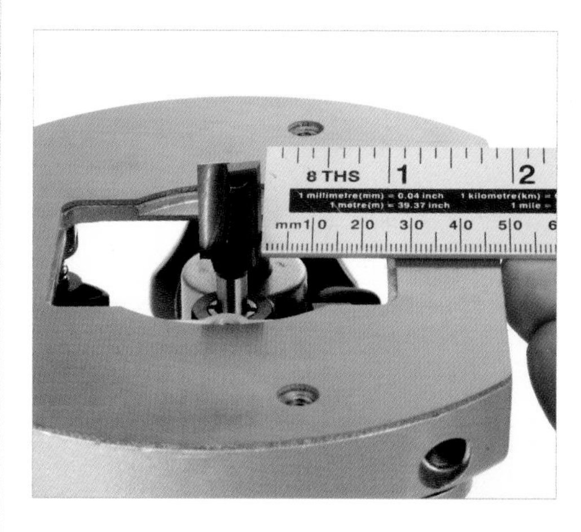

Then measure off this distance on the workpiece at both ends of the cutting line, working to the left-hand side of the groove. Position and clamp a straight guide against these lines. The procedure is slightly simpler if you're using a round-based router as you can measure the distance from the cutter to the edge anywhere around the base.

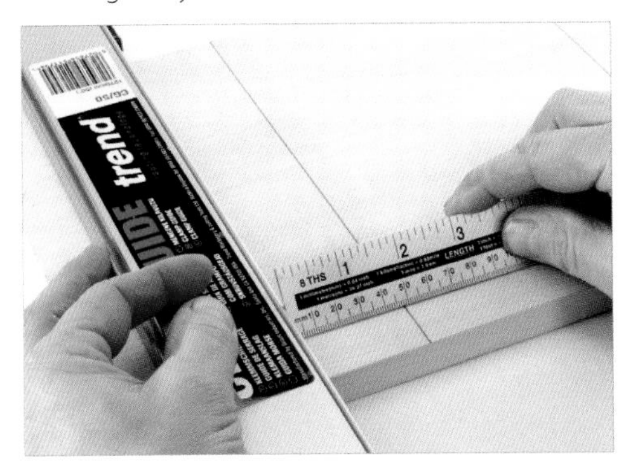

The other way of positioning the guide is to stand the router on the face of the workpiece at one end of the required groove with the cutter's edge against the cutting line. Mark the edge of the base plate on the workpiece, or even better, slide the edge of the straight guide up to it and lightly tighten. Repeat with the base at the other end of the line, re-check the first setting and then fully tighten the clamp.

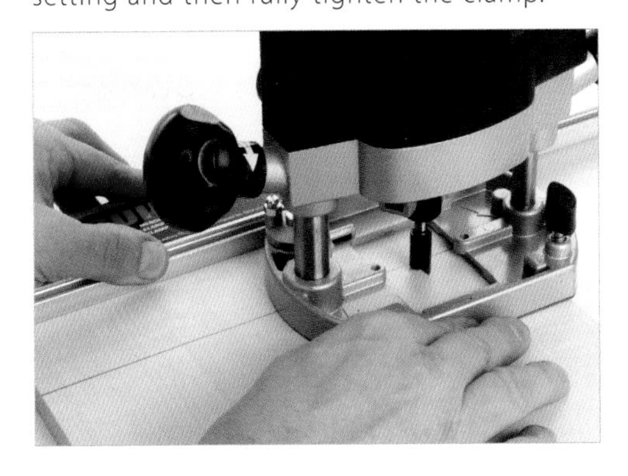

Tip

If you do a lot of work with a particular router/bit combination, machine up a piece of thin MDF or plastic to be exactly the same width as the distance between the edge of the router and the cutter and use this to position the fence clamping line.

Feed direction

When you are using a straight guide, always cut from left to right to maintain the correct feed direction i.e. against the rotation of the cutter as this will have the effect of pulling the router into the guide edge rather than allowing it to wander off line.

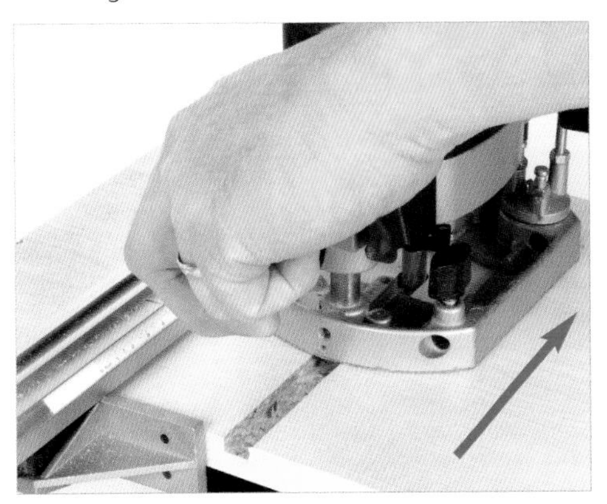

If you need to make more than one pass to get the required width of groove, make the second cut to the left of the first one to maintain this pulling action.

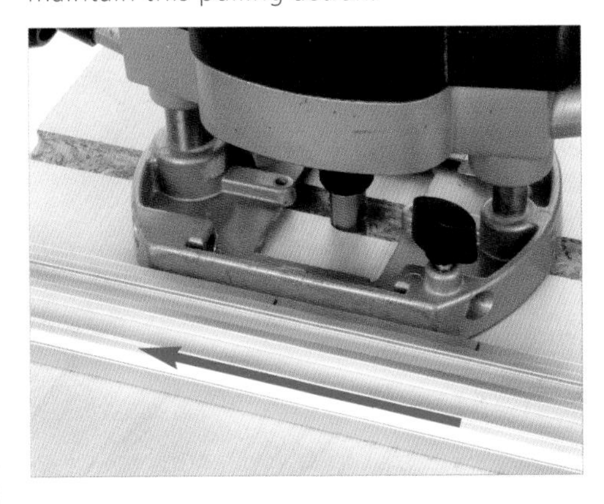

A very quick way to make multiple cuts without having to reposition the guide each time is to use a thin spacer sandwiched between the guide and the router for the first cut and then remove it for the second one. This ensures that you can reproduce the same groove width each time.

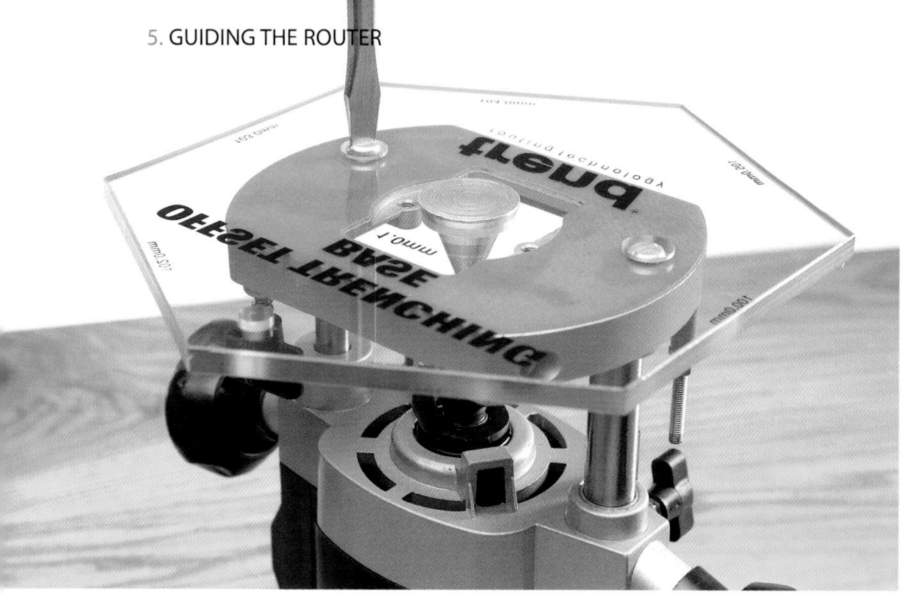

You can buy a special base for just this sort of application. The Trend Offset Trenching Base, allows you to cut wide grooves by varying which face of the base you run against.

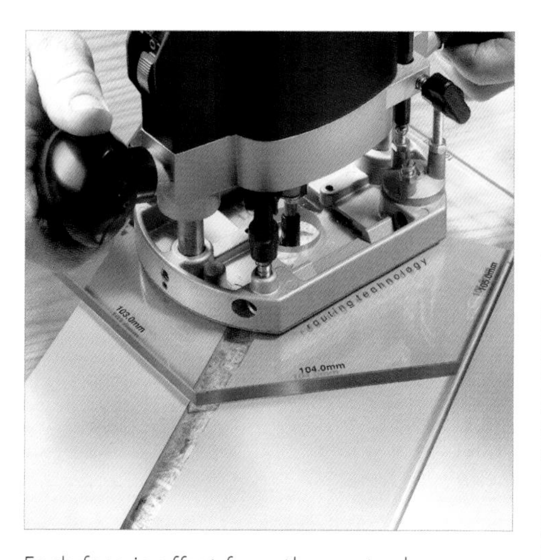

Each face is offset from the centre by a different amount ranging from 1mm to 5mm. With this in place, you can cut six different groove widths with the same cutter and fence settings.

Cutting parallel housings

Sometimes, it is necessary to machine a series of equally spaced housings which can be both difficult and time-consuming if you try and position the guide by measuring each time. Instead, just screw a spacer batten to the underside of the straightedge and the job becomes foolproof.

The spacer batten must be a smooth sliding fit in the groove and is fixed to the underside of the straightedge at the distance equal to the required housing spacing, less the base plate/cutter edge margin. It must also be perfectly parallel to the guide edge. Cut the first housing at the end of the work by clamping the guide across the workpiece with the batten uppermost.

Remaining housings are then cut by dropping the spacer batten into each previous cut. If you're making matched components like a pair of bookcase ends, clamp each pair edge to edge and cut across both faces in one pass, to ensure they are identical.

Stopped housings

If you don't want the grooves to run right across the width of the work as for instance in a stopped housing, you can fix stops to the top face of the straightedge to limit the travel of the router.

This can either be screwed or clamped to the guide for a one-off application, or made to be fully adjustable by cutting a slot in the guide and locating the stops with a coach bolt and wing nuts. Make sure that there is a gap underneath the stop so that sawdust cannot accumulate between the base and the stop and cause a false reading.

Cutting across uneven surfaces

If you need to cut across an uneven surface it is obviously impossible to get the router to run smoothly and produce a consistent depth of cut.

In this case make up a stepped straightedge by gluing together two lengths of relatively thin material, something like 8 mm MDF is ideal. Make one piece wider than the other by slightly more than the base plate to cutter edge measurement. Fix them together so that the back edges are lined up and then trim the bottom edge parallel to the top by running the router base against the upper edge.

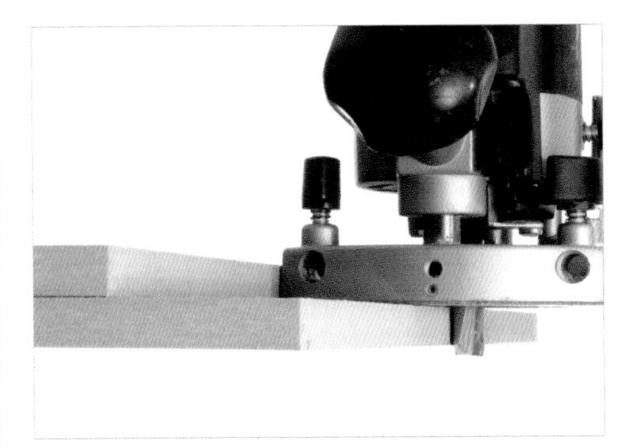

The guide can then be used in the same way as the normal straight guide, clamping it at either end to bridge the uneven surface.

If you're removing the waste or ground from a flat area, such as a relief carving, the router must somehow be supported straight and level above the surface while the waste material is cut away and there are several methods for achieving this.

Here are a few examples:

1. On narrow surfaces the edges of the area can be left to allow the base to span between them.

2. On wider surfaces the cutting operation can be planned to leave raised areas which are then cut away later by hand, or by fitting temporary support blocks over the cut face, or you can fit a large sub-base to the router to allow it to span over a wide area.

   If this is cut from a transparent material like acrylic you'll get a clearer view of the cutter.

3. If there is no support available from the workpiece, span it using ski pads fitted to the ends of the router side fence rods, but your bench must be absolutely flat for this to work accurately.

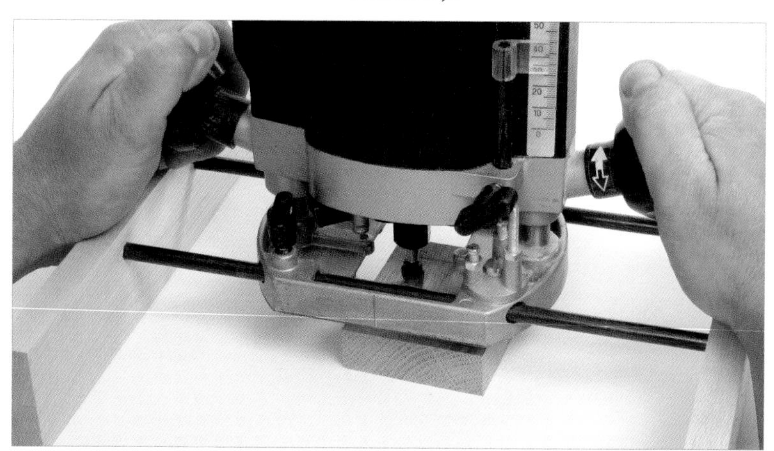

For extra rigidity if the cuts are likely to be heavy, make up a support frame and mount the router on an adjustable sliding carriage.

This can be made up quite simply using scraps of timber, although there are more sophisticated ready-made versions that fulfil a range of support functions if you anticipate extensively doing this type of work.

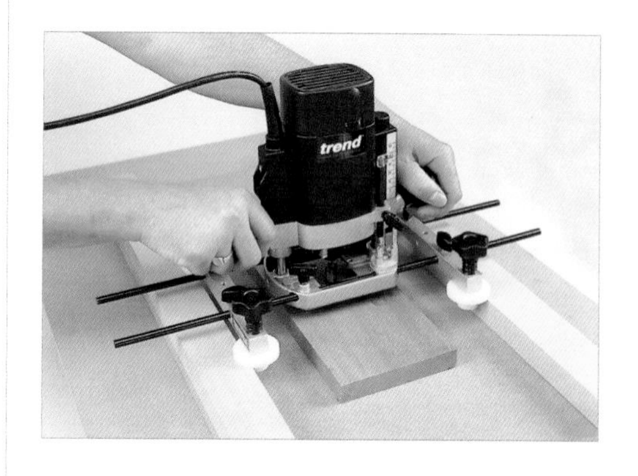

Tip

If you are removing a wide area that is recessed to an edge such as a half lap joint, always cut the shoulder first and then start the waste removal from the end of the work and gradually move the cutter inwards to ensure that half the router base is always firmly supported. Working the router in the opposite direction will gradually reduce the support, eventually causing the base to drop into the cut.

Straight cutting with a guide bush

Sometimes a groove has to be really precise and simply relying on running the base of the router against the straightedge may not be accurate enough. There is the chance of a tiny amount of wander if the router is not kept firmly against the guide throughout the cut.

To avoid this, make up a straight guide with a slot cut along its centre line to take a guide bush, but the cutter/guide bush combination must be carefully matched to produce a free running slot with no side play.

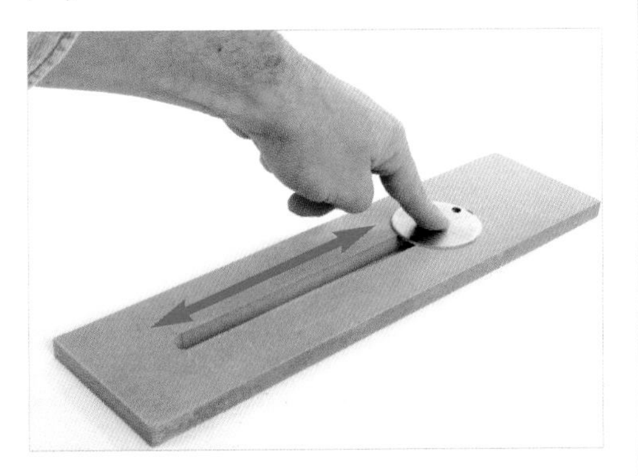

Frame Guides

If you need precision, along with a degree of versatility and do not want to use a guide bush, then it is useful to make up a frame guide by linking two straightedges together to form a square routing frame.

This allows you to cut wide housings or slots, by spacing the two straightedge slightly wider apart than the width of the router base. Remember to feed the router against the cutter rotation to ensure the router is kept firmly against the guides at all times. Any waste between the cuts can be removed using the router freehand.

A further refinement of this idea is to make an adjustable wooden frame using coach bolts fitted with wing nuts. If the straightedge and their linking pieces all have suitable slots cut along them, the frame can be setup for a variety of different cuts and you can also add clamping lugs to simplify mounting the frame, as well as sliding stops for cutting stopped housings.

The router base can either slide directly on the frame members or fit it to a sub-base. The slotted arrangement of the fences also allows the guides to be set at an angle across the workpiece and the frame can be used to cut louvre and angled housings across the work.

A metal ready made version of this frame is available as the Trend Varijig.

This highly accurate, adjustable frame allows you to cut rectangles and squares.

It also incorporates an anti tilt block for the router if you decide to use it with a guide bush rather than guiding with the router base itself.

All these grooving cuts are effectively inside cuts, with the router bit cutting both sides of the groove and they rely on the router being held firmly against the edge guide. If you do not concentrate fully during this operation or the guides become loose in any way, the cutter will go off-line. This sometimes happens if the density of the workpieces suddenly varies, for instance if you hit a particularly hard knot. Whilst there is relatively little danger to the user, the cut will not be what you intended and will probably wobble off line.

For this reason it is sometimes beneficial to make the cut with two different diameter cutters, the first one slightly narrower than the second one, as the light cut from the second pass is less likely to be deflected off line and there is also room for the chips to escape cleanly as well.

Tip

After clamping the guide in position, always check with a square or mitre gauge to ensure that the position is still perfect and has not moved slightly during the clamping.

Working with guide bushes

The guide bush is perhaps the most useful way of guiding the router, and widens the scope of the handheld router for both amateur and professional user alike.

They are used in conjunction with a straightedge, jigs and templates and sometimes even just the edge of the work itself, to produce both curved and straightedge work. They can also be used for cutting out, trimming or decorative edge moulding and offer the facility for cutting panel mouldings and other recessed surface applications. They are also used with a wide range of templates and jigs for such applications as comb jointing, dovetailing and cutting tenons.

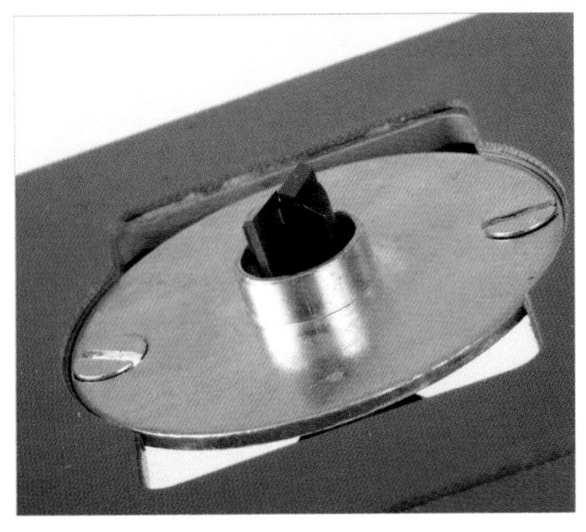

The guide bush is effectively a small ring fence and stands proud of the underside of the router base plate. On high quality routers they are designed to be a precision fit and concentric to the cutter to ensure that there is always a constant distance between the cutting edge and the template during use. Whether the guide is a straightedge or curved template, this constant margin is vital so that the guide bush faithfully reproduces the shape. They are also used with jigs for precision drilling using all the advantages of the plunge action of the router, e.g. for dowel drilling or hinge sinking.

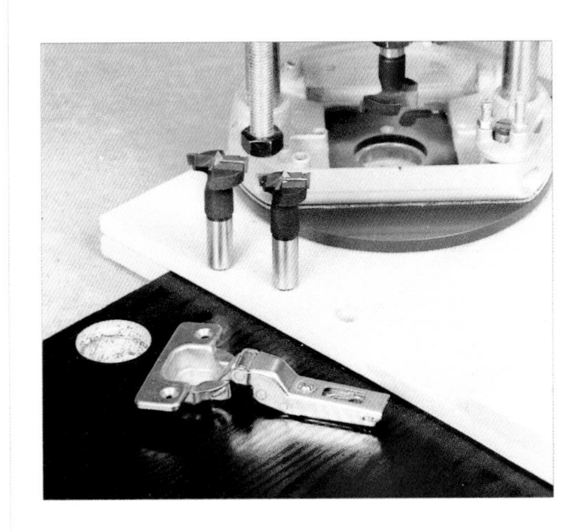

For precise working, the guide bushes need to be accurately manufactured in steel. This obviously makes them expensive, particularly if you require a range of different sizes.

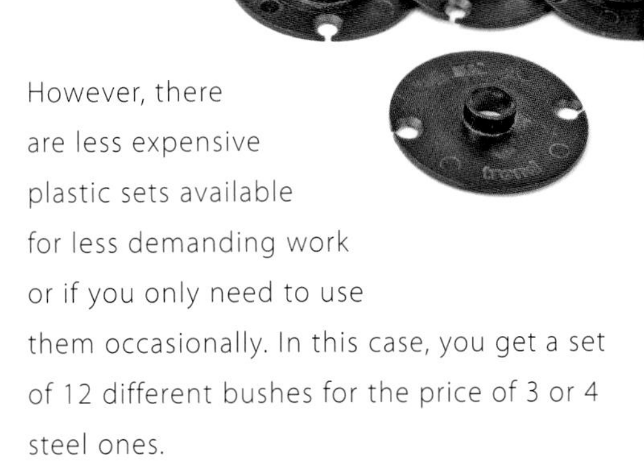

However, there are less expensive plastic sets available for less demanding work or if you only need to use them occasionally. In this case, you get a set of 12 different bushes for the price of 3 or 4 steel ones.

One of the snags of fitting the guide bush is that the mounting plate can compromise the effectiveness of the dust extraction facility by effectively blocking off the cutter from the point of extraction. To overcome this problem, some manufacturers supply bushes with a skeletal form to minimise any obstruction and maintain the necessary airflow.

In order to accommodate different diameter cutters, guide bushes are available with outside diameters ranging from 8 to 40 mm. By using different combinations of cutters and guide bush diameters, you can easily vary the dimensions of the finished workpiece.

This is particularly useful for cutting stepped recesses or variations in fluting or panel moulding using a single template.

Adapters and sub bases

Not all router manufacturers offer a complete range of guide bush sizes, or even the facility to fix them. However, with these routers it is still possible to fit guide bushes using a sub-base or adapter plate. This is screwed to the underside of the router base plate and is suitably recessed to take a full guide bush range.

The Trend Unibase is a universal base plate designed to fit all popular routers and take their vast range of guide bushes.

Fitting guide bushes

Various methods of mounting the guide bush are used by different router manufacturers, the most common being to machine a circular recess, concentric to the cutter on the underside of the base plate. The flange of the guide bush can then be set flush into the recess and secured with two countersunk screws.

Other methods involve bayonet fittings held by a spring lock or two-piece bushes held by a threaded locking ring.

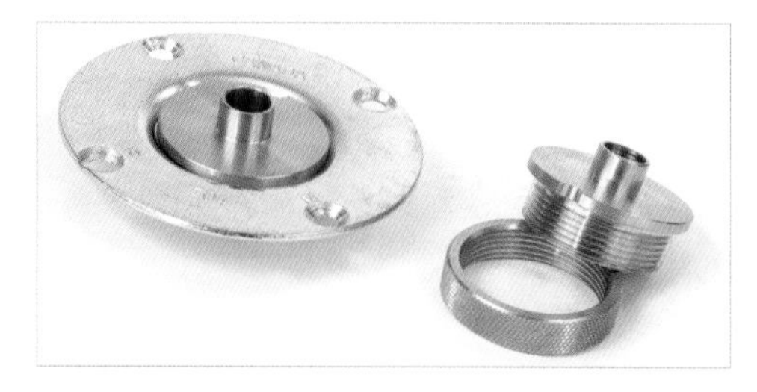

Before fitting a guide bush, always clean out any resin or dust from the bush recess. Make sure that the flange lies flat, with the screw heads recessed below the base plate. If left proud, they will score the face of the work. It is vital that the guide bush is truly concentric with the cutter and for this purpose, some routers are supplied with an alignment tool that is temporarily gripped in the collet.

Any flat thin, stable material will do for making templates, MDF is an economical choice for one-off applications. But if you intend using a particular template frequently, it might be worth making it from either acrylic sheet, Tufnol® or solid laminate, which are available in sheets of varying thickness.

It is equally important that the material used for the template is thicker than the projecting guide bush. If it is not, the router

Tip

Some applications may require a much bigger area of contact between the bush and the template to prevent it riding up over the edge. To stop this happening some heavy-duty routers are fitted with long guide bushes that can be adjusted to give the required amount of protrusion below the base.

will not sit down squarely, the cut cannot be accurate and there is a danger of scratching the work with the end of the guide bush.

In some situations it is only necessary to use a very thin template in which case the depth of the guide bush spigot can be reduced by filing it down.

Cutter clearance

When you are selecting a guide bush and cutter combination, always make sure that the clearance between the cutting edges of the cutter on the inside face of the bush is not less than 2.5 mm. This is to allow the waste to clear quickly in use and prevent the cutting edges from overheating.

Guide bush margins

To take account of the difference between the cutter and the guide bush diameter, it is necessary to calculate the amount of offset, called the guide bush margin (GBM), and then add this margin into your calculations for the template dimensions. If you are making an external template where the guide bush follows the outside edge, subtract the margin from each edge of the required workpiece dimensions. On the other hand, if you're making internal templates where the guide bush follows the inside edge, the margin must be added to each edge of the workpiece dimensions.

DIA. CUTTER	Outside Dia. / Ref.	GUIDE BUSH														
		GB10	GB11	GB12	GB14	GB16	GB17	GB18	GB20	GB22	GB24	GB26	GB28	GB30	GB32	GB40
inches	mm	10 mm	11 mm	12 mm	14 mm	16 mm	17 mm	18 mm	20 mm	22 mm	24 mm	26 mm	28 mm	30 mm	32 mm	40 mm
7/64	3	3.5	4	4.5	5.5	6.5	7	7.5	8.5	9.5	10.5	11.5	12.5	13.5	14.5	18.5
1/8	3.2	-	3.9	4.4	5.4	6.4	6.9	7.4	8.4	9.4	10.4	11.4	12.4	13.4	14.4	18.4
5/32	4	-	3.5	4	5	6	6.5	7	8	9	10	11	12	13	14	18
3/16	4.8	-	-	3.6	4.6	5.6	6.1	6.6	7.6	8.6	9.6	10.6	11.6	12.6	13.6	17.6
13/64	5	-	-	3.5	4.5	5.5	6	6.5	7.5	8.5	9.5	10.5	11.5	12.5	13.5	17.5
7/32	5.5	-	-	-	4.2	5.2	5.8	6.2	7.2	8.2	9.2	10.2	11.2	12.2	13.2	17.2
15/64	6	-	-	-	4	5	5.5	6	7	8	9	10	11	12	13	17
1/4	6.3	-	-	-	3.8	4.8	5.4	5.8	6.8	7.8	8.8	9.8	10.8	11.8	12.8	16.8
5/16	8	-	-	-	-	4	4.5	5	6	7	8	9	10	11	12	16
23/64	9	-	-	-	-	3.5	4	4.5	5.5	6.5	7.5	8.5	9.5	10.5	11.5	15.5
3/8	9.5	-	-	-	-	-	3.8	4.2	5.2	6.2	7.2	8.2	9.2	10.2	11.2	15.2
25/64	10	-	-	-	-	-	3.5	4	5	6	7	8	9	10	11	15
7/16	11	-	-	-	-	-	-	3.5	4.5	5.5	6.5	7.5	8.5	9.5	10.5	14.5
15/32	12	-	-	-	-	-	-	-	4	5	6	7	8	9	10	14
1/2	12.7	-	-	-	-	-	-	-	3.6	4.6	5.6	6.6	7.6	8.6	9.6	13.6
-	13	-	-	-	-	-	-	-	3.5	4.5	5.5	6.5	7.5	8.5	9.5	13.5
-	15	-	-	-	-	-	-	-	-	3.5	4.5	5.5	6.5	7.5	8.5	12.5
5/8	16	-	-	-	-	-	-	-	-	-	4	5	6	7	8	12
-	18	-	-	-	-	-	-	-	-	-	-	4	5	6	7	11
23/32	18.2	-	-	-	-	-	-	-	-	-	-	3.9	4.9	5.9	6.9	10.9
3/4	19	-	-	-	-	-	-	-	-	-	-	3.5	4.5	5.5	6.5	10.5
-	20	-	-	-	-	-	-	-	-	-	-	-	4	5	6	10
7/8	22.2	-	-	-	-	-	-	-	-	-	-	-	-	3.9	4.9	8.9
1	25.4	-	-	-	-	-	-	-	-	-	-	-	-	-	-	7.3
1-1/8	28.5	-	-	-	-	-	-	-	-	-	-	-	-	-	-	5.7
1-1/4	31.8	-	-	-	-	-	-	-	-	-	-	-	-	-	-	4.1

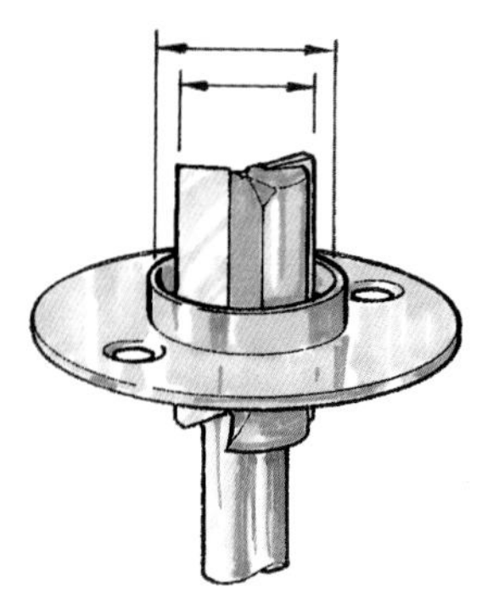

To calculate the guide bush margin, subtract the cutter diameter from the outside guide bush diameter and divide by two.

$$\frac{\text{Guide bush diameter} - \text{Cutter diameter}}{2}$$

For example if your cutter is 12mm diameter and the guide bush is 22mm then the GBM is 5mm.

$$\frac{22 - 12}{2} = 5$$

The versatility of the guide bush can be even increased still further by using guide bush collars that slip over standard bushes.

As well as giving you further variations in the spigot diameter, these bushes are also accurately sized to account for the guide bush margin and when used with the appropriate cutter, allow you to use a single template to cut both the male and female shape. This is particularly useful if you want to cut an inlay and its perfectly matched recess.

Using guide bushes

When you are using guide bushes the router is applied in the normal way, if necessary reaching the final depth in several steps. Position the router over the template or guide edge and slide the guide bush up against it. Follow the template in the correct direction, keeping the bush tight against the guide edge. If you feed the wrong way the cutter will deflect away from the template edge, as it would when using any other guide.

Self guided cutters

For trimming and moulding workpieces with curved or straightedges, the use of self guiding cutters offers the simplest and most direct solution.

These cutters are guided by a bearing either fitted to the cutter shank or on the end of the cutter. Self guiding cutters can be used to follow either the smooth edge of the workpiece or a template fitted above or beneath it.

Cutters with a solid pin acting as the guide are an alternative to bearing guided equivalents. An advantage is that the pin can be ground to a very small diameter allowing the cutter to work really close into a tight corner.

There is inevitably friction between the wood and the fixed pin, making it difficult to avoid the pin overheating and marking the surface of the wood.

Bearing guided cutters on the other hand should leave a virtually blemish free surface, provided the bearing is in good condition, free of resin build up and able to rotate freely.

The principle with these guided cutters is exactly the same as that of using a guide bush and initially it appears a quicker and easier system to set up and operate, with no complicated calculations involving guide bush margins.

However, the use of self guided cutters is more limited regarding variations in depth of cut, and the cutters themselves are often limited to a single purpose only. They are also more expensive than their non-bearing equivalents and the bearing will eventually wear, whereas a metal guide bush should last for ever. Nevertheless, self guided cutters are a very useful and important part of router work in both hand-held and fixed applications and often allow you to work in situations that might not otherwise be accessible to the router, such as previously installed window frames or worktops. In use, the bearing or pin on the self guided cutter follows the guide edge contour precisely to reproduce the cutter profile evenly along the workpiece.

Consequently, the guide edge must be deep enough to support the bearing face as the profile is cut, with no risk of it breaking or crumbling. It must also be finished perfectly flat and smooth, as any hollows, areas of raised grain or resin and glue deposits, will be reproduced on the cut edge of the workpiece.

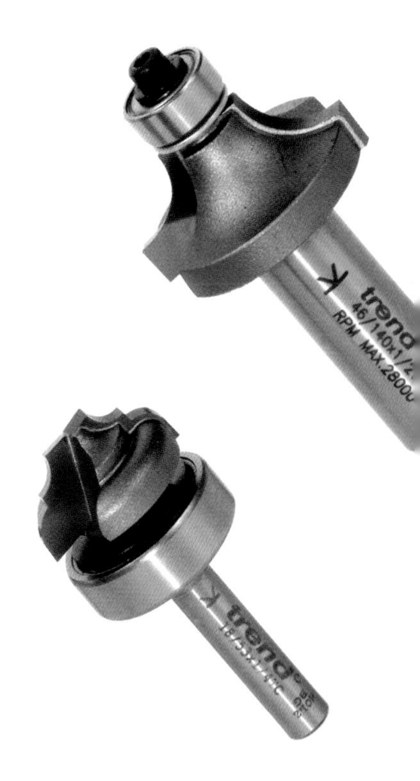

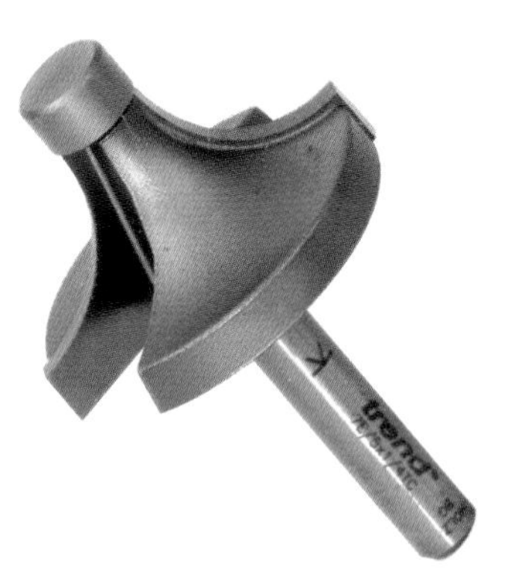

End mounted bearing guided cutters

Bottom mounted guide bearings are fitted over a precision ground spigot on the end of the cutter, which has an internal thread that allows the bearing to be held in place with a small Allen headed screw.

Before using one of these cutters, check that the bearing is secure with the supplied Allen key and that there is no slack in either the mounting or the bearing itself. With continual use it is possible for the retaining screw to work loose, so test this occasionally. If it drops off in use, your work will be ruined.

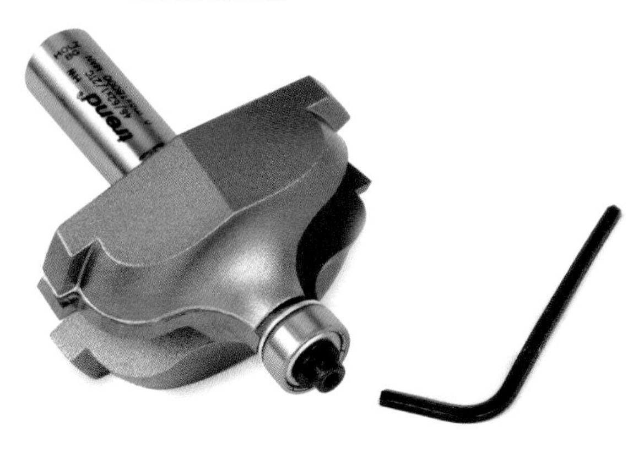

Avoid generating unnecessary side pressure by forcing the bearing against the work or template. As well as the danger of bending or even snapping the cutter, this generates excessive heat that will burn the edge of the work. Running the bearing hot will also melt the internal lubricating grease causing the bearing to seize and possibly disintegrate.

Larger cutters are sometimes fitted with more robust, heavy double duty ball races.

Tip

You can do a lot to minimise contamination of the bearings by always allowing any glue, used to fix laminates or veneers, to dry thoroughly before trimming it with the cutter.

It is therefore important to maintain the bearings on these cutters properly. Regular surface cleaning is an essential precaution, but never try and clean a bearing by soaking it in solvent, as this just dissolves the internal grease which cannot be replaced. Instead carefully scrape off any large deposits of resin or glue with a sharp blade, taking care not to scratch the surface of the metal. Then wipe the bearing edge carefully using a rag moistened with solvent, keeping it well away from the top and bottom bearing faces.

The combination of very high speed and fine dust inevitably means that bearings have a limited life and must be replaced as soon as they start showing any sign of stiffness.

If you anticipate heavy usage for a particular cutter, it might be worth investing in shielded bearings which have rubber seals giving improved protection from dust and dirt.

Some workpiece materials are particularly sensitive and will mark if you use a conventional bearing on the cutter, e.g. Corian. A range of plastic sleeved bearings are available for use with these materials and the bearings may be shaped as well to provide maximum support.

On some cutters, like 90° trimmers, the diameter of the bearing is perfectly matched to the cutter diameter, so a problem may arise when the cutter needs to be reground. The sharpening process always reduces the diameter of the cutter slightly, so professional resharpening will enable the bearing size to be reduced accordingly. The problem is obviously less critical with moulding cutters where the small variation in profile after grinding is probably not significant.

Bearings can also be mounted on the shank of any standard cutter to turn them into a self guided one. If the bearing exactly matches the diameter of a straight cutter it can be used for trimming operations, when a template is mounted on the top of the work, which is often easier as visibility is better.

Bearings are held in place with small collars that incorporate a tiny fixing screw.

Cutting with self guided cutters

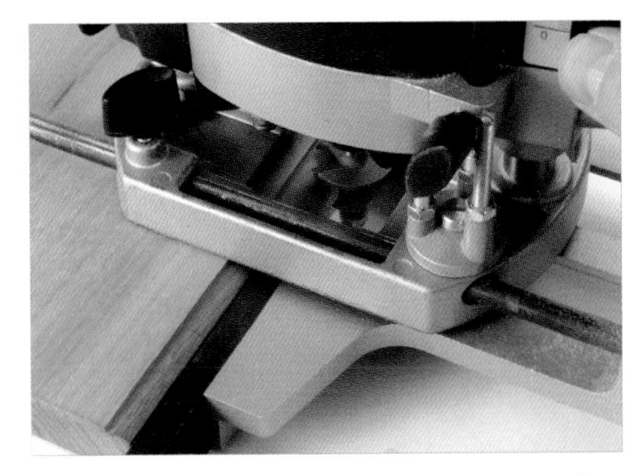

When using self guiding cutters it is usually recommended that the full depth of cut is achieved in a series of shallow steps as you would undertake with a standard cutter. This is not always possible with some profiles, so either use the guide fence or fit a larger diameter bearing to limit the depth of the initial cuts.

The final depth may be limited by the depth of the guide edge remaining. If this is not sufficient, position a batten or false guide edge above or below the workpiece. As a general rule, bearings should not be run against any edge less than 3 mm deep.

Shank mounted bearings must again be run with plenty of edge support from the template. If you're making shallow cuts, it may be necessary to increase the thickness of the template to provide an adequate bearing surface.

Bearing diameters

The width or profile of a cutter can be altered by changing the guide bearing to one of a different diameter. For example a standard rebate cutter can be used to cut rebates in a variety of widths.

Decorative moulding cutters can be used with different bearings to cut several variations on the basic profile.

A range of different sized alloy bearing rings are available for some of the heavy duty cutters which have two bearings. This allows different depths to be cut with the same bit. These are secured between the two bearings allowing a wider range of self guided operations.

Freehand routing

The term freehand routing can be applied to two different situations and it is worth taking a look at both.

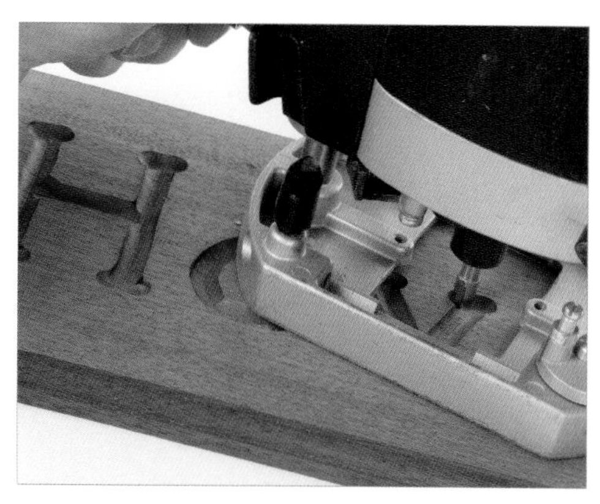

Firstly, freehand usually means using the router without any form of side-fence, bearing guided cutter, template or straightedge. This is perfectly possible, but it does need a steady hand coupled with intense concentration and is generally used for roughing out and removing waste material.

Freehand routing techniques can also be used to produce textured surfaces as well as for lettering and carving work.

The other type of freehand work involves using just the router motor unit without any base. Carving and engraving jobs can be carried out using multi-flute burrs or rasps, the motor unit being handheld and used as a rotary file. Cut away the waste using a coarse rasp to start with and then finish off with a fine burr to leave the required amount of texture.

It is important that you only use dedicated multi-flute burrs and rasps for these applications, never try and use conventional router cutters.

Controlling the router

With freehand routing, it is particularly important that the direction of feed of the router into the wood should always be against the rotation of the cutter and only light cuts should be made to avoid snatching.

This ensures that there is always some resistance against the cutter, helping you to control its path. Hard knots, twisted grain and other defects in the timber may cause the router to snatch or wander. The force you require to guide the router also varies depending on whether you are working down or across the grain and there is no substitute here for practice and experience. Find a piece of scrap material and make some trial cuts in various directions to get the feel of it. Try following a marked line and see how the rotation of the cutter tries to push you off course. For some shapes it may be that you cannot follow the normal rules of routing and you may have to feed in the 'wrong' direction.

Any router can be used freehand, but ideally one of the smaller lightweight models is best, as these have excellent visibility through the base plate and only generate minimal rotational reaction making them easier to control.

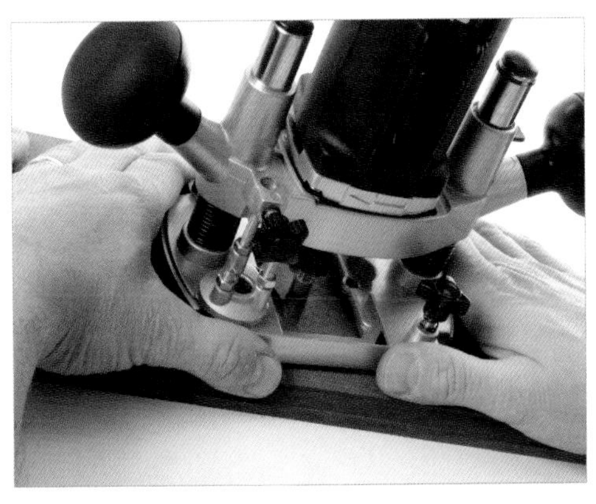

You can increase this control further by holding the router by the base, with your hands close to the surface of the work to produce a damping effect that minimises the tendency of the router to veer sideways. A large sub-base fitted with handles is an even better method, offering greater safety and reducing the risk of the router tipping as it cuts. It goes without saying that you should always keep your fingers outside the base plate area.

For more precise lettering work you can use templates from a range of pre-formed ones that are available in a range of typefaces, or cut your own from thin plastic or MDF.

6. JIGS AND TEMPLATES

The amazing versatility of the router can be increased even further with the addition of a variety of jigs and templates. Most of these arrangements are alternative means of guiding the router and enable you to carry out repeated operations with both accuracy and safety.

Jigs v templates

The terms jig and template are often used synonymously although there are in fact subtle differences.

A template is normally a flat plate made from thin MDF, plywood or plastic which is attached to the work and acts as a master pattern for the router to follow, allowing numerous identical shapes to be cut or profiled. Templates must be cut very precisely and although there are a lot of ready made patterns you will often need to make your own to suit specific jobs.

A jig on the other hand, is usually a more sophisticated arrangement that enables you to securely locate either the router or the workpiece, giving you suitable control to rout precise repeatable cuts.

The work needs to be clamped firmly within the jig to allow this repeatability and the jig itself must be strong enough to retain its accuracy and withstand constant use.

There are five basic methods for guiding the router when using jigs or templates:

1. A metal guide bush fitted to the router base.

2. A roller bearing guide fitted to the end of the cutter.

3. A roller bearing guide fitted to the shank of the cutter.

4. The base of the router runs along the edge of the template.

5. A shaped sub base is fitted to the router base to run against the template.

Making your own jigs

The most effective jigs are undoubtedly the simplest, as these are quick to use and can be tailored to suit each individual situation.

Sometimes they are made for just one particular operation and then discarded, but usually a well constructed jig can be used many times over, so it is worth investing some time and effort into making it properly.

For a jig to work properly, you must take account of several important design considerations, the most important of which is accuracy. The whole idea of a jig is that it allows you to perform exactly the same operation every time you use it. If it has not been made accurately enough to deliver this basic requirement you might as well not bother and save yourself some considerable frustration.

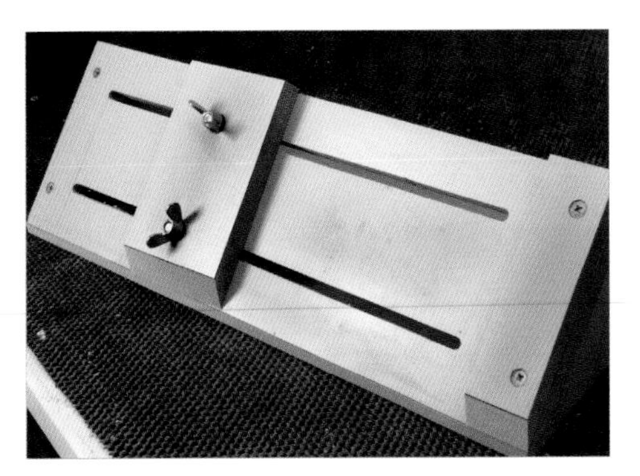

Many factors influence this accuracy; the jig must be stable and have some facility that allows it to be clamped firmly to the work.

The jig must also confine and guide the router precisely along the intended path, so it must be strong enough not to be deflected by the forces generated during the cut. The router must also slide freely within the jig, so mating surfaces must be smooth and protected if there is any likelihood of repetitive wear, which could compromise the accuracy.

It must also be quick and easy to remove and replace the workpiece accurately, so some form of datum stop and quick release clamps are required on most jigs.

In some situations, it is necessary for the router to cut through into the jig itself, so allow for this by making a particular component replaceable, or by incorporating a sacrificial work pad.

Most importantly, the jig must be safe, holding everything securely and allowing you to work with your hands well away from the cutter.

Jig making materials

You can use a variety of different materials to make a jig, though MDF is particularly good as it is flat, perfectly stable and relatively cheap. Although it doesn't take screws too well on the edges it does glue together easily.

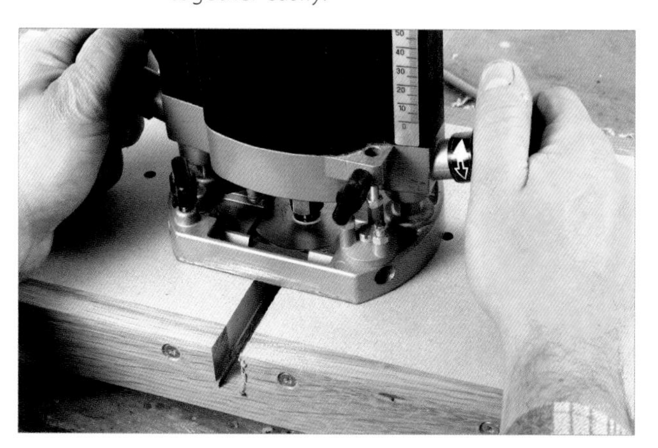

Solid timber may seem an attractive alternative for jig making as it is so much stronger, but large pieces are liable to move, even when seasoned properly. So its use should be restricted to smaller structural components rather than important guiding surfaces. Even small amounts of natural movement are enough to destroy the accuracy of a jig, so combining hardwood with MDF achieves the best of both worlds.

Good quality plywood is another very solid jig making material though it is considerably more expensive than MDF and often not as flat.

Other plastic materials are also available, but due to their higher cost, are best restricted to only the most critical parts of the jig, (normally the guiding template) but even then, only if it is going to be used frequently. Tufnol is a superb material that is smooth and strong and can be machined with most TCT cutters. The cheaper alternative is clear acrylic sheet, which again is easily machined, but is more brittle.

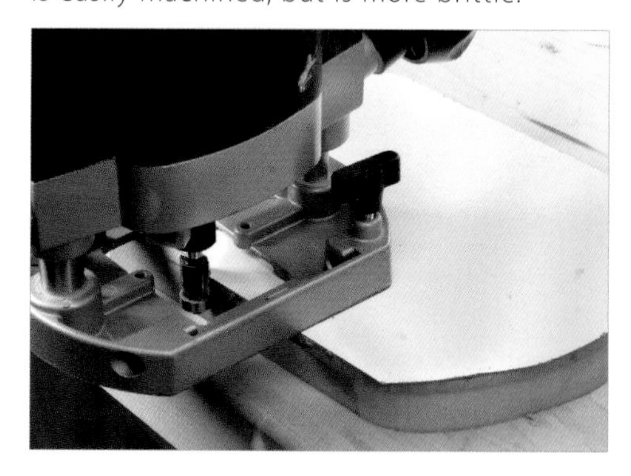

A good compromise is to use MDF for the majority of the jig and then cover any surfaces that are subject to wear with a layer of laminate.

This is easily applied using an impact adhesive, leaving it slightly oversize and then trimming back with a suitable bearing guided cutter.

More sophisticated jigs will need removable or adjustable components. You can buy a huge range of jig making accessories from specialists router suppliers, like Trend.

Levers, threaded inserts, scales and template making material, as well as double sided tape and toggle clamps for holding the workpiece in the jig are all available.

Having made your jig, it is obviously important to hold the work securely within it and you may have to adopt various holding strategies.

These depend on the type of work, but as well as the toggle clamps mentioned above, other alternatives include the use of spikes, eccentric cams, double-sided tape, wedges, abrasive paper, special mats and vacuum beds.

Sometimes the work has been predrilled as part of its manufacture and this hole may be used as a means of locating and securing it. In fact, any clamping method can be used, as long as it doesn't interfere with the path of the router or restrict the removal of the work from the jig.

You will soon build up quite a collection of different jigs so it is worth labelling each one with what it does and also make a note on it if there are any particular cutters or guide bushes that are needed for its use.

Attaching the router to a jig

Some of the most useful jigs and work aids need to be fitted directly to the router base. When you are purchasing a router make sure it has suitable tapped holes in its base. Look for routers with the TBC logo which is a standard configuration for many bolt on sub bases and router table fixings.

For future reference, when you start making jigs and templates, it is a good idea to make up a pattern of your router base.

Alternatively, if your router has a detachable soleplate, the job of making this template is very much easier. Simply remove the soleplate and fix it with double-sided tape to a piece of thin MDF which has been roughly cut to shape.

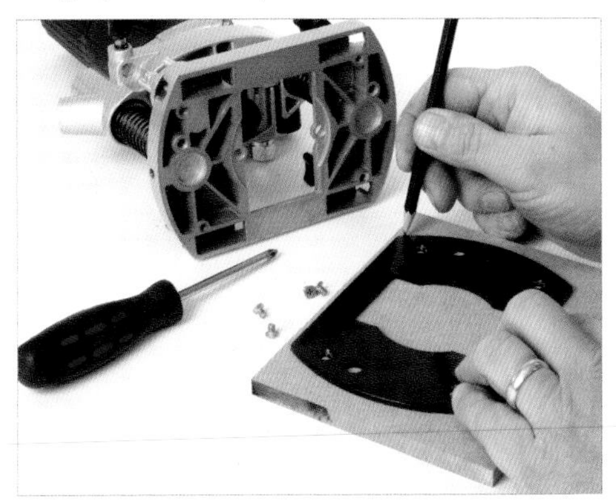

Then use a flush trimming cutter in the router, minus its soleplate, to produce a perfect pattern.

The fixing holes are easily located using the soleplate as a guide.

If the base is not detachable, a pattern can be made by drawing around the router base and then cutting or sanding the MDF to shape.

The fixing holes can be accurately located by making a couple of sharpened studs from appropriately threaded bolts, cutting off the heads and sharpening one end.

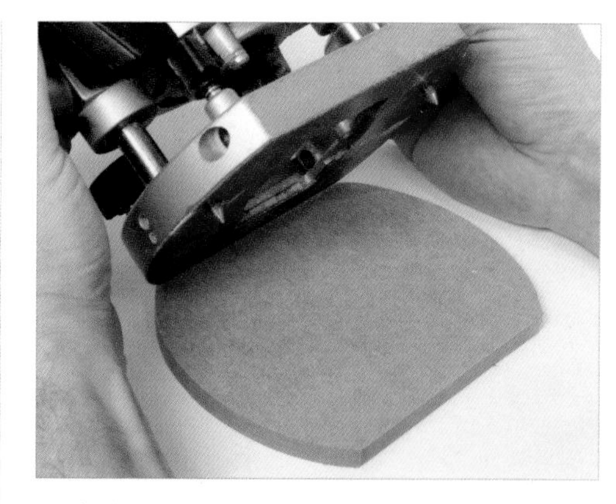

With these screwed into place in the base so that the points are just sticking out proud, press the router down onto the template and the hole centres will be marked perfectly.

The alternative is to use the Trend Unibase that is drilled to accept most routers.

If the router doesn't have any fixing holes other than those for the guide bush, you can always the use the guide bush itself as a template to get the holes accurately located.

Tip

Once you have made a base pattern you can then make a range of false bases from MDF, though for some applications, where you need good cutter visibility, Perspex may be a better alternative.

Simple work aids and jigs

The range of homemade jigs is virtually limitless and you will no doubt design and develop some of your own to suit specific applications. However, there are a few simple jigs that are so universally useful and quick to make that every router user should consider making them. Here are just a few:

Base extension

Often on edge moulding jobs there is very little support left for the router, particularly if it is a narrow workpiece or you are working round a corner.

In this situation, it is so easy to accidentally tilt the router and leave an unsightly scoop in the mould. Those routers with very large base openings are particularly vulnerable.

Beware of making this extension plate too thick or you will reduce the depth of the plunge capacity of the router. 6mm or 9mm material is plenty thick enough.

For larger and heavier routers this setup may still not provide sufficient support and a larger base extension with two guide handles may be necessary.

Centre finder

This is often called a 'drilling base' as it allows precise location for plunging cutting holes in the workpiece. Although somewhat limited, the router makes an excellent drilling device, particularly on large workpieces where the holes are too far in to be reached with a drill press. The router is able to cut a perfectly clean 90 degree hole to a precise depth.

This particular jig needs to be made from Perspex and is best made by first fixing it to the base of the router.

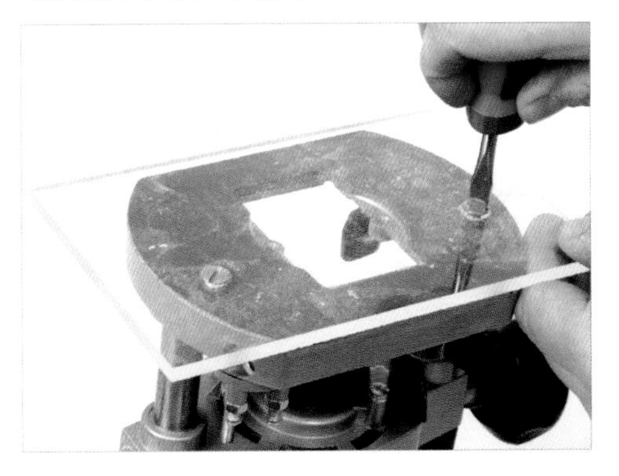

Then plunging down with a V cutter to mark the centre point.

Now remove the Perspex and scribe the crosshair lines at 90° to each other, with the intersection centred on this marked point.

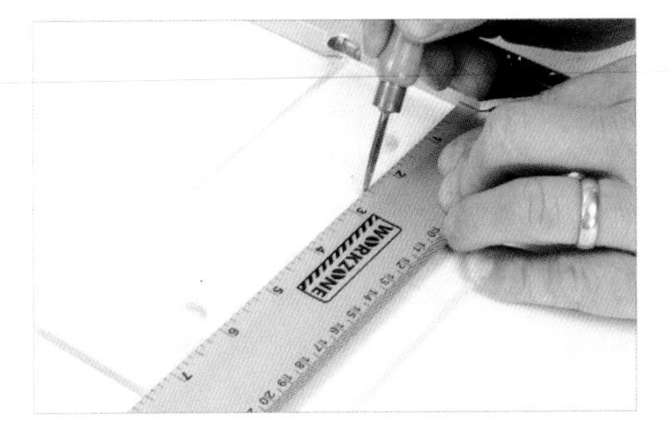

Replace the Perspex on the router and drill through it with a cutter slightly bigger than the one you'll be using for the drilling operation.

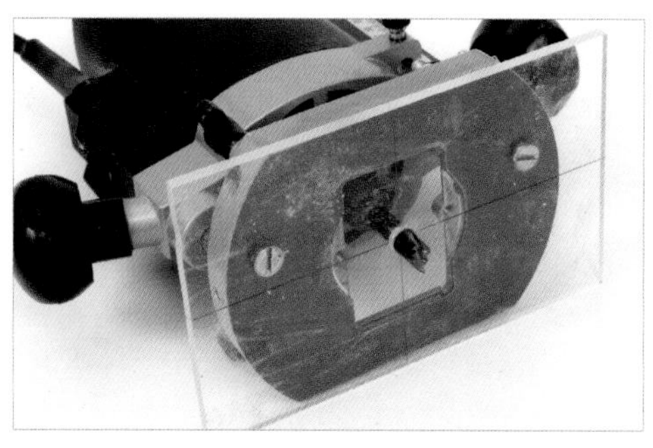

To use the jig, the location of each hole is marked on the workpiece with intersecting lines and the jig just needs to be lined up with these before plunging in with a suitably sized cutter.

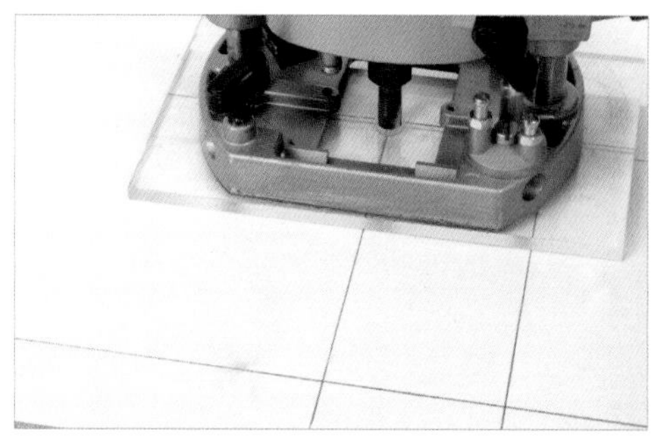

You can even bore holes at an angle by adding shims to one end of the base though this makes precise centering more difficult.

A variation on this is to locate the router onto the drilling template using a guide bush which is a close fit in the template.

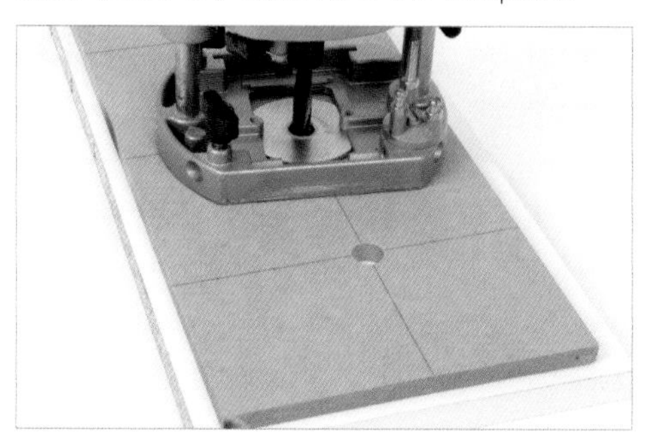

Trimming jig

This simple jig is designed for quickly trimming the end of boards to exact length and leaving a perfect finish across the end grain, something not normally possible unless you have a panel cutting table saw.

All you need is a perfectly straight timber batten about 250 mm long and no thicker than the material being trimmed. Stick this to a piece of MDF with another perfectly straightedge, making sure that the two form a right angle. Make this MDF slightly longer than the widest piece you anticipate trimming and also make sure that the batten end is flush with the edge of the MDF.

Cut the workpiece to within about 2 millimetres with a saw, then clamp it to the jig or use some double-sided tape to hold it in place, lining up the end of the batten with the cut line. Now use a bearing guided trimming cutter to run across the end of the board using the edge of the MDF as the guide.

This will result in a perfectly clean and square cut in both planes and is a wonderful aid if you have a batch of boards to prepare for a project such as a bookcase.

Housing jig

The simple housing joint is one of the most useful for building shelf units and cabinets. Cutting the necessary groove with a router makes it almost foolproof, providing you can guide the cutter accurately.

This jig is very similar in construction to the trimming jig but is made with a heavier section batten which extends well beyond the end of the MDF fence. Use it with a bottom cut two flute cutter, but this time use the base of the router running against the fence as the guide.

You must maintain positive pressure against the fence at all times to prevent the cutter wandering off course. If you don't have a cutter of exactly the right size, take two passes with a narrower cutter, moving the jig to the required amount.

After the first groove is cut, it is a simple matter to line up the jig for each subsequent housing by positioning the edges of the cut groove in the batten against the marked lines on the work.

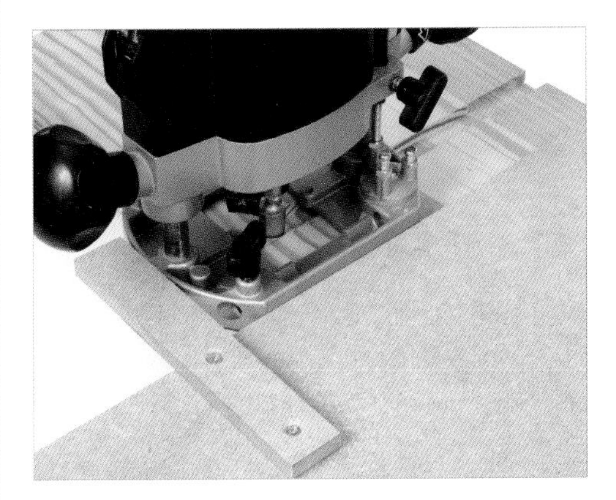

If the housings are to be stopped, you can either stick or screw stop blocks onto the MDF to limit the amount of travel of the router.

Self centering mortising and slotting jig

This is another very simple jig which allows you to cut slots or mortises that are perfectly centred along the workpiece edge, no matter how thick it is.

Again, you will need a sub-base but this time fix two dowels or metal studs into it, about 75mm apart, but centred on a line through the centre of the base.

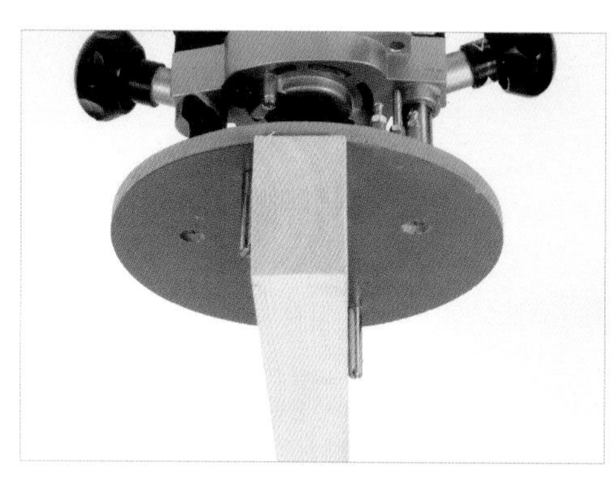

To use the jig, mark the limits of the required groove on the workpiece, position the router over the work, holding it so that the pins are on opposite sides of the edge. Maintain gentle twisting pressure at all times to keep them both in contact, then plunge and cut the slot to the required depth.

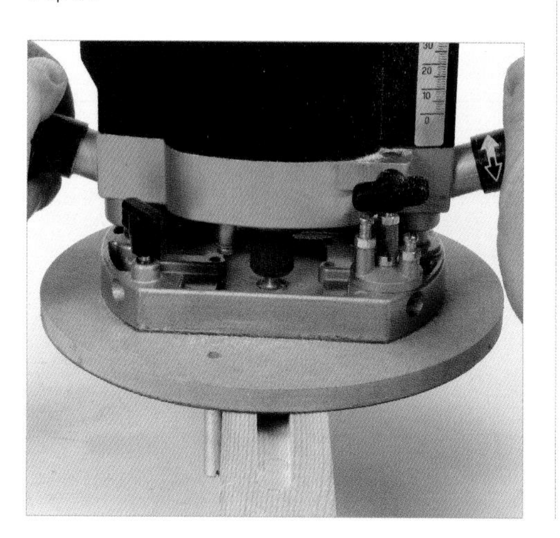

The slot will be perfectly centred. If the work is particularly narrow, it may be necessary to reposition the pins closer together or you will not be able to use the jig close to the end of the work.

Corner rounding jig

It is often necessary to cut matching rounded corners on the end of table tops and you can very quickly make up the jig that reproduces exactly the same curve each time.

The jig itself is an exact size template of the corner with two thin hardwood stops fixed along adjacent edges.

All you have to do is roughly cut each corner to shape with a jigsaw, then clamp the jig underneath the work and run round the corner with a bearing guided flush trimmer to produce a perfect radius each time.

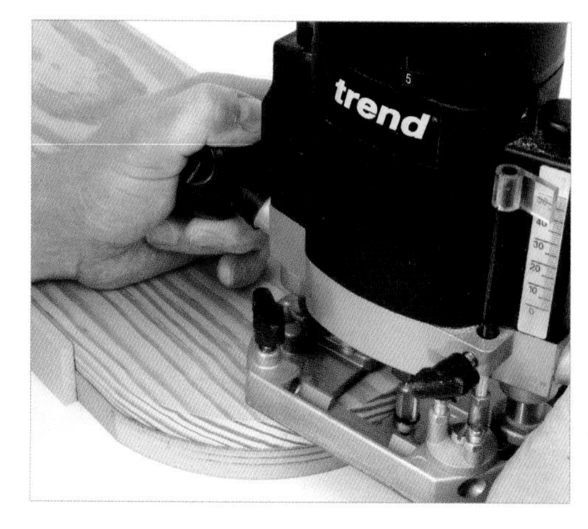

More elaborate jigs

Although simple jigs are usually the most effective, it sometimes becomes necessary to make them more elaborate, often building in integral clamping for quick change over and repositioning.

Hinge jig

Forming the recess for a hinge can sometimes be quite tricky, particularly if the grain of the timber slopes diagonally.

It is important to get the housing perfectly flat and the router is the ideal tool for this job.

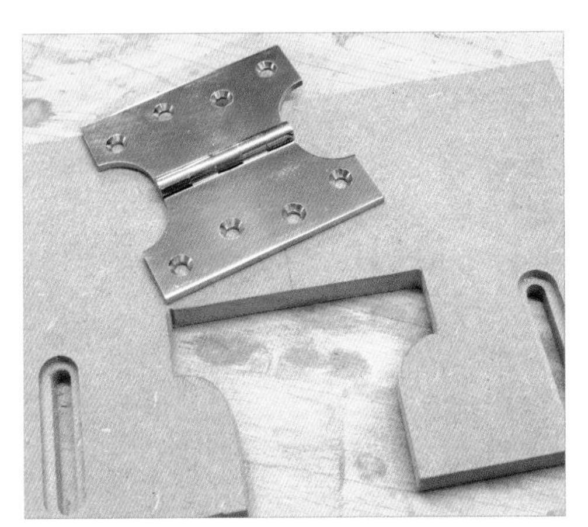

The jig in this case consists of a template fitted to a hardwood batten, the template being slotted to allow it to slide from side to side. For this jig, the guide bush is used in the base of the router and the template must be cut to suit the specific hinge size, but allowing for the guide bush margin.

To calculate the margin, deduct the cutter diameter from the guide bush diameter and divide by two.

Cut the template from Perspex or MDF allowing extra width and length to provide enough support to prevent the router from tipping. Scribe a centre line across the back of the template.

This template is fixed to the batten using bolts and knobs, and once positioned, the whole assembly is firmly clamped to the door with the jig centre line aligned with the centre of the recess. The template can then be slid backwards and forwards to adjust the width of the recess.

Tip

The corners of the recess are necessarily rounded, but these are easily squared out using a conventional chisel, but for a quicker result use the Trend Corner Chisel.

Adjustable housing jig

This is a more sophisticated version of the simple housing jig, as it is fully adjustable and provides complete control over the path of the router. There is no chance of it wandering as can happen with the simpler straightedge arrangement.

A few hours spent constructing this jig will quickly be rewarded by years of frustration free slot cutting, and housing joints will become a pleasure rather than a trial.

The jig is used in conjunction with a guide bush on the base of the router. You can either set the two cross boards so that the bush just slides easily between them using a cutter to the width of the groove you want, or if you want a wider groove open the cross boards out and run the bush down either side of them.

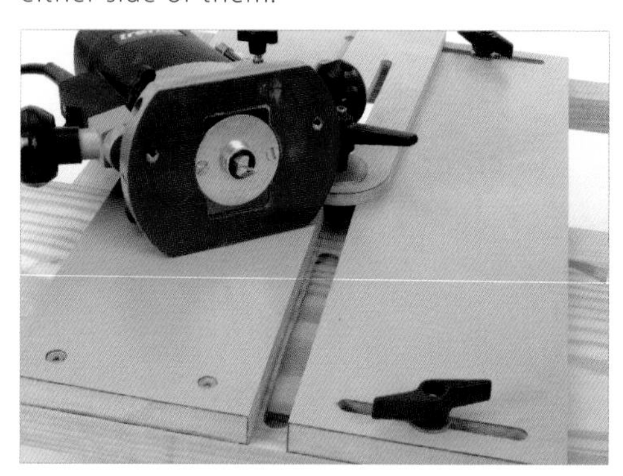

An end stop is easily fitted if you want to form stopped housings.

Comb jointing jig

The finger or comb joint is a very strong way of joining two pieces at right angles for a box or a drawer, and the result can be quite decorative as well. There are several ways of forming the joint, but now that the use of wobble and grooving blades is illegal on a circular saw, the router is one of the best tools for the job. Once you have made this jig it can be used time and time again on a variety of different projects.

For this one, the router has to be fixed underneath the table of the jig and again you can use the base template to position the mounting holes, making sure that the cutter ends up central in the hole of the top. Use a fine height adjuster as well if you have one, as it makes precise setting of the joint size so much easier.

The extra overhang of the table allows you to clamp it in position on your workbench, this way you can quickly dismount it and easily put it away when it is not wanted.

Panel raising jig

The traditional fielded panel has made a significant comeback in the design of modern reproduction furniture and because of this a full range of dedicated profile forming cutters are now available.

Whilst these cutters are very effective, the majority of them are very large in diameter, which in turn necessitates the use of a router table and a heavy-duty router.

However, for the smaller workshop, where fielded panel production is a relatively rare event, a less expensive alternative is available. With this jig, you can still produce fielded panels using just a medium duty router, provided you have a large diameter straight cutter with bottom cut and a suitable guide bush with good clearance to fit over it. Even in very hard timber, the fielding is soon perfectly formed with very clean edges round the edge of the central raised portion.

Multiple grooving jig

Multiple grooving is a common operation in woodworking and the router is the perfect tool for the job. The grooves may be widely spaced, as in shelf housings, or they may be close, like drawer runner grooves. No matter what the purpose, it is essential that the grooves are evenly spaced on matching components or the job will not line up.

The answer is usually to make a simple jig consisting of a plate of MDF fixed to the base of the router with a suitably sized guide strip or slide screwed to it to locate in the previous slot. These are usually custom made jigs and discarded at the end of a job.

More sophisticated adjustable versions like this allow you to cater for a variety of groove widths and spacings.

You form the first groove with either the router side-fence or using a straightedge as a guide. Then position the slide in this groove and adjust the router position for subsequent grooves.

Tenon

There are various ways of cutting a tenon joint, but with its consistent depth cutting, the router lends itself to the job particularly well.

This simple jig allows you to cut several components at once, considerably speeding up the process and is ideal for semi batch production. Precise control of the cutter depth makes for an accurate joint with perfect reproducibility.

In effect, it is just a guide fence that clamps square across the ends of the work, but with a sliding support to prevent the router tipping as you cut away the joint. The same jig can also be used for cutting halving joints, the only necessary variation being the depth of cut you set on the router.

Thicknessing jig

There is no doubt that the most effective way of surfacing any piece of timber is by using the conventional combination of a planer and thicknesser, but sometimes you come across a job where this approach just doesn't work or the equipment is not available.

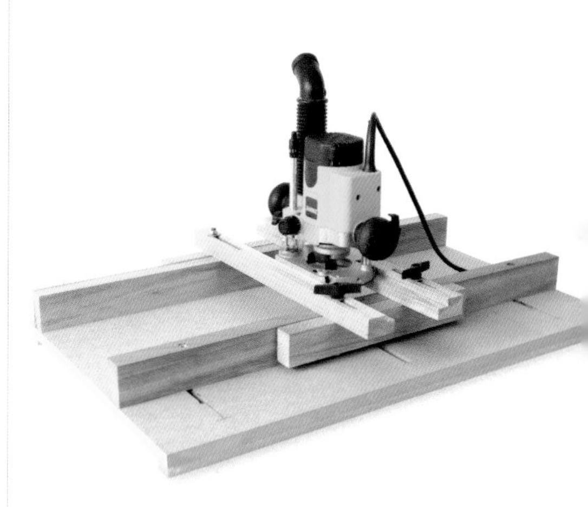

For instance, some workpieces may have very interlocked grain, which is impossible to plane in any direction. Also, the board may be so badly warped that it is difficult to control its orientation for the initial surfacing cut. You may even need to plane the end grain, which is not easy on a planer.

With its cutting action at 90° to that of a standard planer, the router is better suited to tackle this tricky thicknessing work and this jig allows you to machine flat surfaces with ease. However, with a few simple modifications, it has further potential for tapered or hollow work as well.

Mitre trimmer

There are dozens of ways to cut a mitre, some of them more accurate than others, but the router is perhaps an unusual choice of tool for the job. However, it is easily capable of producing the quality cut essential for close fitting mitres, a quality that is not consistently achievable using other methods.

To use this jig you need a router with a guide bush and a suitable two flute cutter. The sizes are not critical; a 12mm cutter with a 20mm guide bush is a good combination. The only essential requirements is that the cutter is really sharp. Larger diameter ones will be more rigid and less prone to vibration.

The router is then rested on the two running strips and passed across the end of the pre-cut moulding to provide the final trim.

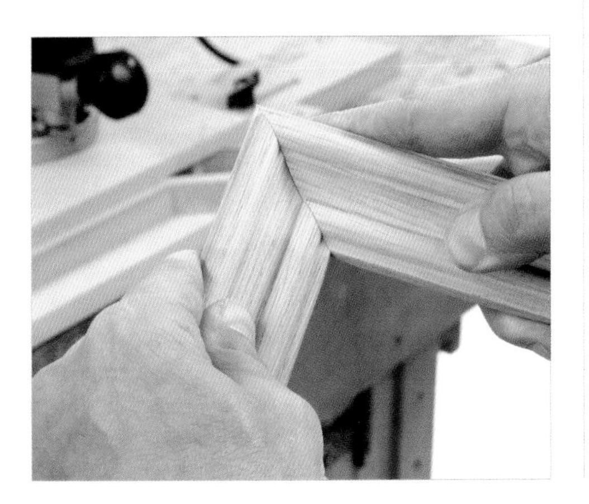

Flush trim

If you use any form of man-made board, the chances are that at some time you will need to lip it, and this can be a tricky operation. Aligning the top edge of the lip perfectly flat with the surface of the board is not easy, particularly if the lipping is slightly warped.

This trimming jig overcomes all these problems and allows you to fit a slightly oversized lip and then trim it off flush with the surfaces of the board. It works with either a narrow lipping or a wider edging, but you will need to use a sharp bit in the router to minimise cleaning up afterwards.

Provided you have the cutter set accurately, you can trim the lipping back perfectly without damaging the board surface, though a fine height adjuster on the router is essential to set the precise depth.

Commercial Jigs

There are also dozens of commercially made jigs. They simplify and speed up many of the repetitive jobs involved in domestic joinery. There are jigs for cutting joints such as dovetails, mortise and tenons, jigs for doors to fit locks, hinges and letterboxes. And for kitchens there is also a large range of worktop jigs.

In fact the list is endless, with other jigs for cutting circles, ellipses, carving and lettering work.

As you would expect, some of these jigs are quite sophisticated and require careful setting up and adjustment. However if used as intended, they are capable of producing work to extremely fine limits and will more than repay the cost of their initial investment.

Dovetail jigs

When cut by hand, the classic dovetail joint invokes nothing but admiration and respect from any woodworker.

Unfortunately, unless you are very skilled and have plenty of time, it is a joint that is beyond the ability of most of us, particularly if there are many to cut. But with a suitable jig, not only does a dovetail joint become a reality, but the speed and quality of the finished job is outstanding and totally repeatable.

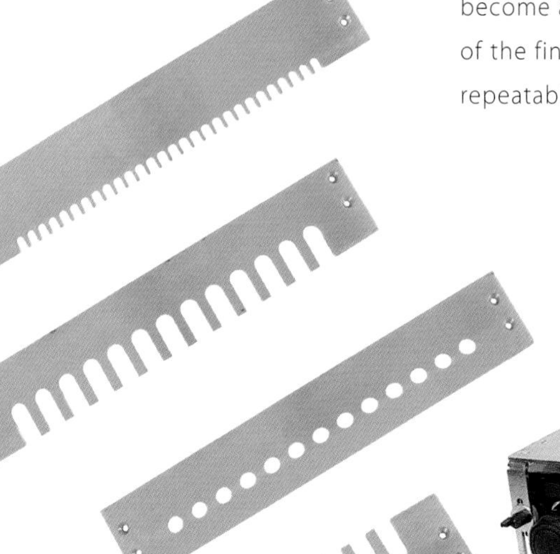

They all work on the principle of having a comb template working in conjunction with the guide bush fitted on the router. The timber is usually held in such a way that both parts of the joint are cut simultaneously.

The initial setting up of the dovetail jig is quite critical and it is essential that your router is fitted with a fine height adjuster for the necessary precise adjustments. Nevertheless, a certain amount of trial and error is always involved to get a perfect fit, so you will need to allow a small amount of spare stock for this purpose.

There are several jigs available depending how much control you want to have over the final appearance. At the lower end of the scale, a basic dovetail jig will cut lap, or rebated dovetails but will not allow you to vary the pin spacing. You can however change the template for smaller joints or even to cut a comb joint or for dowelling.

For carcase work there are some jigs that will hold material up to 600 mm wide.

More elaborate jigs allow you to vary the size and layout of the pins and tails and also cut proper through dovetails, rather than being restricted to the lap joint. These may initially seem rather complicated, but in fact many of the jigs are extremely simple to set up and you can change the start point of the joint, or the thickness of the material without the need for major adjustment.

At the top of the range there are very sophisticated dovetail jigs that allow you total control over the joint profile, to such an extent that you end up with a dovetail that looks hand cut, but which has in fact been cut in just a few seconds.

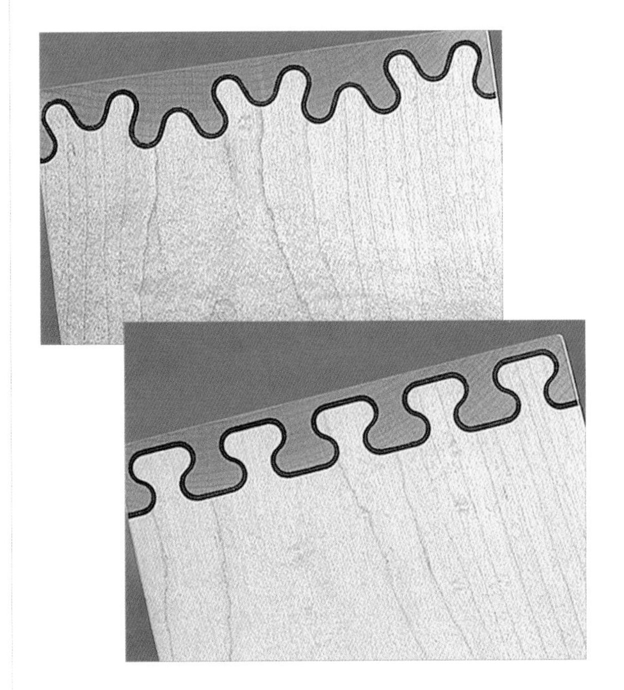

With the addition of special templates you can also use this jig to cut other wonderfully exotic joint patterns, the only limit being the degree of your creativity.

Mortise and tenon jigs

Mortise and tenon joints are used in many forms of joinery work such as frames for panel doors, carcases for furniture and cabinets legs and rails for tables and chairs. Traditionally, they were cut either by hand, or by using different machines for each operation.

However, you can simplify the whole procedure using the router in conjunction with a mortise and tenon jig. On the better quality jigs, once it is set up to cut the tenon, the mortise is automatically set, which ensures a totally accurate fit each time. No repetitive marking out is needed; all you have to do is change the cutter and guide bush to switch between the two applications.

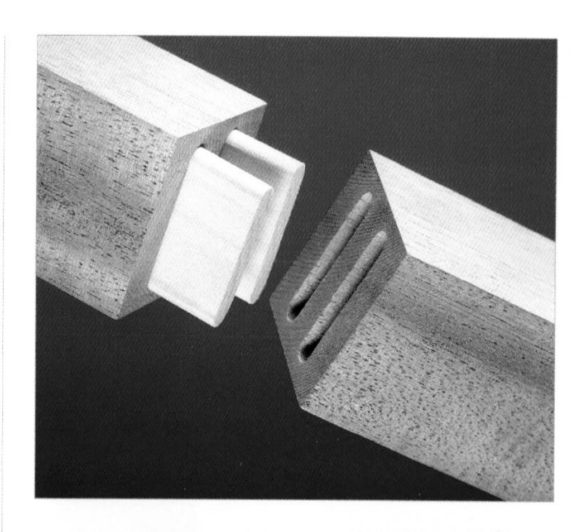

The jig is adjustable in both planes to allow angled or compound tenons to be cut, as well as the normal square ended versions. You can also use it to cut all the other forms of mortise and tenon such as haunched and mitre, as well as for drilling dowel holes.

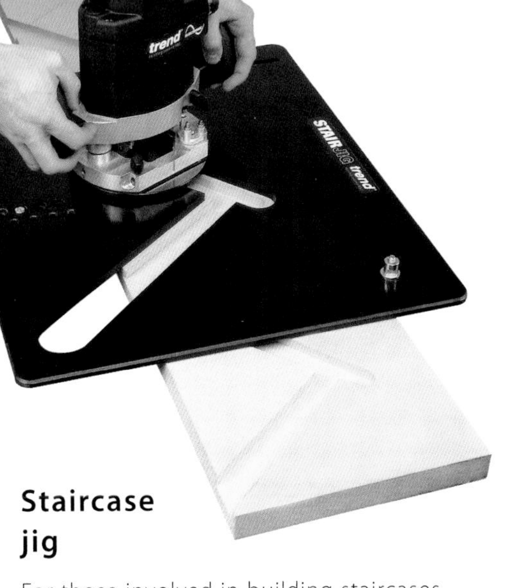

Staircase jig

For those involved in building staircases, special housing jigs are available for accurately routing out the housings in the strings. As there is inevitably a lot of material to be removed, such jigs are normally used with a heavy-duty router and feature a reversible fence so each string can be matched perfectly.

Letterbox jig

Another job which is difficult to cut out neatly by hand is the letterbox opening in a door. However, the use of a simple jig allows you to remove the waste quickly and accurately, again using a heavy-duty router with a long reach 1/2" shank cutter.

The jig can be adjusted for size and is quickly set up, with the opening remaining perfectly square at all times.

Worktop jig

The professional way to join two post formed worktops at right angles is to cut a butt and scribe joint. Although this can be done by hand, it requires some considerable skill to produce a close fitting joint that is virtually invisible and watertight.

A dedicated worktop jig will allow you to cut a perfect joint, as well as the necessary recesses for the connecting bolts. More refined versions also provide cutting guides for the ends of Peninsula tops.

Jigs are available for a variety of worktop widths and even allow for a faultless joint where the two tops need to be joined out of square to each other.

Hinge jig

The professional version of the hinge jig works on the similar principle to the one you can make yourself, but allows for multiple hinge positions or different sized apertures to be cut out in one setting.

Made from extruded aluminium, it can be used either on-site, or in a joinery shop and is fast and simple to operate. The hinge is actually used as the pattern so setting up is both quick and simple and there is no need for the conventional time-consuming marking out. Obviously, the corner of the recess is left radiused, but this is quickly squared up using a corner chisel.

Lock jig

This jig uses a set of interchangeable templates to cut both the mortise and the faceplate recess for a variety of different sized locks. Always a difficult job to do by hand, the deep mortise is cut very cleanly even on hardwood using a suitable long reach cutter. Once again, you will need to square out the corners of the faceplate recess.

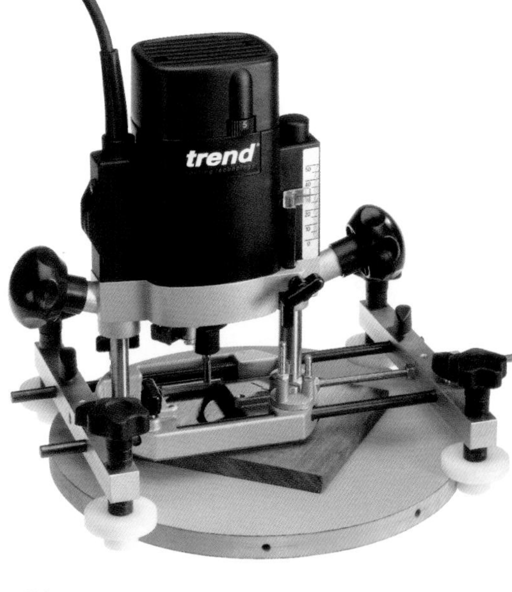

Pivot Frame Jig

The pivot framed jig is a particularly versatile setup, performing a number of valuable routing applications. Its main function is to create an artificial centre point around which the router can be rotated using a circular template. However many other uses have emerged, for instance you can use it as an anti-tipping device for template routing, or as a ski frame for surface routing, or even as a beam trammel for cutting rings, scalloped designs and decorative patterns.

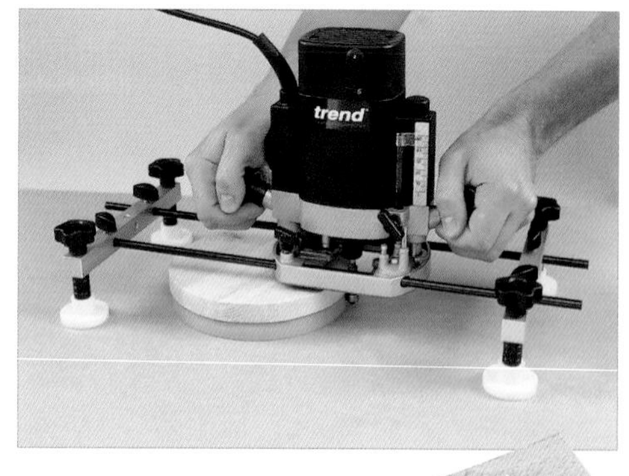

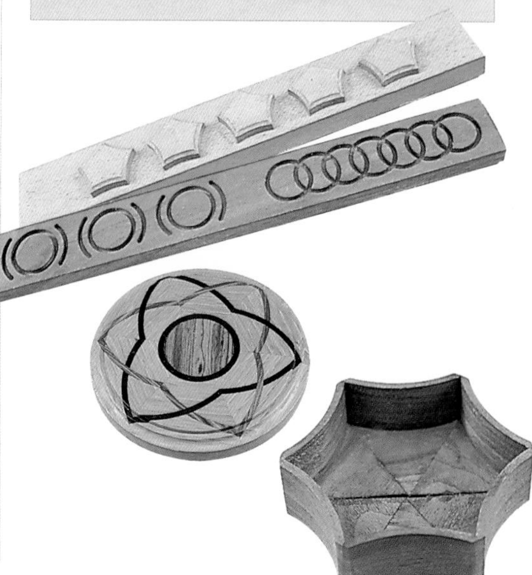

Ellipse and circle cutting jig

This is designed to enable virtually any router to cut an accurate ellipse or circle and is ideal if you are a cabinet maker forming tabletops, arches and the like. Using a router with this jig is perhaps the only way to get the perfect circular forms necessary for high quality work.

Routabout hole cutting jig

It is often necessary to have access points for pipes and cables beneath wooden floors. This jig allows you to cut the 250 mm diameter openings and then place the waste piece into a spacer ring as a removable lid. Suitable for 18 and 22 mm thick wooden floors the jig, yet again, demonstrates the versatility of the router for a wide range of applications.

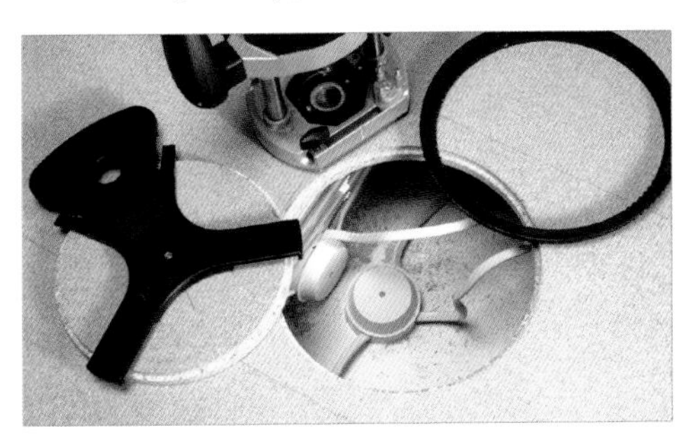

Varijig

This adjustable jig allows you to make up square or rectangular frames to any dimension, which can then be used to machine recesses, slots, panel moulds etc.

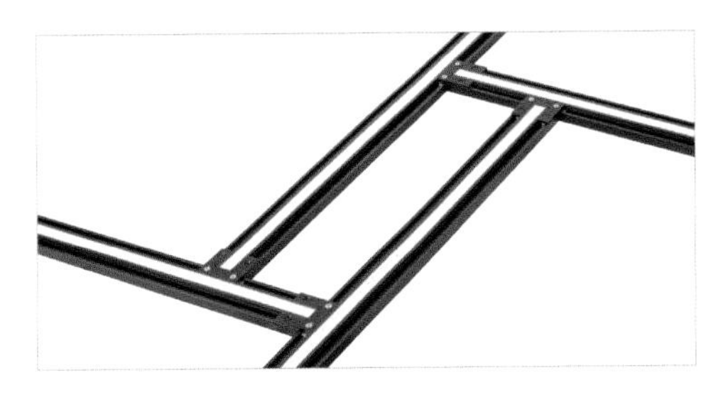

Draining groove jig

This simple jig allows you to cut the draining grooves in solid timber for Belfast type sinks. The jig is specially shaped to produce grooves which are very slightly sloped to assist the water to run away.

Templates

Like routing jigs, templates simplify many routing operations involving both regular and irregular shaped work and also offer an accurate method of performing repetitive operations such as recessing, edge or panel moulding, edge trimming, slotting and dowelling. As we have already seen, templates may form part of a jig, the purpose of the jig being to quickly and accurately position the template on the workpiece, or to hold the template for cutting several workpieces for simultaneous machining.

The advantage of using templates is that most of the difficult work is done in producing the actual template itself. It provides accurate repetition and avoids the risks of mistakes when cutting the work freehand. So not only does a template save time when cutting matching components, but it also eliminates much of the risk of making a mistake.

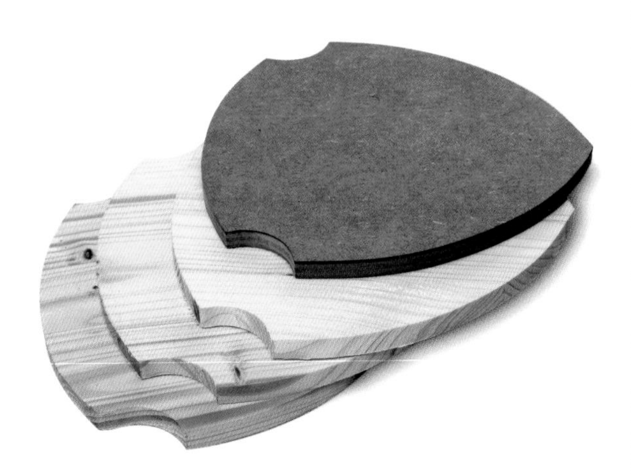

For the professional user, this is vital as it speeds up the work flow and minimises material wastage. Each piece cut from a specific template will be identical with the next.

Templates can be used with guide bushes or bearing guided cutters.

If you are using a bearing guided cutter, the template is easier to make as it is exactly the same size as the workpiece, but it doesn't allow you to control the depth of cut, essential for work such as inlaying.

With a guide bush, the situation is a little more complicated and the template obviously has to be cut over or under size to allow for the guide bush margin, but you do have control over the depth of cut.

Also, by fitting different sized guide bushes in the router you can use just one template to cut different sizes.

Another difference between the two guiding methods shows up at external sharp corners, which become slightly radiused if you are using a guide bush.

Templates should be designed to afford as much support for the router as possible. In situations where the router overhangs the edge of a template, or the template extends beyond the edge of the workpiece, levelling blocks should be fitted to prevent the router tilting and producing a cut that doesn't register properly with the template.

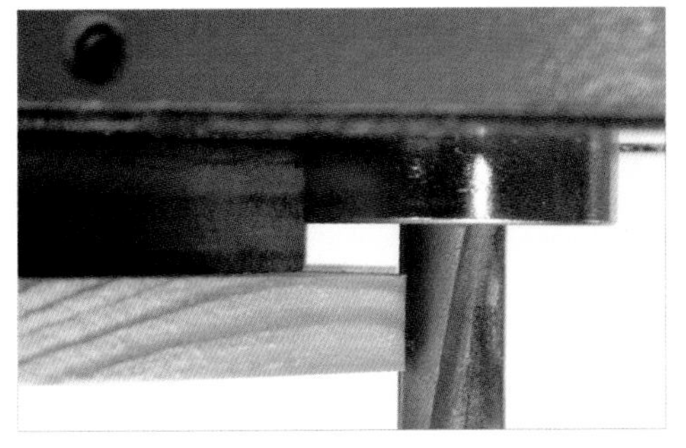

The template obviously has to be strong enough that it does not distort during use, but if you're using a guide bush it is also important that the thickness of the template material exceeds the depth of the guide bush ring and allows a clearance of, at least 1 mm, between the tip of the ring and the surface of the workpiece.

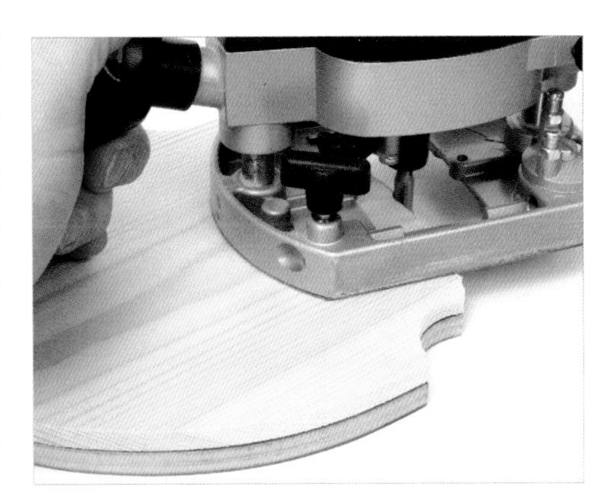

It is essential that the template is followed in the correct direction to keep the ring tight against the guide edge. If you don't, the cutter will deflect away. Remember to work anti-clockwise on external templates and clockwise for internal templates to maintain this correct orientation.

There is a necessary compromise to be made as regards to fixing the template on the work. It needs to be perfectly secure to accurately reproduce the pattern, but you should be able to remove it easily for repositioning on the next piece. In some situations, simple locating blocks and the downward pressure of the router will hold the template in place, but it is always advisable to secure it further with cramps or some other holding device.

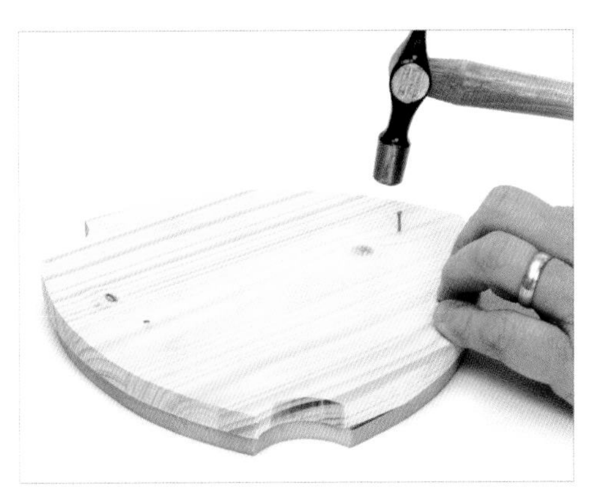

On painted or concealed work, the template can be simply pinned or screwed in place.

On flat work it can be held in place with double-sided tape provided the surfaces are dust and grease-free. If you anticipate using a particular template frequently, seal the surface with sanding sealer and you'll then get much better adhesion with double-sided tape.

Templates can be cut from any piece of smooth surfaced sheet material that is easy to work and finish. Although it must be thick enough to keep the guide bush clear of the work, it must not be so thick that it reduces the depth of cut. MDF is suitable for general use, but for templates likely to be used more often, materials such as 'Tufnol' or non shattering plastic are recommended. All the edges must be finished really smooth as any unevenness will be reflected on the finished cut. Ideally try and use the router itself for this shaping as it will leave the template edges smooth and square without requiring any further cleaning up.

Although you could theoretically use the router with a template to actually cut out a shape, realistically, this is rarely practical, you would have to use large diameter cutters to prevent them snapping and the amount of time and waste involved is prohibitive.

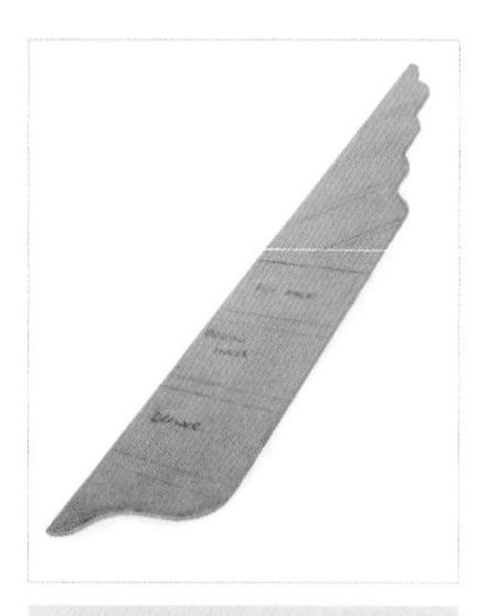

Tip

For accurate positioning, centre lines and other alignment marks can be drawn on the template to match up with corresponding points drawn on the work.

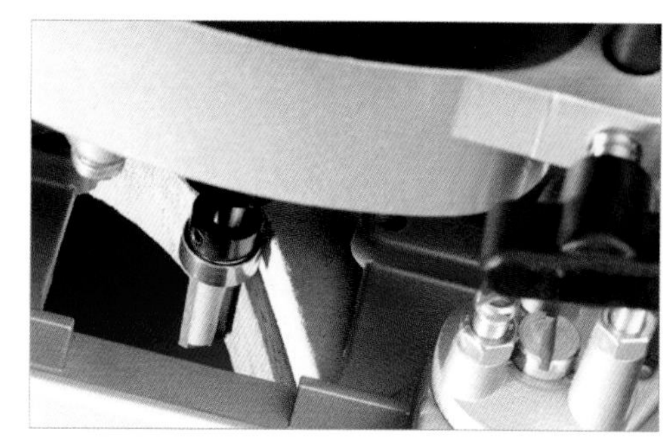

To reduce the time and wear on the cutter, cut the workpiece roughly to size with a bandsaw or jigsaw and then use the router in conjunction with the template to trim back the exact dimension.

The most basic template is a simple straightedge which is either clamped or stuck to the workpiece. This allows you to make a trimming cut if you use a bearing mounted cutter, or to cut grooves if you use the guide bush and a two flute cutter.

For better control, particularly for grooving, or for critical cuts like worktops, the double straightedge is better, with the guide bush running within a suitable slot cut in the template.

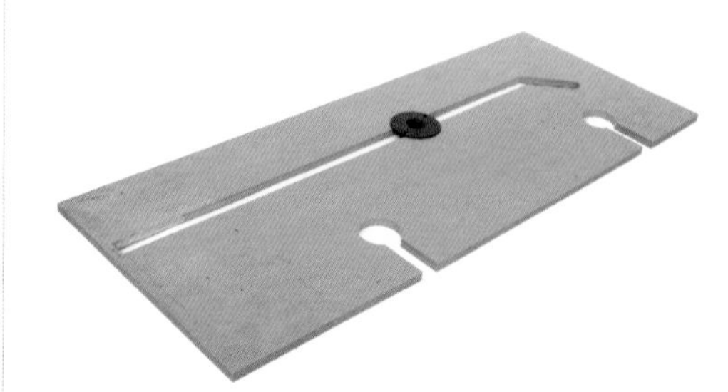

Some of this work may be possible using the standard side-fence supplied with the router, but using a template gives much more capacity, particularly when working with large boards which the side-fence simply cannot reach.

Circular templates are also very useful to cut and trim curves to a required smooth shape. The finished result is entirely down to the quality of your templates, but you can then use the router to cut circles, round corners and ovals as well as holes and recesses.

To form a circle template first cut a smooth sided hole with a suitable hole saw. For accuracy, do this on a drill press and clamp the template material securely to make sure it doesn't move.

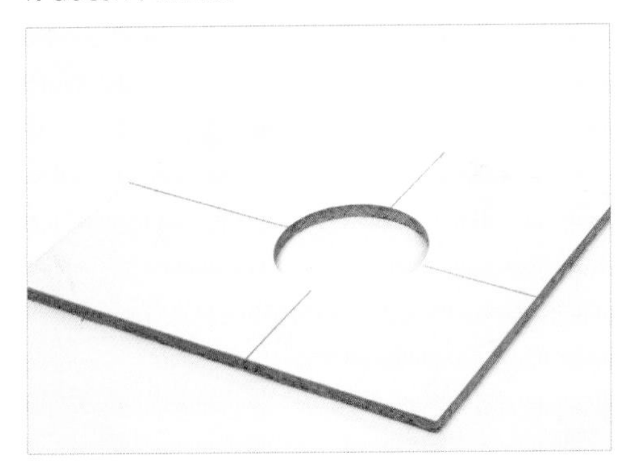

From this one template a series of decreasing diameter templates can be cut using different guide bush and cutter combinations.

To cut templates of a larger diameter use a self guiding rebate cutter. In the centre of the new template, cut the hole roughly to size with a jigsaw and then tape or pin the new template over it.

With the rebate cutter fitted in the router, set the depth of cut fractionally deeper than the template material (the cutter will cut slightly into the surface of the first template). Position the router with the bearing through the hole in the top template and cut away the waste by running the bearing around the inside edge of the bottom template.

Guide bushes can also be used with templates for locating the router when fitting dowels or support pegs for shelves etc. Mark out the centre-point of each dowel position on the template or a square edged piece of clear plastic. Drill a hole equal in diameter to the guide bush. Locate the template over the workpiece by either fitting locating blocks or by scribing lines across the guide bush hole and then with the router securely held, plunge in to drill the hole.

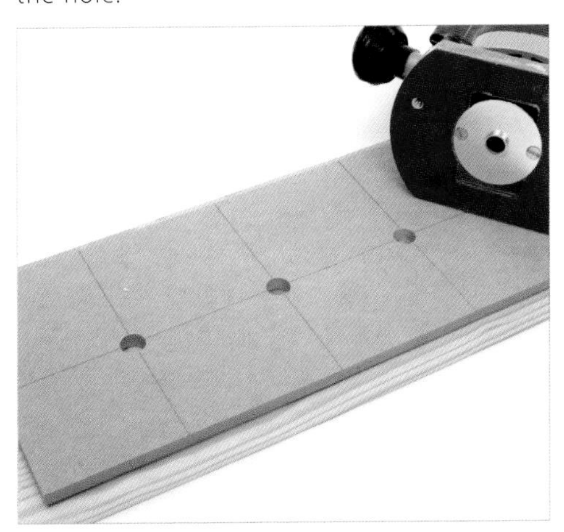

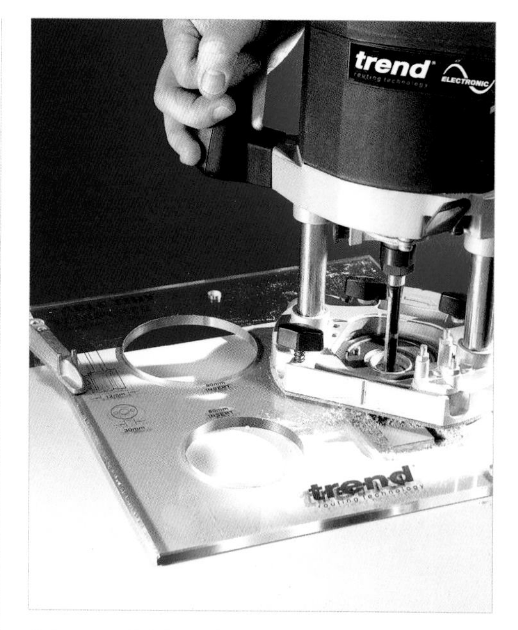

Other useful bought templates are available for fitting cable tidies in desktops and for repairing damaged areas of timber.

Proprietary templates

There is an equally large range of ready-made templates available for more common applications. The advantage of manufactured templates is that they are usually of better quality than those you can make yourself and the finish produced from the cutter is therefore better.

Others allow you to use the router for more artistic purposes such as inlay or panelling work.

For sign work there are dedicated templates for cutting numbers and letters that only require the use of a small guide bush and a suitable cutter.

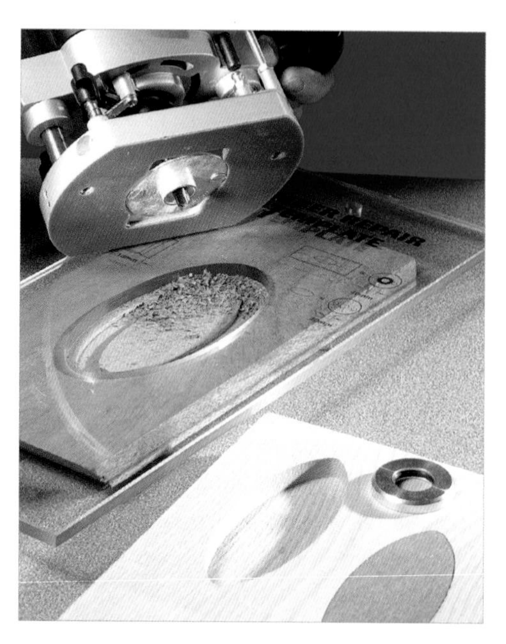

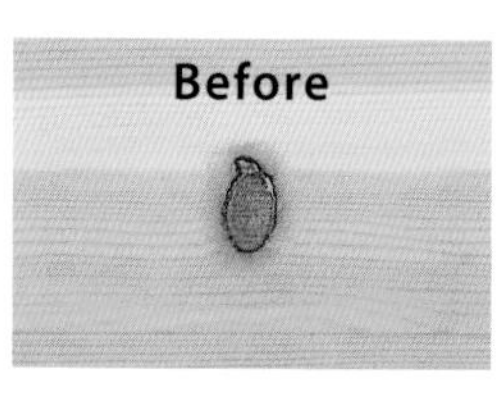

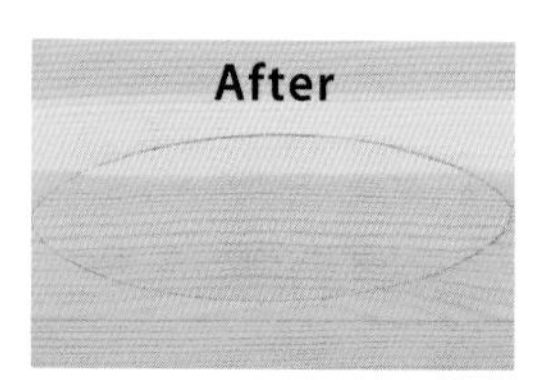

7. ROUTING TECHNIQUES

Most techniques are basic woodworking operations, but the router makes them quick and easy to apply. The variety is endless, if you add in a few jigs and templates, you will soon start devising your own techniques to harness the incredible versatility of the router.

Edges and rebates

Edges

Routers excel at cutting decorative edges and rebates with a vast range of cutters available to produce a variety of different moulded profiles. Edge machining operations are usually carried out using either the router side-fence or a self guiding cutter.

Plain cutters without any form of bearing have no built-in guide and therefore need to be used with the side-fence, but a common problem here is that of 'run in/run out' at the beginning and end of each cut, as there is only limited contact and support at this stage.

The simple remedy is to fit an elongated false wooden fence to the router, giving a longer and more stable support for many moulding operations.

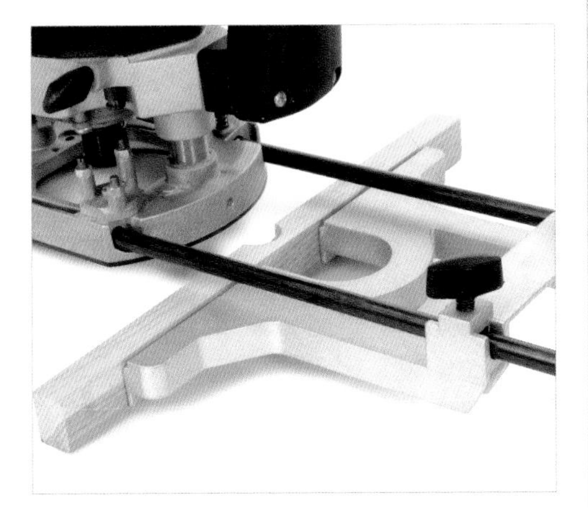

In many instances, even better control is obtained by fitting a larger sub-base to the router to further minimise the risk of it tipping during a cut.

Rebates

To cut a rebate it is preferable to use a straight cutter which is slightly larger in diameter than the width of the finished cut. Set the side-fence so that the cutter extends beyond the fence faces to the width of the required rebate.

If your cutter is too small in diameter to make the rebate in one cut, remove the waste by making two passes. This is often almost as quick anyway, but remember not to strain the cutter by trying to take too much in one pass and cut the rebate in a series of steps until the full depth is reached.

Tip

Although not essential, a fine fence adjuster does make precise setting for operations like rebating, very much easier.

An alternative to using the fence is to make use of a guide bush and template. This has the advantage that by using two different diameter cutters you can both trim the work and cut the rebate using the same guide bush and template. Secure the work to the bench with a sheet of thin waste material beneath it, or fix it near the edge so that there is enough overhang to keep the cutter clear during the trimming cut.

Fix on the template allowing for the guide bush margin and use the smaller diameter cutter first to trim a perfectly square edge, and then just substitute the wider cutter to form the rebate.

Self guiding rebate cutters are a quicker option and can be used to machine both straight and curved edges. However, the width of the rebate is restricted to the standard cutter and bearing sizes, but you can achieve some variation in the rebate width by changing the bearing diameter.

Tip

To give the bearing enough clearance, the workpiece should be clamped overhanging the edge of the workbench. If this is not possible, raise it up using a spacer block so that the screw and washer holding the bearing are clear, but make sure everything is held firmly when you start adding layers like this.

The bearing is simply run against either the edge of the work or against a template which is attached above or below it.

The final depth will probably once again need several passes, but check that there is still sufficient edge width left for the bearing to run on.

You need at least 1/16" in most timbers, although some species with a very heavy grain structure may require a wider support.

Mouldings

The same procedures can be used to apply decorative edge mouldings, but in this case it is even more important that the edge of the work is properly finished square and smooth, as any irregularities like chips or ripples will be mirrored by the fence and especially by a bearing.

You can make considerable variations to the profile produced by some cutters by adjusting how the fence is positioned relative to the axis of the cutter.

Similarly, with self guided cutters, changing the bearing to a different size will also vary the profile and as usual, make several passes for deep cuts.

To minimise tearing and burning, you should try to maintain the correct feed direction, but if the grain of the work is distinctly angled it may be better to roughly remove the bulk of the waste working the 'wrong' way and then finish off with a light finishing cut in the 'correct' direction to even it all out. However caution is required when using this technique, see page 104 for further information on 'back cutting'.

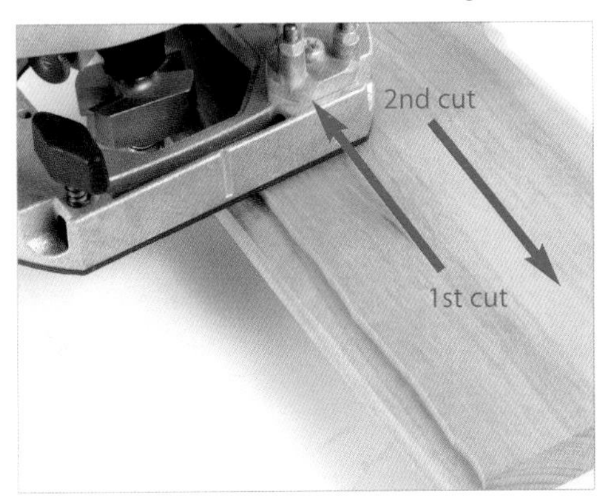

For all edge moulding work it is very important that the work is held securely, and you can usually clamp it so that at least one edge extends beyond the workbench.

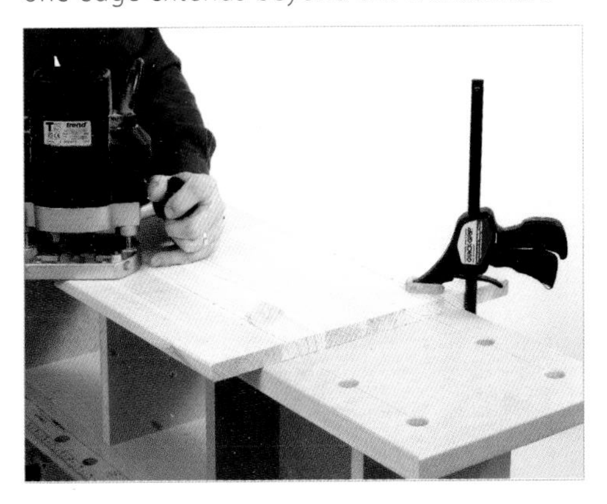

Alternatively, use a router mat to prevent the work moving around. This is a better option provided you are not making very heavy cuts, as there are no clamps to obstruct the path of the router. Smaller pieces for edge routing are sometimes more difficult to hold and you cannot rely on the router mat to hold it firmly enough to prevent kickback. One solution is to stick it temporarily to a larger piece of scrap, using either double-sided tape or hot melt glue.

If the required moulding cuts away the full edge face of the work, the router will need to be guided with a guide bush and template in the same way as the rebating procedure outlined above. Alternatively, fit a pattern to one side of the work and then use a bearing guided cutter.

Curved and irregular shaped edges can also be moulded or rebated using plain cutters, but now guided by an edge follower.

This handy little device is attached directly to the side of the router or the side fence rods and consists of a small diameter wheel at right angles to the axis of the cutter. This then acts as a fence to run against either the edge of the work or a template mounted beneath it.

Always begin any cutting sequence on the end grain sections as there will inevitably be some spelching at the end of the cut. This will then be removed by the long grain cut.

End grain cuts are always harder work but it is vital to keep the router moving steadily to avoid scorching or burn marks. If you do get any of these burns they are notoriously difficult to remove, but you can try making a very light finishing pass in the 'wrong' direction. Sometimes a further quick pass applying plenty of pressure to the router is enough to deepen the cut fractionally and shave off the worst of the scorching.

Grooves and housings

Grooves and housings are just slots in the face or edge of pieces of timber and are usually used as a means of jointing them together. Although they are essentially the same thing, a cut made parallel with the grain is usually referred to as a groove, whilst one across the grain is called a housing.

A typical application for a groove is to locate the panel in a framed construction, or a drawer bottom. Housings are usually bigger than grooves and are used for more constructional purposes, for instance, to fix shelves into bookcase ends.

Grooves

It is even more important that the work to be grooved is securely held before you attempt to make the cut, as there is little scope for cleaning up if the cut wanders off line. Straight grooves near the edge of the work can all to be cut using the side fence as the guide. However, as with the edge moulding, consider extending the fence to minimise run off problems at the start or end of the cut.

If you're making a stopped groove, you can either plunge the cutter in and out at marked pencil lines, or for more reliability, clamp on temporary stops.

Grooves cut further in from the edge of a board will require the use of a straightedge, either in the form of a timber batten and two G clamps, or one of the purpose-made straight edges with built-in clamping facility.

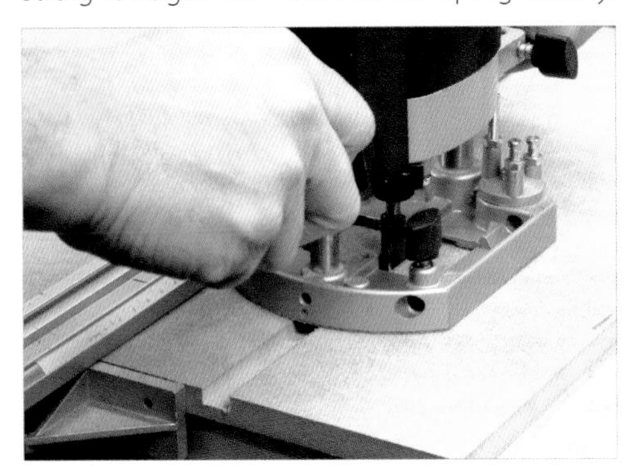

If the groove is wider than the largest cutter you have, it can be enlarged by making two or more parallel passes. Always make the first cut closest to the edge guide, cutting in stages right down to full depth, and then adjust the fence to widen the groove by the required amount.

Wide boards can be very effectively jointed by gluing a loose tongue into grooves cut along their edges.

This can be achieved using a standard straight cutter and guide fence with the workpiece clamped on edge, but some additional side support will be necessary to stop the router tipping if the edge is very narrow. Alternatively, using two side fences will usually provide the necessary extra stability.

A better method of cutting edge grooves is to use a slotting cutter mounted on an arbor, as this allows the work to be held flat and therefore provide more stable support for the router base.

The depth of cut of the groove is controlled by the diameter of the guide bearing fitted to the arbor. It may be necessary to limit the depth of cut for the initial passes on difficult timbers by mounting the side fence. This is then removed to achieve the final depth.

A variation of this idea is to mount two cutters on the same arbor, and use this combination to cut the classic tongue and grooved joint.

Butt jointing has never been the most attractive or effective way of fixing one square piece of wood to another.
The natural and inevitable expansion and contraction of timber will always distort a butt joint leaving an irregular line.
One way of overcoming such a problem is to exaggerate the joint by creating a mould or profile along the joint line helping to disguise any overhang, bowing, wavy or damaged edges and make the joint look consistent. Here are just a few examples showing how this can be achieved.

Tip

For a series of regularly spaced housings, use a spacer batten or a simple jig that locates in the previously cut groove.

Housings

By definition, housings are nearly always cut across the width of the work so you cannot always use a guide fence. In this case you will again have to resort to using a straightedge, though, if this is a regular requirement, it is worth making up a dedicated housing jig.

Housings often have to be made in pairs, as for example on either side of a bookcase. In which case, get them identical by clamping both workpieces edge to edge and then machine across them both.

Offset base

An offset trenching base is another very quick way of making different width grooves using a single cutter.

As the name suggests, each edge of the base is offset by different amounts from the centre hole, so by varying which edge is used up against the straightedge, you can get an instant offset off up to 5 mm in 1 mm steps.

If the housing runs right through the width of the board there is always the problem of spelching on the rear edge where the cutter breaks through.

Avoid this by clamping a waste piece against the back edge and running the cut through into it, or alternatively, cut all housings first and then run a plane along the edge to clean up the break-out.

Circles and curves

The router is the ideal tool for cutting and moulding clean and accurate circles and curves. If they have a constant radius the curves can be cut by pivoting the router around a fixed point using an adjustable trammel. Most routers can be used with circle and ellipse trammels both for cutting the initial shape and for applying a decorative edge profile. Alternatively, the shape can be cut first using a trammel and then a decorative moulding applied using a bearing guided cutter in the conventional way.

Trammels

The trammel consists of a rigid rod carrying an adjustable centre point that locates in or on the surface of the work, allowing the router to be swung round in an arc.

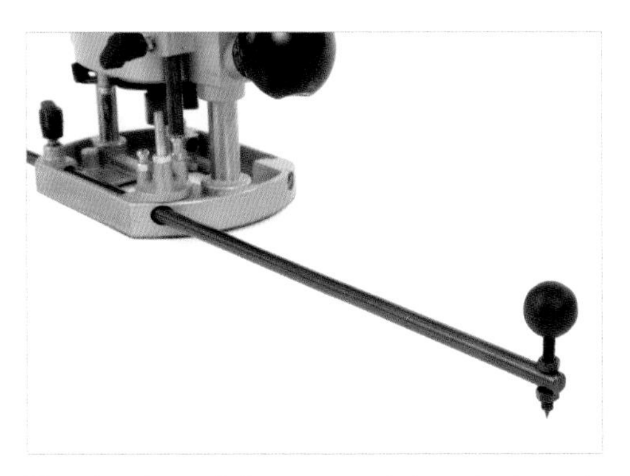

The simplest of the trammels is a single rod fitted into the base of the router and held in place by one of the fence bar clamps. You can even make your own by drilling a hole through the end of one of the fence rods and then using a nail as the pivot point.

Alternatively, you can buy an attachment point to fit over the end of a fence rod, this slightly more sophisticated arrangement allows the point to be raised and lowered above or below the base of the router.

To set the radius of the circle or arc, the cutter flutes are lined up with an axis taken from the centre of the cutter to the trammel point. To cut internal circles and arcs the cutter diameter is deducted from the radius.

For external circles and arcs, the cutter diameter is added to the radius. In both cases the radius is set between the trammel point and the nearest cutting edge.

With some jobs, the trammel can be located in place by simply pressing the point into the face of the work.

On more decorative work where you don't want to spoil the surface, the point can be located into a thin piece of scrap timber secured to the work with double-sided tape.

If the required radius is much larger, a single rod trammel will probably not be rigid enough and may flex in use, causing variations in the radius of the curve as the router is swung around.

For maximum rigidity, these larger diameter circles are better cut using either a twin rod trammel or a flat beam version that incorporates a sub-base for the router.

Adjustable beam trammels are available such as the Trend router compass with a variable radii up to 610mm.

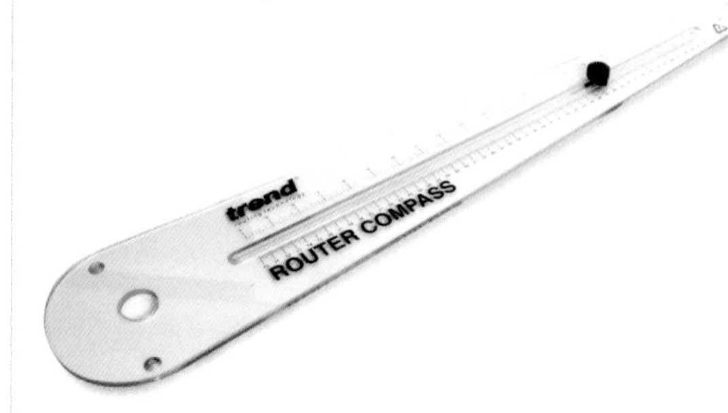

Made of clear acrylic plastic, it has a sliding fulcrum that runs in a central slot with a graduated scale, which allows precise radius setting. The whole thing fits directly to the base of virtually any router. The width of support provided by this arrangement prevents any tipping and allows for a super accurate cut.

You can easily make your own version of this trammel using MDF or Perspex, with a pin or bradawl driven in the work at the required pivot point.

When you're using a trammel the router must swing smoothly, so ensure that the centre point is securely located and only feed against the rotation of the cutter. This braces any side force along the trammel rod axis, rather than pulling away from the centre, which could possibly dislodge the centre point. Be aware though that the correct direction of cut is not always obvious, but if you remember to work anti-clockwise round the outside, and clockwise round the inside, you should not go far wrong.

To Illustrate this, consider cutting the curve on the top of a door panel. This is an outside shape so you need to cut anti-clockwise. However, if you're cutting a hole in the front of the door this is an inside shape, and the cut needs to be in a clockwise direction.

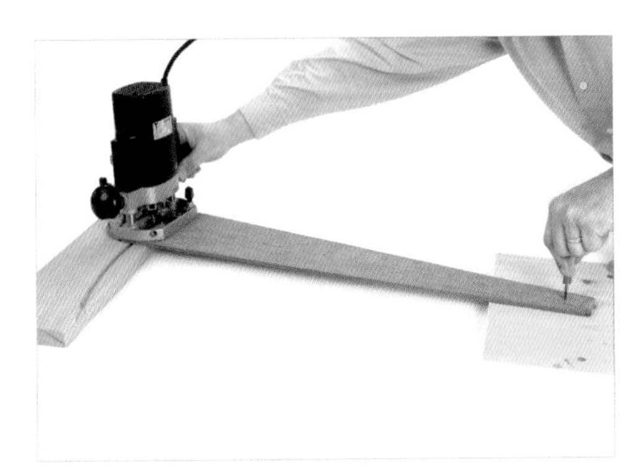

Of course, the centre point of the trammel is not necessarily always located on the work itself and for the very large curves the pivot point can be rigged up on a piece of scrap mounted elsewhere on the bench.

Be careful that the point of the trammel does not enlarge the centre hole as you work, as this will spoil the accuracy and prevent the cut matching up perfectly when you complete the circle.

Cutting a complete circle is quite straightforward, though one of the biggest problems is keeping the cable out of the way, so ideally, support it from a hook in the workshop ceiling.

In order to maintain a smooth and steady movement, swing the router as far as you can until your arms start to cross and then quickly swap them over to complete the cut, trying not to stop completely during the changeover, or you will leave a tiny burn mark.

The problem with all these trammel bar arrangements is that the smallest radius you're able to cut is determined by the router base size, which may be too big if you want to cut small diameter circles.

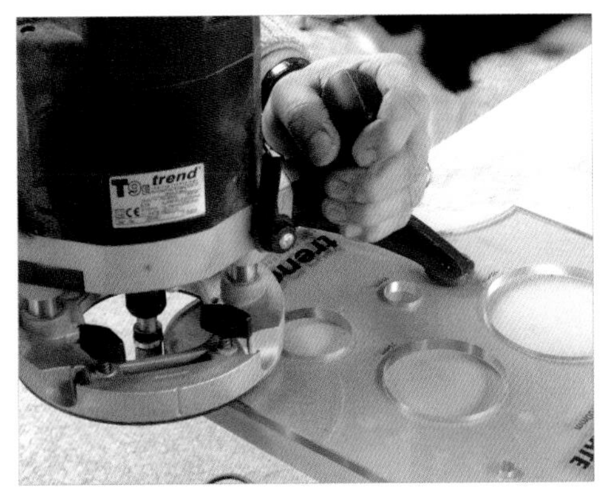

One alternative is to buy a hole template that is predrilled with holes of various diameters. You can use this either with a straight cutter and guide bush, or by using a template profile cutter which has a top bearing. Although the pre-drilled holes are of fixed diameter, a variety of other sizes can be obtained by varying the combinations of cutter, bearing and guide bush.

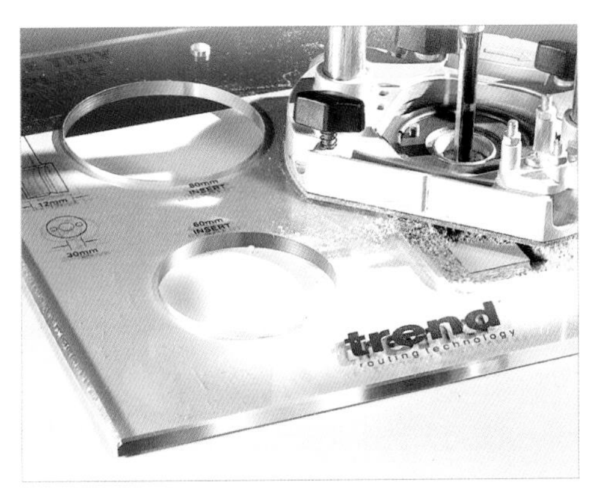

A dedicated version of this template is used to cut the holes in office desks for cable tidy inserts.

Tip

If you're making repeat cuts using the same centre point, it may be better to replace the sharp trammel with a small diameter rod that locates in a matching hole drilled in a pad that can be stuck temporarily to the bench or the work.

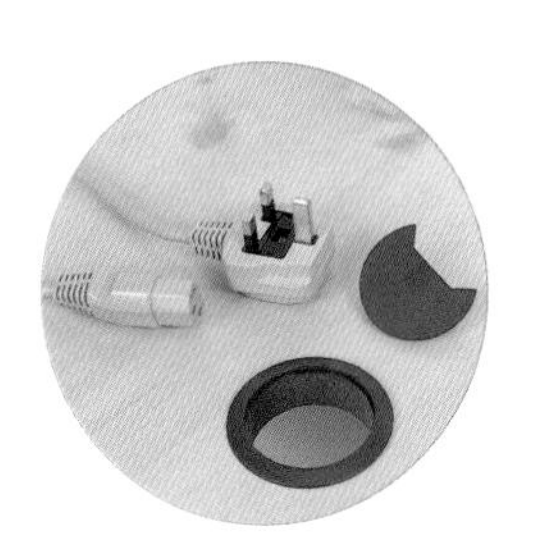

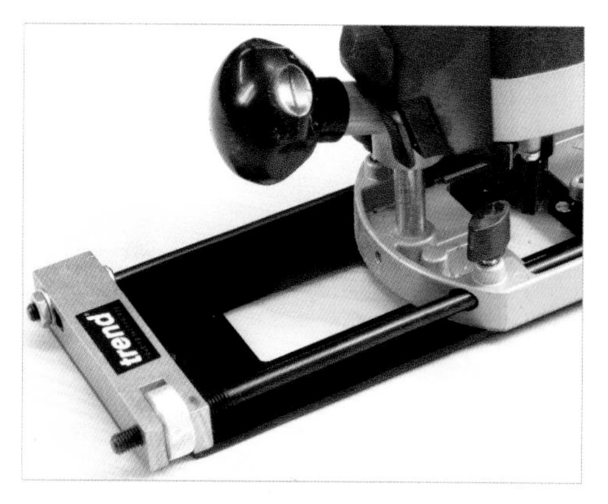

The N compass made by Trend uses the guide rod holes like a conventional trammel, but here the pivot point is now mounted on a plate that fits underneath the router, so it can be used to cut circles down to 25mm in diameter. Threaded rods are available to boost the standard 200mm maximum diameter.

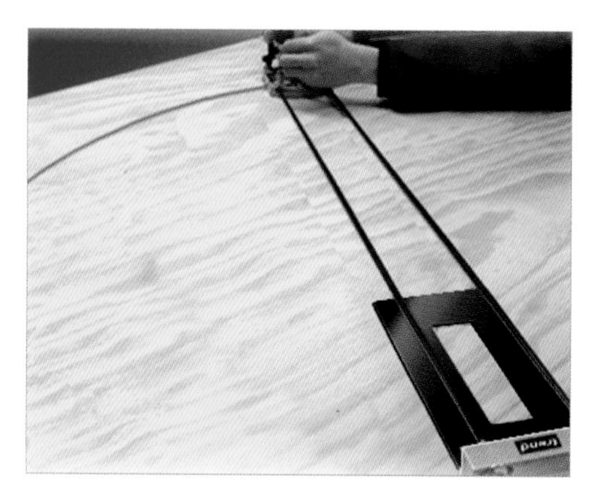

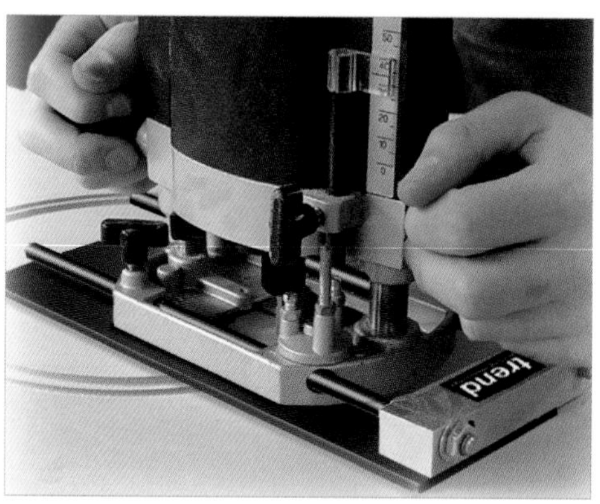

Ellipses

Trammels are not restricted to fixed radius cuts, but can also be used for cutting ellipses or ovals allowing you to make table tops, decorative cut outs, or to make openings in mirrors, picture frames etc.

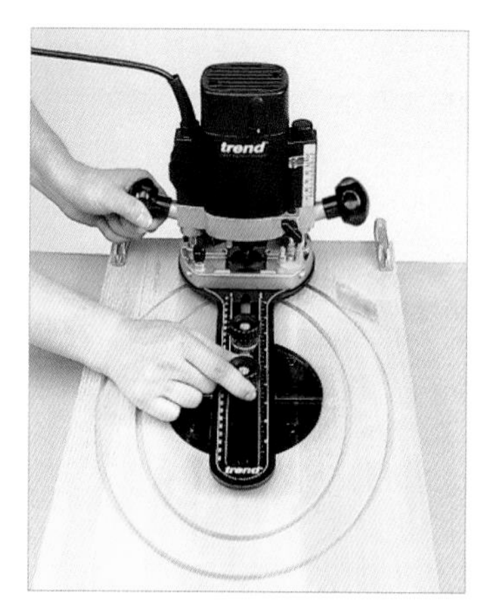

You can buy ready made jigs in various sizes which can adjusted to perform any type of ellipse cutting, or alternatively you can make your own.

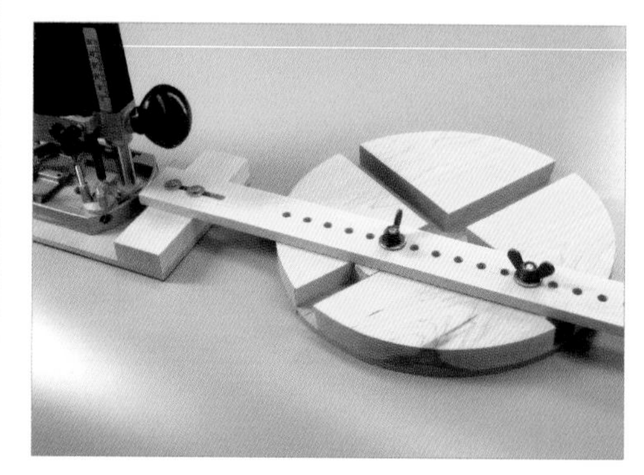

With these jigs, the trammel arm is pivoted about two points, which slide in slots cut at right angles to each other on a centre plate.

This centre plate is attached to the workpiece and the pivot points are set out to represent the length of the major and minor axes of the ellipse. The router is then guided round the plate to cut the ellipse.

Theoretically, as both pivot points are held securely in the slots, the router can be moved in either direction, as there is no danger of them becoming dislodged. Cutting the wrong way, i.e., feeding with the direction of cutter rotation can be beneficial in some timbers as it minimises break-out and leaves a smooth and clean edge finish. However, make sure you have full control of the router as it can snatch doing this and may damage the cutter and/or the work.

Pivot Frame Jig

Much of the work covered by the circular and ellipse trammels can be combined into a single jig in the form of the Trend pivot frame jig. This jig is able to perform many other valuable routing operations like planing, template routing, ski frame carving and trimming work. It can also be used for other circle applications such as adding decorative designs and patterns to a variety of different projects.

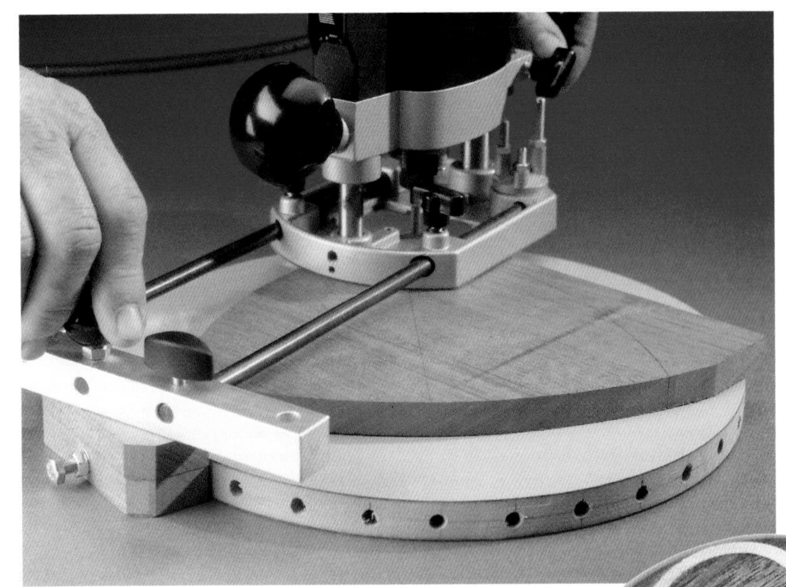

Circular and ellipse cutting, edging and trimming can also be accomplished using the router mounted in a fixed position either from above or below the workpiece. For these applications the wood is rotated anti-clockwise in a router table set-up and clockwise when the router is mounted in the overhead mode. The workpiece can even be motorised, and index points around the jig add a host of other decorative possibilities unique to this set-up.

Drilling and boring

Many router users have not yet realised the very real advantages of using a router for drilling.

The plunging facility of the router is designed to enter the work at a perfect 90 degree angle and this combined with the speed of rotation will produce perfectly accurate and clean cut holes, provided you use suitable cutters. Using the depth stop on the router ensures that all the holes are drilled to an accurate size and constant depth.

You cannot use normal wood drills because their flute design is not suitable for the high speed rotation of a router, but there is a range of special-purpose bits just for router use. These include straight bits, dowel drills, plug cutters and spiral bits, along with more specialised tooling such as hinge sinkers. However, many of these bits are designed to work at a specific speed, so you will need to use them with a variable speed router. Always follow the manufacturer's recommendations.

Tip

No matter what cutter you're using to drill with, it is usually better to plunge in stages, raising the cutter between each cut to help clear the waste. This is particularly important with large diameter cutters.

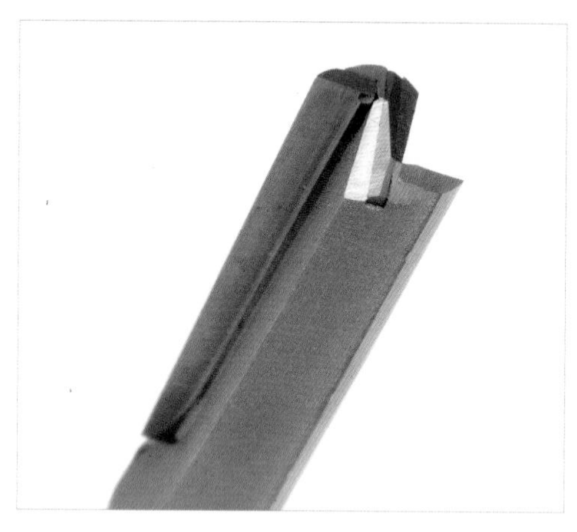

Any cutter that is used for boring must be ground with bottom cut and ideally have a clearance angle of approximately 20°. Whilst this is relatively easy to achieve on HSS cutters, it is more difficult on small diameter TCT ones.

For this reason solid TC cutters are better if you need to cut clean, small holes without burning. However, straight fluted standard cutters may have problems clearing the swarf, particularly on deep cuts, in which case up-cutting spiral versions are preferable.

The main problem of using the router for drilling is that it is difficult to centre it accurately. Some cutters actually have a central spur which makes alignment much easier, but it is not so easy on standard square ended cutters.

Overcome these problems by scribing centring marks on the base plate of the router which can be lined up with centre lines drawn on the workpiece.

Some routers may actually have the centre marks cast in the base by the manufacturer, otherwise mark the router base yourself with this simple procedure.

Draw lines at 90° to each other on a piece of flat material. Fit a symmetrical pointed cutter into the collet and bring the tip down onto the intersection of these lines. Square up the router base parallel to one of these lines and then mark the centring points on the router base plate.

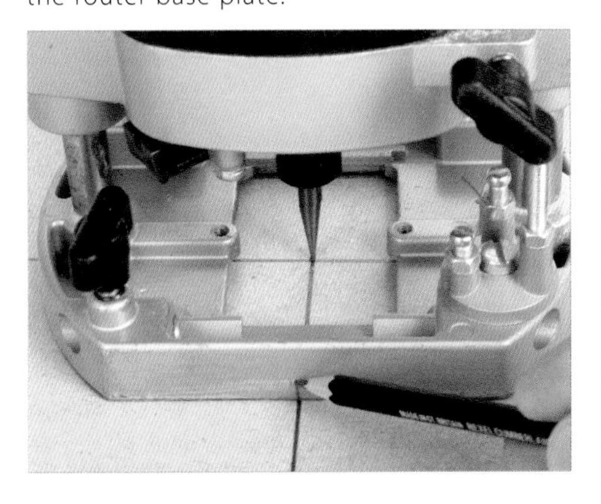

To make them more permanent, try engraving them using a small triangular file.

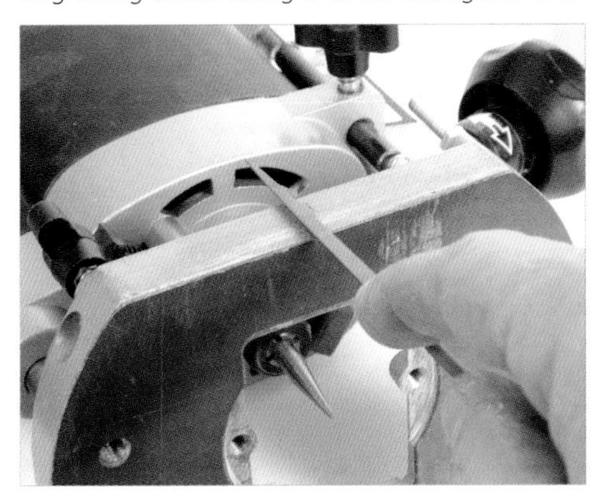

Another way of centring the router is to make a Perspex sub-base. Extend the edges of the sub base beyond the width of the router base to give alternative line up points.

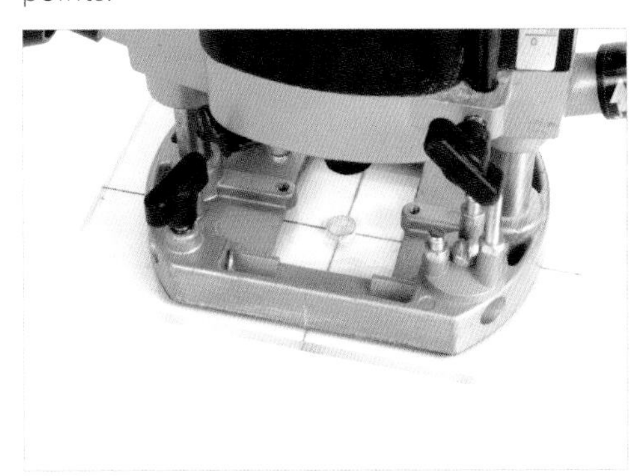

Because the base of the router is deliberately smooth to prevent it marking the work, it is sometimes difficult to hold it perfectly still while you are drilling. Minimise the risk of any unwanted movement by sticking some fine grade abrasive paper to the underside of the base using double-sided tape, but keep it well away from the cutter.

For a more secure location, a better way is to use a guide bush template. For this, drill a hole that exactly matches the diameter of the guide bush in a thin piece of MDF. Scribe the cross lines on this base as before and then clamp it in place over the required

drilling point. Now the router can only fit in one place and cannot move.

Add tapered spacers to this template to allow you to drill holes at an angle. However, this arrangement may be difficult to hold in place securely as you start drilling so use locating battens that are clamped across the surface of the work if necessary.

Hinge sinkers

Round hinges are very common in the furniture industry, particularly for kitchen cabinet doors as they are so very easy to fit and adjust.

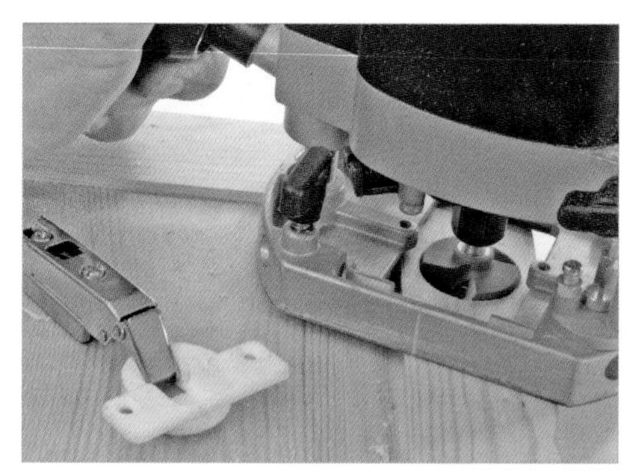

Although they require a large diameter hole, this is easily cut using the router and a hinge sinking cutter with a suitable locating jig to provide precise positioning. Take care not to exceed the maximum stated speed and cut the hole in two or three stages to allow the waste material to clear.

Tip

Check the maximum speed of rotation carefully, as many plug cutters need to be run with the router speed set as slow as possible to reduce the risk of burning.

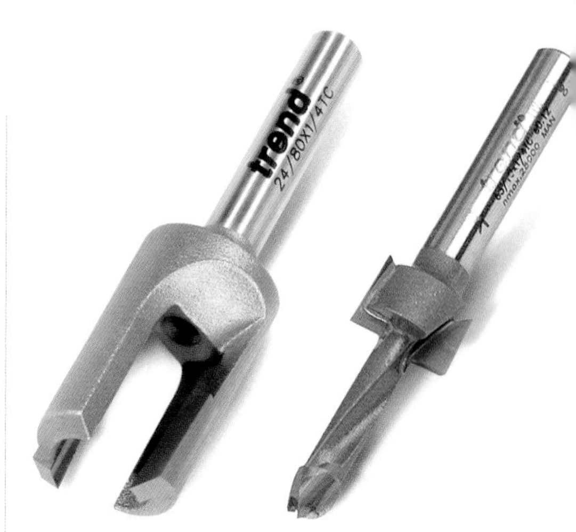

Plug cutters and counterbores

If you want to conceal screw heads or surface blemishes, use a counterbore to drill a clearance hole for the screw shank and then countersink or counterbore it all in one operation.

Plug cutters can then be used to cut tight fitting pellets from matching timber, which are then glued into the counterbored holes. The plug is trimmed flush with the surface to leave an almost invisible repair.

The counterbore bits have a locating spur which is normally enough for accurate positioning, but a simple locating jig, or template with a guide bush can be used for absolute precision. If you are working on curved surfaces like handrails, a shaped mounting block can be fitted underneath the locating jig.

Ideally, plug cutters should be used in an overhead mounted plunging router, with the waste material being securely clamped to the table.

However, if they have to be used in a handheld router, a simple jig can be used to hold the router still while the cutter starts to enter the wood. Use a router mat to prevent the workpiece from sliding out of position.

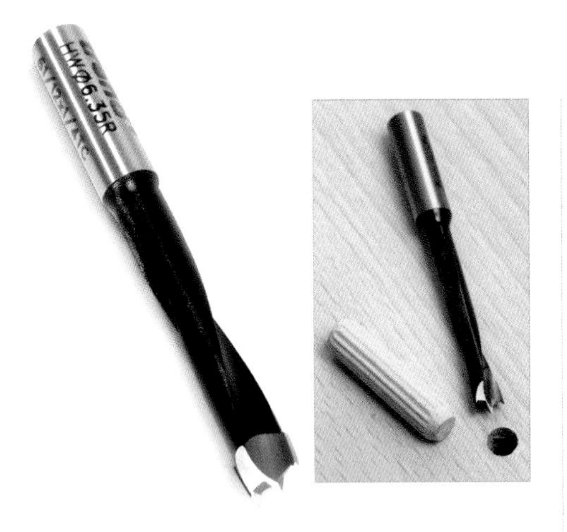

Dowel drills

Short, slow-spiral router doweling bits can be used in the router up to speeds of 22,000 rpm to produce perfect clean holes, but need to be used with a template for accurate alignment or spacing.

They are available in all the sizes to match standard wooden dowels, but the 5mm diameter is particularly useful for drilling holes for shelf supports.

Special templates are available for multiple drilling applications such as this. Used in conjunction with a small diameter guide bush, this is a foolproof method of spacing repetitive holes, though simpler shopmade jigs are very easy to make.

Most of the dowel drills have tungsten carbide tips and can be used on both manmade boards and natural timbers.

The concept of drilling with the router can be extended into all sorts of decorative applications. Cutters with bottom cut facility such as V and cove cutters will produce shaped dimples and indentations that can be used to add surface decoration to furniture and panel work.

Carving

With its ability to remove wood quickly and cleanly, the router is an obvious choice for a range of wood carving functions. However its use for freehand carving is mostly confined to small routers with de-mountable bodies which accept burrs and rasps.

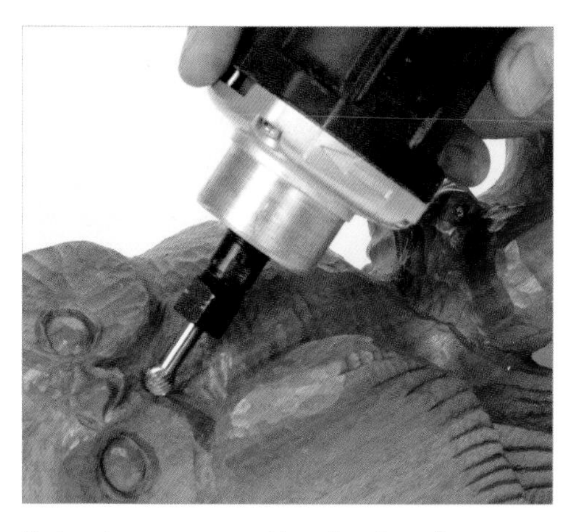

Trying to use conventional cutters for carving with the router handheld would be extremely dangerous, as you are unable to control any snatching or kickback. A variation on this is a dedicated carving machine in which single or multiple routers are mounted in a large frame and all the routers are moved simultaneously by tracing a guide stylus over a three-dimensional master pattern. In this case the routers are held securely so they can be fitted with conventional cutters for quick stock removal.

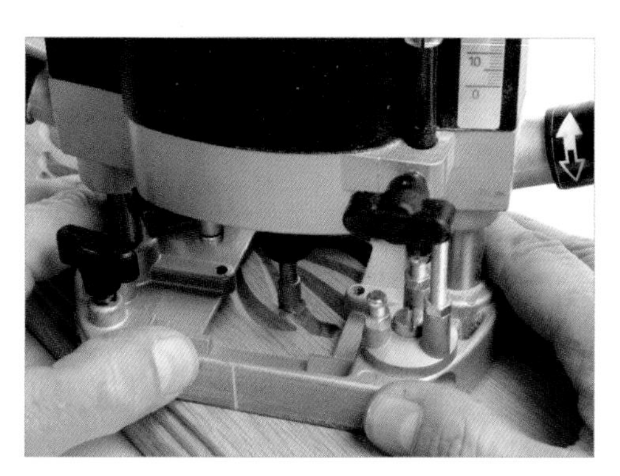

However, the handheld router is superb for relief carving when you want to add some decorative detail to panels or drawer fronts. You can do this freehand using the tip of a cutter to follow a marked line. The larger the cutter you use, the more erratic the progress of the router will be. But you can get better control, particularly if there are knots or grain variations in the timber. Hold the edge of the router base instead of the side handles, steadying your hand on the work and pushing it gently along each line to achieve the required designs. Patterns can be drawn directly onto the work or onto paper, which can then be stuck down onto the work surface. As the cut is relatively small and shallow, there is little chance of burning, even if you work slowly, but the quicker and more fluid you can get the movements, the smoother the resulting surface will be.

There is also a range of devices to simplify relief carving work and these offer endless decorative possibilities. The Trend Routasketch uses a light-duty router to cut freehand words and sketches by simply following a line drawing or template.

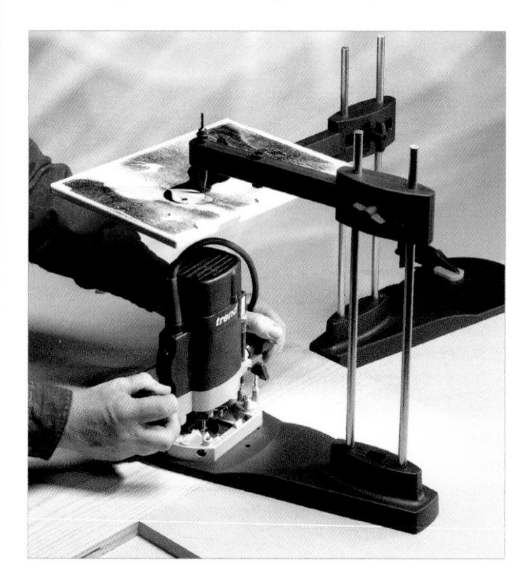

Other letter carving or sign writing systems rely on following letter and number templates using a pantograph arm, or by adopting standard template and guide bush procedures.

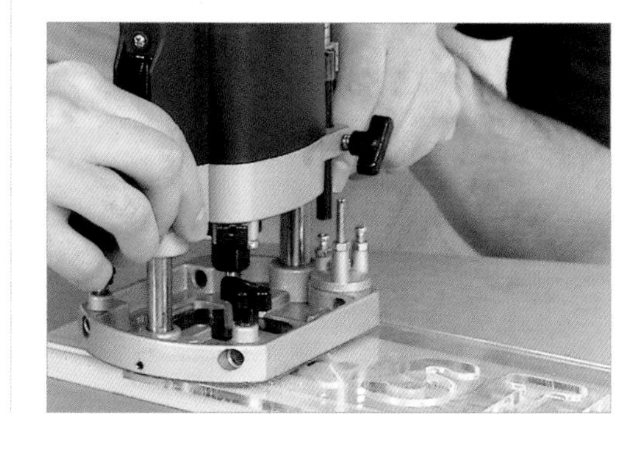

The Router Carver is a slightly different concept in that it allows you to create variable depth woodcarvings, using a 45 degree engraving tool, which is housed in an aluminium cone shaped bearing guide. This is moved over templates which are clamped or pinned to the workpiece. The templates have accurately shaped slots with varying widths, which means that as the bearing guide is moved over them, the depth and therefore the width of the cut varies automatically. There are numerous designs to choose from and they are ideally suited for panel doors, chair backs and even for cutting rosettes around drawer handles. The main advantage of this system is that the pattern is totally reproducible each time.

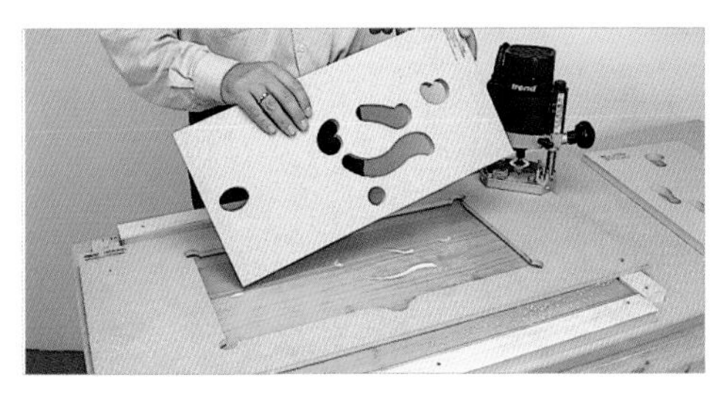

For relief carving, where large areas of waste often need to be routered away, extra supports in the form of ski bars may be necessary.

Decorative routing

The router really comes into its own when you want to start applying decorative effects to your work. With such a vast range of cutters available, the possibilities for decoration are endless, and a single cutter can often be used in several different ways to produce a variety of different effects.

Because there are so many possibilities it is impossible to cover them all in detail. However, it is worth taking a brief look at some of the main groups of cutters to see just what effects you can achieve with them, but experiment further to produce variations of your own.

Chamfer and V groove cutters

These cutters are available with a variety of different angles and are primarily used for engraving, chamfering and for imitating the tongue and groove effect on manmade boards. Bearing guided versions are used for a whole range of decorative edge details. Vary the depth of cut and change the guide bearing diameter to produce cuts with or without quirks.

Chamfers are often used in furniture making to soften hard edges on legs or panels.

Shallower angle cutters can be used for simple bevelling work on thick timbers, or for cutting the precise angles required for building up staved work.

Ovolo and rounding over cutters

This very large group of cutters has many useful functions, particularly for edge moulding. An ovolo cutter is essentially the same as the rounding over but has small quirks on the top and bottom of the radius. If you are using a bearing guided version, by simply changing the diameter of the bearing you can obtain both the round over and ovolo effects.

Standard ovolos are quarter radius, but flatter versions are available for applications like false panel work, and larger ellipse shaped profiles, used for architraves and hand rails.

Small ovolos can be used to disguise joints or multiple versions on the same cutter. They produce a bead profile, again, ideal for false panel work when guided around a template.

Bead and reed

Single bead cutters are used to produce nosings and decorative edges, often referred to as 'staff beads'.

These can be in the form of either a full round profile, or one with quirks on either side, like a double ovolo.

The corner bead cutter is particularly decorative and can be run twice, with the second cut at 90° to the first to produce a fully round bead on the corner of legs or cabinets.

Variations of the standard bead cutter in the form of the classic staff bead, produce a more elaborate profile for edge moulding applications.

Beading cutters are often used on the meeting stiles of double doors to balance the rebates, or on round frames and linings to disguise the joint line.

Reeds are just multiple beads combined on a single cutter, either with all the beads having the same radius or with different combinations of radii on the same cutter.

Radius and cove cutters

These are the reverse of the ovolo cutter and are used singly to produce drip grooves and the like, or with several parallel cuts, to produce decorative flutes, as for instance, on pilasters of a fireplace.

Flutes have many attractive possibilities and when used with a suitable jig, can be tapered to match the external profile of a leg.

When a radius cutter is used on the edge of the work, the resulting profile is referred to as a cove, and bearing guided versions are available for just this purpose.

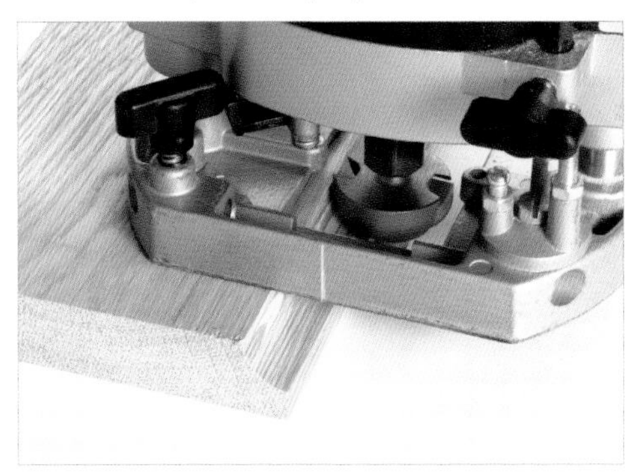

A more elaborate version of the standard cove cutter is the Cavetto mould which incorporates two quirks to add more detail. This cutter can be used either as an edge mould, or to create panel effects by using the whole width of the cutter.

Ogee cutters

The ogee is another classic decorative shape, being a mixture of cove and ovolo profiles in various combinations.

It creates a particularly attractive edge moulding and wide flatter versions are especially useful for disguising the thickness of table tops and shelves.

Panel moulding

This is a very useful technique for improving the look of large flat surfaces by cutting some form of imitation panelling. You could achieve this by just planting some moulded sections on the surface, but the most attractive effect is achieved by actually routing on the board faces. Many of the plain cutters already described can be used for this purpose although there are some dedicated profiles specifically designed for panel moulding. Obviously, they have to be guided in some way and the normal arrangement is to make up a template and use this in combination with a guide bush in the base of the router. An alternative is to use the cutter with a bearing mounted on the shank, again in conjunction with a suitable template.

Raised panel moulding

The more traditional way of producing a panel effect for doors is to mould individual infill pieces and then set them in a suitable frame. You can achieve this effect with the router but all the cutters are necessarily very large and you will require a heavy-duty router, normally mounted under a router table, and running at a lower speed.

Raised panel moulding with big cutters cannot normally be achieved safely using the router handheld. Cutters can be either plain or self guiding and can be used with templates to produce shaped tops to the panels.

An alternative method for raising square panels is to use a vertical cutter which then allows the use of smaller, less powerful routers. These can be handheld, but only providing that there is adequate support for the base of the router.

Combination mouldings

It is possible to build up the required profile using different cutters, making several passes at a variety of width and depth settings.

But you have to plan ahead a bit with this technique to be sure of retaining enough bearing surface to work off for the subsequent cuts.

Alternatively, you can build up a large moulding from several separate pieces, each having a different profile, a technique ideally suited for very heavy sections like cornices.

Linen-fold panel

Previously the preserve of the hand carver, it is now possible to cut specialist decorative effects like Linenfold panels using specially designed cutter sets. These use several cutters working in combination to produce this most traditional panel decoration.

Inlaying

Inlaying is another very common woodworking operation, either for decoration with banding and strings, or for setting in various types of hardware such as hinges and escutcheon plates. This job is ideally suited for the router with its ability to cut perfect, even depth recesses in both straight and irregular patterns.

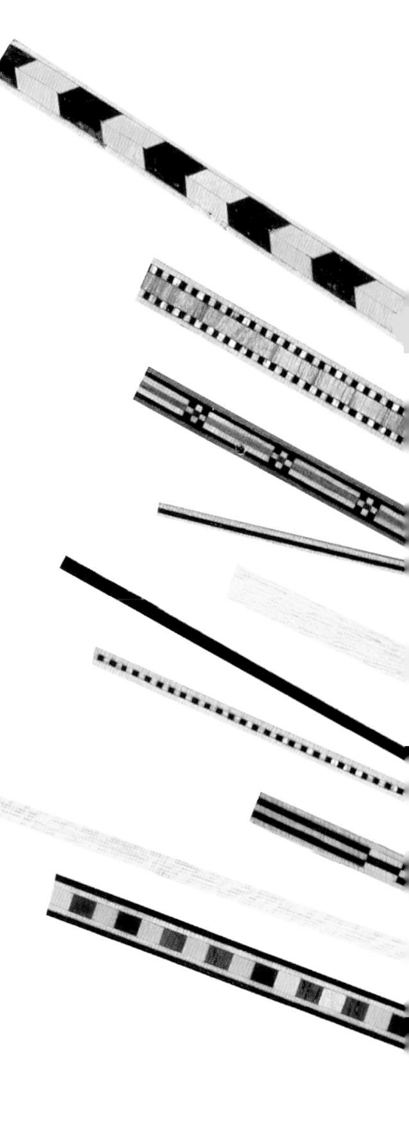

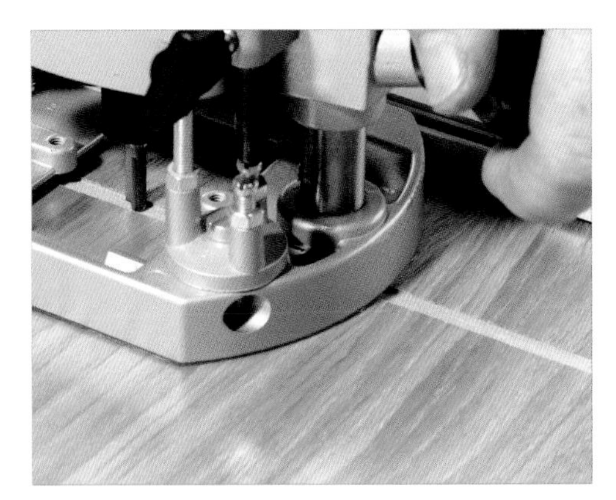

Straight line inlays are usually used as decorative edging on flat panels and are set into very shallow grooves cut with a router bit equal in width to the inlays strip, but cut to a depth of slightly less than the thickness of the inlays. This type of cut is easily produced using the standard edge guide on the router, or by using a straightedge in the conventional way.

For more continuous use, special inlay cutter sets are available, and although these have a limited number of widths, they are supplied with different diameter bearings to vary the depth.

However, inlay bandings and strings are not limited to straight lines and you can apply the same principles for curved work, guiding the router with a trammel, circle cutting jig or by just cutting freehand. If the inlay is following the edge of a tabletop for instance, it is simpler to use an edge following device, or make up your own from a block of wood shaped with the curve to match that of the workpiece. This is simply held on the router base with double sided tape or screwed to the side-fence.

Inlays may also be shaped in the form of motifs, often round or oval. Again the shapes can be cut freehand, after tracing around the outer edge of the inlays, or for more regularly used motifs, make a suitable template and use this in conjunction with a guide bush in the router.

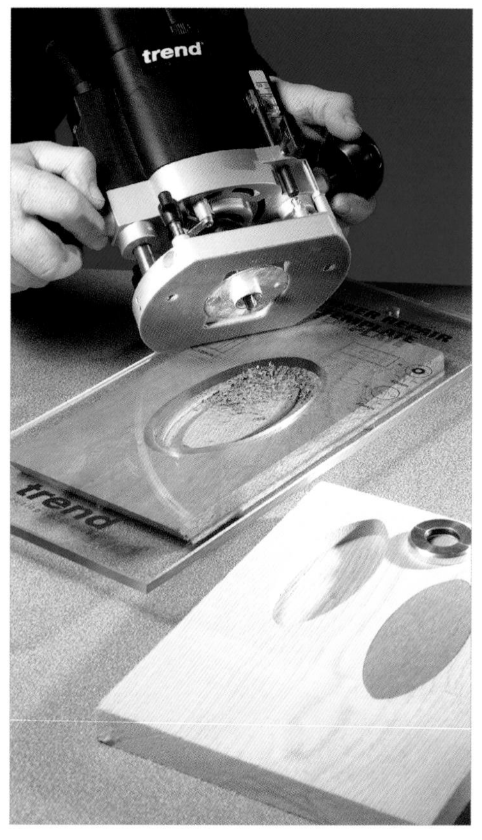

A very handy technique is to use two different sizes of guide bush with the same template and cutter, enabling you to cut both the inlay and the required recess for it to fit into. As well as insetting decorative detail, this technique is also useful as a means of patching over surface defects such as bad knots.

The size relationship between the cutter and guide bush for this technique is as follows:

Outside diameter of large bush minus the bit diameter equals the outside diameter of the smaller bush plus bit diameter.

The larger of the two guide bushes is used to remove the groundwork leaving a recess of a suitable depth for the inlay. The smaller diameter guide bush is used to cut the inlay itself which is then a perfect fit in the recess.

Cabinet hardware is inlaid into recesses in a similar manner. You can again use the router freehand, or use templates. There are factory made jigs for installing hinges and locks, or you can make these up yourself for one-off jobs

Router lathes

The router lathe is another standard accessory useful for three dimensional work with the router, like turning spindles and columns, or tapering and fluting on round, square and faceted workpieces. It also is used for cutting barley twists, spirals and diamond fluting.

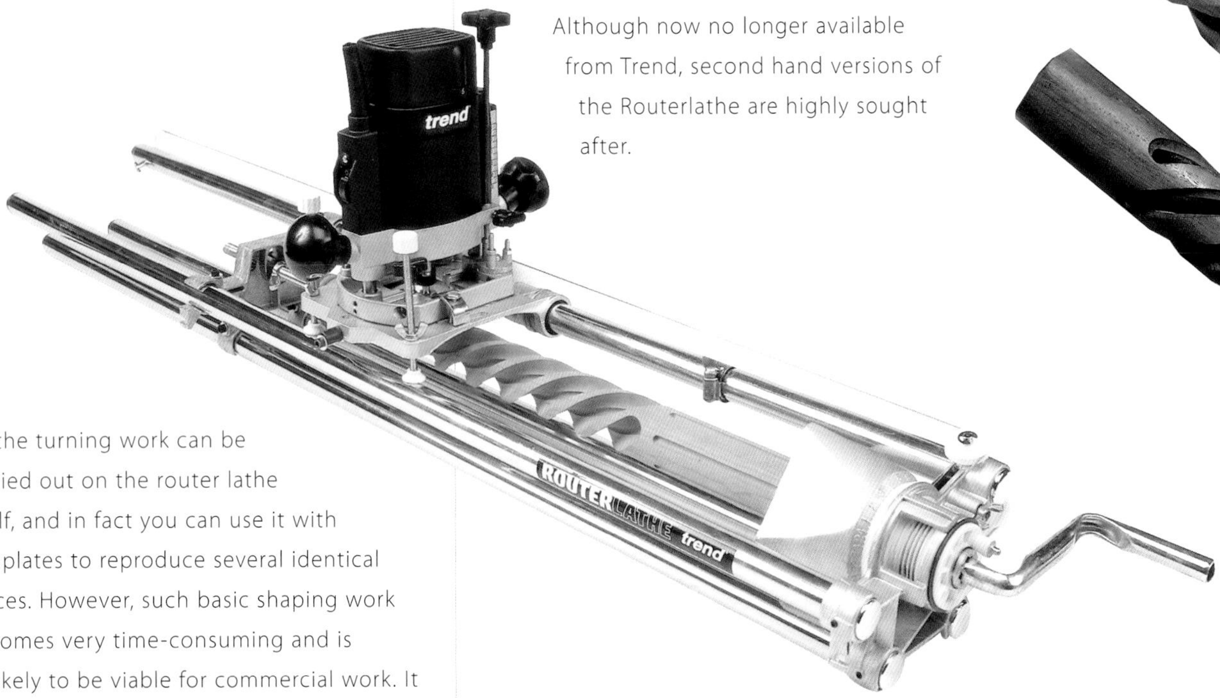

All the turning work can be carried out on the router lathe itself, and in fact you can use it with templates to reproduce several identical pieces. However, such basic shaping work becomes very time-consuming and is unlikely to be viable for commercial work. It is best carried out on a commercial wood lathe, with the router lathe being reserved for adding the final decoration.

A router lathe consists of a head and tailstock mounted on tubular rails, with the router fixed to a sliding plate which in turn is connected to a winding mechanism. To operate the lathe the router in wound along the workpiece by turning a crank handle on the headstock with adjustable stops being provided to limit the length of travel. The pitch of any spirals produced is determined by the diameter of the winding drum, as this sets the ratio between the speed of rotation of the work and the speed of the router moving along it.

On the simplest machines, this ratio is not variable and is normally set to give a pitch angle for twists of about 45°. More sophisticated router lathes allow you to vary this pitch angle. Right and left hand spirals can be cut by changing the connection of the drive wire. The tailstock is adjustable in height to accommodate tapered work and a dividing plate at the head end allows you to index around the work for multi-start fluting.

For straight line fluting, the work remains stationary and the router is run along its length.

Although now no longer available from Trend, second hand versions of the Routerlathe are highly sought after.

The router lathe is actually an extremely versatile device and when used with a variety of different profile cutters, is capable of producing some highly decorative effects, albeit rather slowly.

An alternative way of adding straight fluting and beading to an existing turned workpiece is by using a box jig, which may be freestanding or designed to fit over the wood turning lathe. They are very straight forward to make up as a one-off to suit the particular job in hand, though it is not difficult to build a universal box jig with a built in height adjustment that can handle a variety of different workpieces.

Whatever you are doing with the box jig, it is usually necessary to make several trial cuts to check on the various depth settings, so always make an extra workpiece for this initial experimentation.

Trimming

In routing terminology, the term trimming means removing a small amount of surplus waste to produce a finished dimension, or to cut back an overhang of laminate or veneer. The cutters are usually of the self guided bearing type with the majority of them being straight, but for laminate work some are angled to provide the necessary bevel where two surfaces meet.

Sometimes a bevelled edge is preferable to a square one to give a more pleasing appearance.

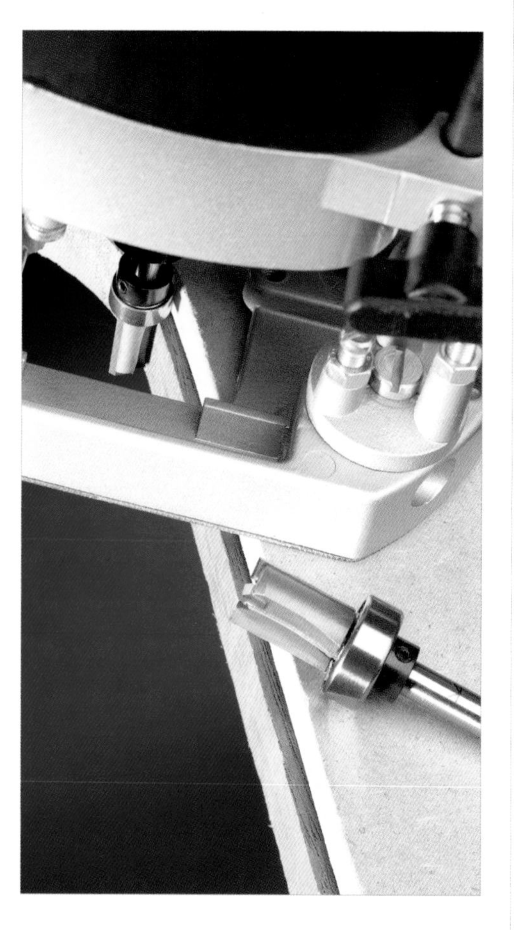

A basic square trimming guide is an essential routing aid that can be used in one of two ways.

Use it to clean up the end of boards using the guide as a bearing surface for the router base to run on. Use a standard straight cutter. Alternatively you can set the guide with only a tiny amount of amount of offset from the end of the board and use it as a template for a flush trimming bit with a bearing.

These flush trimming bits can also be used freehand to cut back any overhangs on assembled joints.

This trimming technique is perfect for squaring the ends of wide boards as it is almost impossible to cut them perfectly unless you have a proper dimension saw.

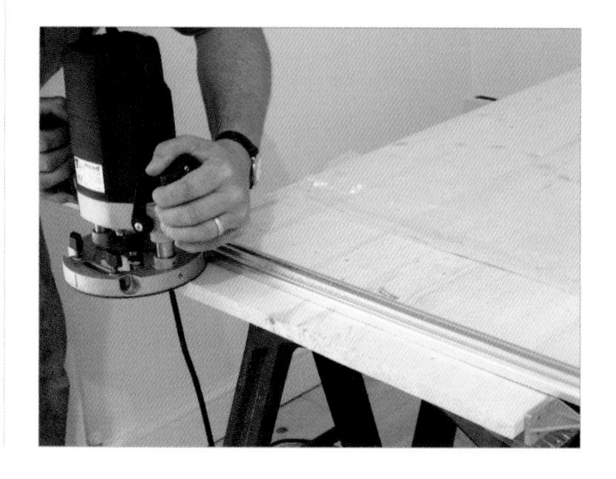

Instead, cut them slightly oversize and then trim back using a straightedge or jig to get a perfect cut without any break-out or splintering, even on veneered panels.

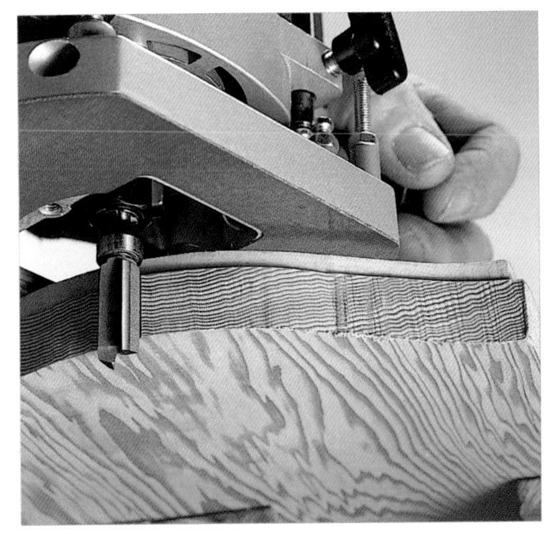

Some trimming jobs may be made easier by positioning the guide templates on top of the work, in which case use a cutter with a shank mounted bearing. Changing the diameter of this bearing allows the component to be routed oversize relative to the template, often handy when making jigs or patterns which need some guide bush margin.

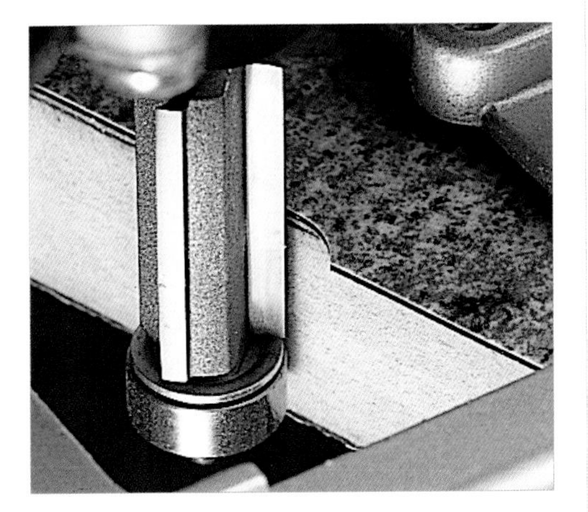

For laminate work standard bearing cutters can be used to trim back a maximum of 3mm overlap. In this situation always make sure the laminate adhesive is properly dry before trimming, to avoid clogging up the guide bearing.

There are self guiding trimmers that have no bearing at all but rely on the diameter of the shank to do the guiding. Pierce and trim cutters allow laminate to be cut back to an existing opening and some are designed for trimming both top and bottom faces simultaneously.

90 degree trimmers are slightly different in that they work from the face of the work and are used for flush trimming hardwood or plastic edge strip to match the existing surface without scoring it.

A fine height adjuster on the router is essential for this job, and the router needs to be fitted with a stepped base to lift the cutter above the projecting overlap of the laminate.

With some trimming jobs it may be necessary to feed the router in the wrong direction to avoid chipping or splitting off existing edges. The router must be used in such a way that the cutter is pushing the edging against its backing rather than trying to flick it off. See 'back cutting' on page 104.

Tip

The projection of the overhang of laminate should be a small as possible to reduce the amount of wear on the cutter. Adjust the depth of the cutter regularly when trimming to spread this wear along the length of the cutter.

8. THE FIXED ROUTER

The workshop value of the router is unquestionable, but its superb versatility can be increased even further by mounting it underneath a table or in an overhead stand.

Hand v fixed

This arrangement effectively turns your router into a small spindle moulder, with all that entails in the way of greater precision, control and safety.

It also allows much larger and more complex cutters to be used, like the profile scribing and panel raising range of tooling.

The router table is perhaps the next most useful purchase after the router itself and even the occasional user will benefit from its extra capabilities.

However, there are other ways of mounting the router in a fixed position, either in an overhead stand or in a machining centre of some sort.

There are of course advantages and disadvantages to each particular method of using the router and you will have to assess the best method for each job as it arises.

Hand routing advantages

- Ideal for machining large workpieces
- Inexpensive
- Increased flexibility
- Ideal for drilling and countersinking

Router table advantages

- Good support for narrow workpieces
- Increase range of available moulds from a single cutter
- Quicker to set up jigs and guides
- More suitable for production work
- Ideal for copy profiling
- More stable when using large cutters
- Increased safety with small workpieces
- Dust extraction is more effective

Overhead stand advantages

- Excellent vision of cutting area, particularly with small pieces
- Good access for cutter changing
- Ideal for template profiling and drilling

Hand routing disadvantages

- Difficult to machine small workpieces
- Easy to make mistakes by poor handling
- Operator fatigue on large runs
- Harder to set up for accurate work.
- Unsuitable for heavy cuts

Router table disadvantages

- Poor access to change cutters
- More difficult to adjust cutting height
- Poor vision for grooving and panelling
- Dust and debris falls into the router body

Overhead stand disadvantages

- Limited throat for large workpieces
- Effective guarding is more difficult
- Access for mounting hold down clamps is limited

The router table

A basic router table consists of a support table, some form of router mounting plate and a straight fence.

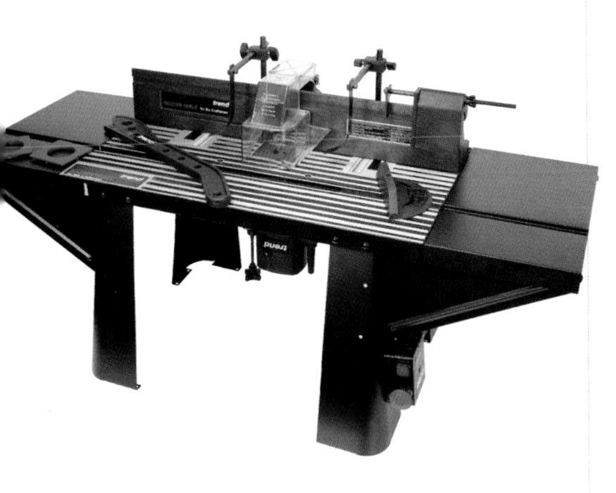

For safety, the cutter must be well guarded and the work needs to be controlled with hold down springs or pressure clamps. Some means of dust extraction is also essential.

The table can be floor standing on its own legs, or it can be mounted on a low stand to house the router for clamping onto the work bench. Proprietary tables vary in construction from heavy cast iron affairs to light plastic mouldings . All have their place, but you will find that the router table soon becomes an invaluable piece of kit, being used far more than you originally anticipated, so think ahead and buy in some spare capacity. Make sure it is stable enough when you start pushing large pieces through it and if necessary, bolt it down to a false base, which can be firmly clamped.

The table top

The tops on most proprietary router tables are either aluminium or steel. However, sheet materials such as MDF and dense particleboard are generally adequate enough if you want to make your own top. Plastic laminate faced board, with a balancing laminate on the reverse side to prevent bowing, is particularly suitable, being both stable and having a low friction surface. It is also inexpensive (off-cuts of kitchen work top are ideal), easy to work and therefore suitable for making your own table. Whatever the material you use, the top needs to be flat, level and smooth with a longitudinal slot to take a sliding mitre guide.

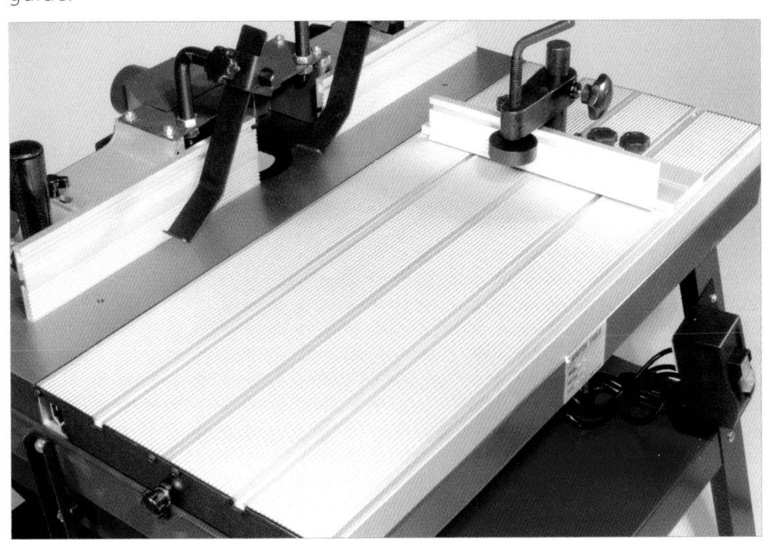

The central hole in the table should be capable of taking insert rings of different diameters to reduce the size of the hole for smaller diameter cutters.

This ensures maximum support at the cutting edge, reduces vibration and hence improves the cut finish. It also minimises the chance of the leading edge of the workpiece snagging in the cutter opening.

The size of router table you choose will mainly depend on the type of work you envisage using it for. Ideally, one around 800 x 600mm (32 x 24 inches) will accommodate most types of furniture and small joinery items. There needs to be enough support so that the workpiece cannot drop or tilt as it is fed into, or leaves the cutter.

For wide or long workpieces, extra support can be provided in the way of a temporary side extension table or in/out-feed rollers.

The table should also be grooved to accommodate a mitre guide, or even better, some form of sliding table or fence.

Tip

If there is no mitre guide available you can still guide the work by using a homemade sled running against the back fence.

If you are involved with miniature work, such as dolls houses, there are dedicated model maker router tables available.

These incorporate all the features of their bigger counterparts, but their small size and precise engineering ensure the necessary high precision for working tiny timber sections.

Mounting the router

Every router table seems to have its own unique method of mounting the actual router, using a variety of holding mechanisms, which often include specifically drilled screw holes to suit a particular model.

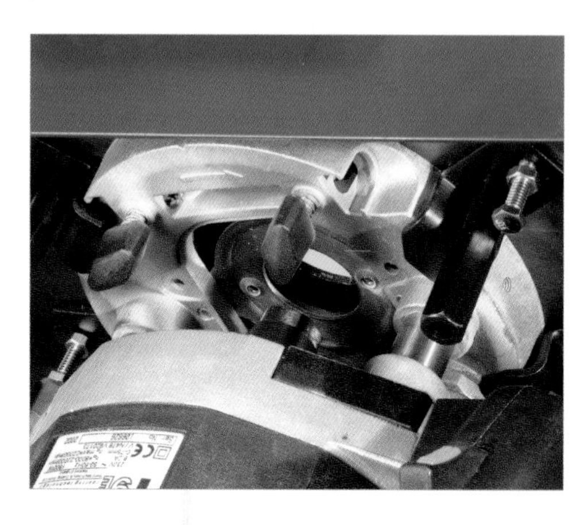

All these methods are inevitably fiddly to set up and you end up leaving a router permanently mounted under the table, it being too much effort to remove it.

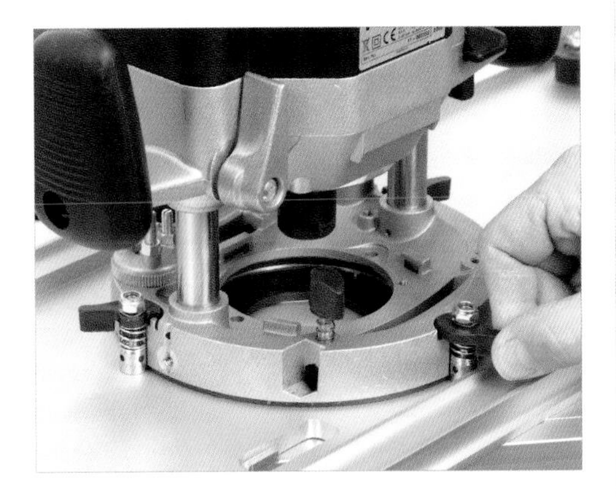

However, with the Trend T11 router and the PRT table, we have seen the introduction of a quick release system that allows the router to be mounted and dismounted very quickly, eliminating the need for an expensive router dedicated solely to table use.

One of the benefits of having a table with a thin metal top is to avoid losing too much depth of cut. Wood based tops tend to be much thicker, with up to 3/4" depth of cut being lost if the router is mounted on the surface. With these thicker tops it is therefore necessary to recess the router base into the thickness of the board, rather than to simply bolt it beneath.

An alternative method is to cut a hole through the table, larger than the router, and then mount the router on a metal plate inset, flush with the table surface. Some tables incorporate levelling nuts or shims to ensure that the plate can be set flush with the table surface.

If all else fails and there is not enough reach, the router spindle can be extended with a collet extension but this does introduce the likelihood of increased vibration and consequent poorer finish from the cutter.

Table fence

To act as a guide for the workpiece, the table needs a rigid back fence that is also adjustable.

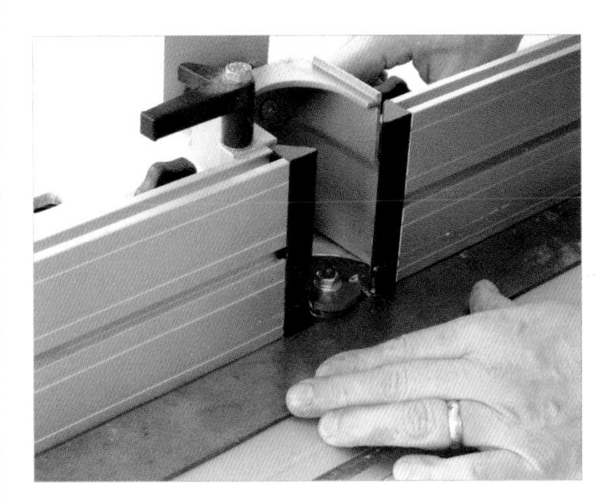

Sometimes it needs to be set a specific distance from the cutter, but at other times it has to be moved to allow the centreline of the cutter to be set back behind the face of the fence, so a good range of movement is essential.

Fence adjustment is ideally carried out using threaded knobs with captive bolts running in slots in either the fence base or the table itself. Alternatively, the fence can be simply clamped to the table at each end. Because the router cutter is spinning on a vertical axis (unlike a sawbench with a horizontal arbor), there is no blade face to which the fence can be set parallel.

However, it is worth trying to set it parallel to the table edge to allow work-holders, and other jigs and guides to be set up easily.

Adjustable faces, like those fitted to the side-fences on portable routers allow the ends to be closed up to the cutter for maximum support.

The table fence should also be fitted with a dust extraction port, which should be positioned directly behind the cutter recess for effective dust removal.

For ultimate extraction efficiency a Y junction hose should be used, with one hose mounted on the router base port and the other behind the projecting cutter.

Ideally, the two halves of the fence should be independently adjustable in and out as well as fore and aft. This allows you to make full face mouldings or edge plane, where fine-tuning of the out-feed face is necessary to maintain support.

If both fences are permanently fixed inline, this offset can only be achieved by fitting a thin shim or thicker false face to the out-feed fence. Similarly, a shaped facing can be fitted over the out-feed face when cutting full width edge mouldings.

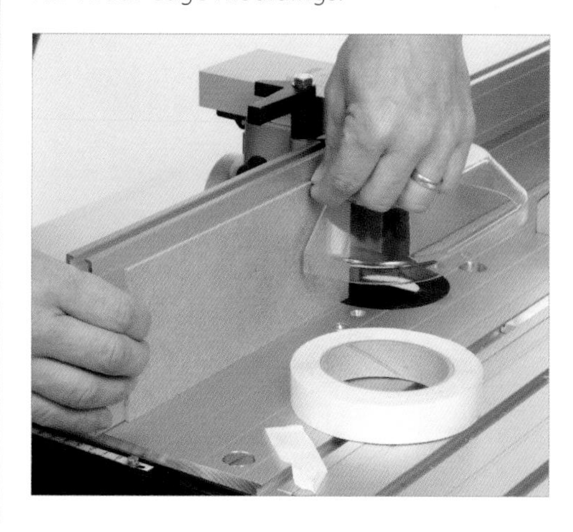

Guards and hold-downs

As with all cutting machinery, adequate guarding must be fitted to prevent accidents.

Ideally, the guard should prevent any part of your hand from getting close to the rotating cutter, but the more protection the better, provided it doesn't interfere with your vision or restrict safe holding of the workpiece.

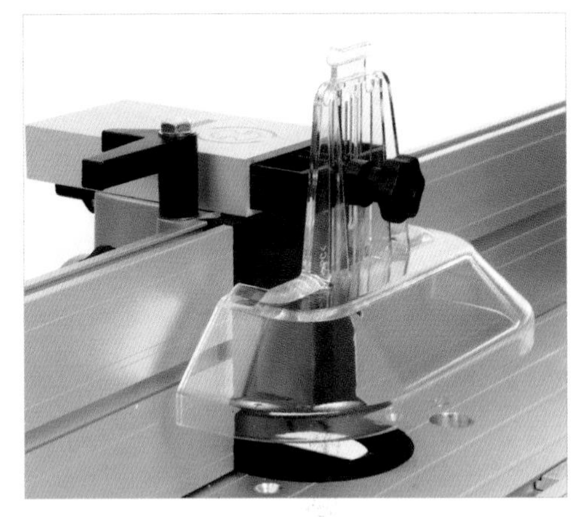

With most table fences the dust extraction hood forms a guard to the back of the cutter. However, the exposed cutter in front of the fence must also be guarded somehow at the start and end of each pass.

The most common method is to fit hold-down clamps or pressure guards.

These not only guard the cutter but also prevent the workpiece lifting from the table surface.

Side pressure guards serve the same purpose, protecting the cutter from the side and additionally holding the work securely against the fence faces.

Where pressure guards are inappropriate, alternative guarding can be purpose made to fit over the cutter. It can be secured to the table fence or a separate rigid bracket. Transparent guards should only be made from shatter proof plastics such as polycarbonate.

Pressure guards may vary from the very elaborate with screw tensioners to simple featherboards.

Tip

For certain operations, particularly with small section material, it is better to make up a tunnel guard which completely encloses both the cutter and the work to ensure a perfectly chatter free finish.

Switching

To avoid the dangers of reaching under the table to switch the router on and off, it needs to be operated via a remote switch fixed to the front (in-feed) end of the table.

No-volt release switches are best suited for this purpose, ideally incorporating an easy to reach knock-off switch to cut the power in an emergency.

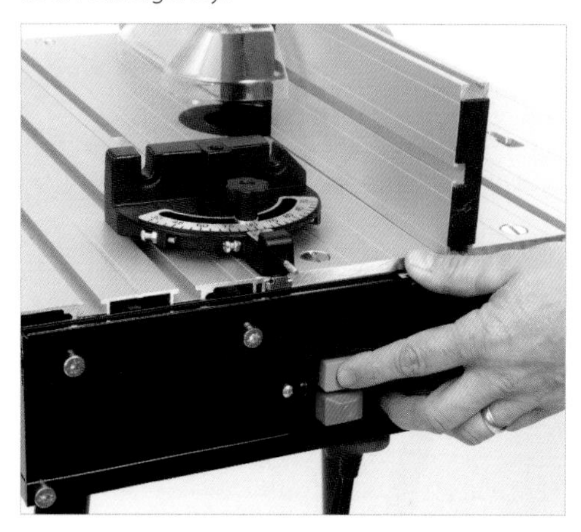

If your router is one of the new type with a 'dead mans' switch you will need to use some form of cover to hold it in the 'on' position, so you can then operate it via the NVR switch.

Router controls

As the plunge action is not required for most operations when using the router inverted, a fine depth adjuster can be fitted to allow precise setting of the cutter height above the table.

This precision is virtually impossible without a fine adjuster and if you have not already bought one with your router certainly get one with the table.

Some tables allow the fitting of a quick raising device which is a great aid, but the Trend T11 router and PRT table allows the router to be raised from the top of the table, a huge benefit only appreciated by those who have previously struggled to make fine adjustments to stubborn and inaccessible table set-ups!

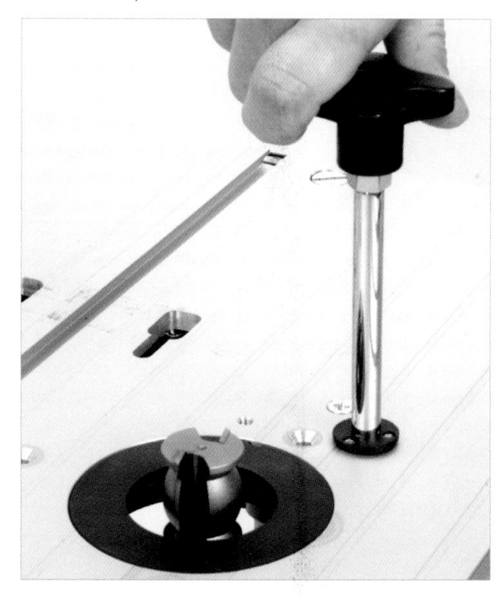

Using the router table

Although generally easy and safe to use, there are a few techniques that will enhance your router table operation.

For a start, the table must be at a comfortable height, which is usually higher than normal bench height to avoid too much bending and stooping.

Feed the timber over the table smoothly and continuously to avoid the inevitable burn marks if you hesitate or stop. Try standing to the right hand side of the table with the left hand holding the stock against the fence, with the right hand one doing the feeding in one long flowing movement.

Because it is easier than using the router by hand, the temptation is to force the wood past the cutter too quickly, so determine a steady feed rate that allows the cutter to work properly and clear the chips without burning or chattering.

Make sure the work is held firmly, either by you or some form of hold down clamp and only take light passes.

Finally, remember that as with hand routing, the finished cut will only be as good as your initial stock preparation, in fact it is probably more important to use quality stock on the router table as distorted material will not slide easily past the fences or through the hold downs.

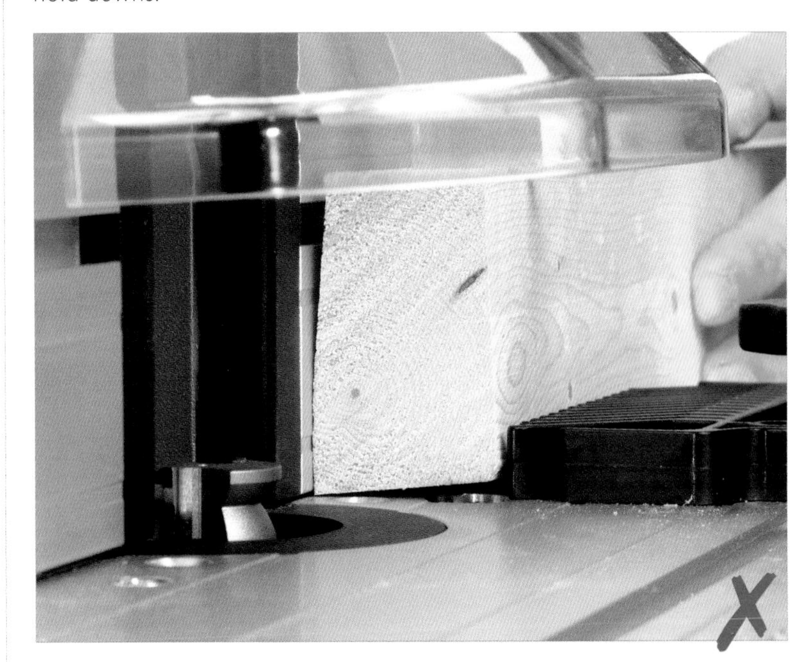

Working safely on the inverted router table

1. For all table routing operations, the full depth of cut should be reached in a series of shallow steps rather than in a single pass. As with hand held routing, the depth of each step will depend on the size of the cutter, shank diameter, cutter profile and router power. Just because the router is firmly mounted don't assume it will take heavier cuts.

2. With the router inverted, the cutter is rotating in an anti-clockwise direction. Therefore the feed direction must be from right to left, working from the front of the table against the rotation of the cutter. Do not run the full width of the material between the cutter and fence or the cutter will grab the work with great force.

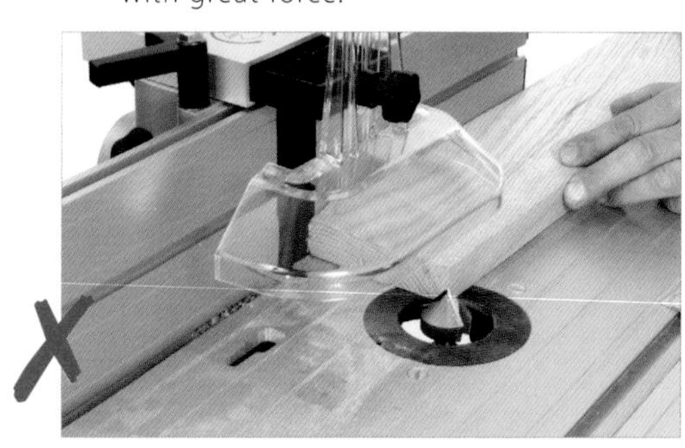

3. Always make edge cuts with the cutter set into the slot in the fence and the edge being machined against the fence face. Never run the material in the opposite direction, i.e. from left to right.

If there is a choice, always use the cutter working underneath the timber rather than on top, as any distortion in the wood may cause it to jam and kickback.

4. If you need to make several passes to widen a groove, take care not to trap the workpiece i.e. adjust the fence so that the bit is cutting on the safe side of the initial cut, this ensures the cutting action pushes the work back against the fence.

Ten essential steps to setting up the router table

A router table may be very simple to use but it does require setting up carefully to maximise its accuracy and safety.

1. Check that the router is securely fixed to the table and centralised in the cutter aperture.
2. Ensure it is disconnected from the power supply before inserting the cutter well into the collet. Don't try and get extra reach by getting the collet to grip the end end of the shank. Try to get at least three quarters of it into the collet and ideally up to the 'K' line mark on the cutter shank.
3. Fit the smallest possible insert ring to close the gap around the cutter, but spin it by hand to check that it is still clear.
4. Set the fence to give the required width of cut, then bring the sliding fences in close to the cutter as well. But make sure they are then locked up tight to prevent them sliding into the revolving cutter when you feed the wood against them.
5. Set the depth of cut remembering that several shallow cuts will always produce a better finish than one heavy one.
6. Check that the router speed is appropriate for the diameter of the cutter, as this is vital with very large diameter cutters.
7. Adjust the hold downs and guards to suit the workpiece dimensions.
8. Plug in the router and connect up to a dust extractor if possible.
9. Start the router and let it run up to the selected speed before starting the cut.
10. Think safety. Ear defenders and eye protection are essential and consider using a powered respirator for ultimate protection. Always use push sticks and safeguard your hands.

Bearing guided cutters

Bearing guided cutters are ideal for use in table-mounted routers, but always remember to feed against the rotation of the bit.

However, remember that any edge defects in the timber will be transferred to the cut if you use a bearing, whereas they will probably be bridged out if you use the wider table fence as a guide.

For straight work, the bearing face should be set flush with the fence faces using a steel rule to align it.

Tip

Avoid leaving the bearing set slightly proud of the fence faces, as the cutter will cut deeper at each end of the pass, as the material will move out and drop back against the fence face as it picks up and leaves the bearing.

Edge rebating

Rebates can be cut on the table using single or two flute straight cutters.

Choose a cutter equal to, or slightly larger in diameter than the width of the rebate. Raise the cutter to a suitable height to make the initial cut 3 to 4mm (1/8 to 3/16 inch) deep. Set the width of the rebate from the face of the fence to the furthest tip of the cutter.

The workpiece can either be held vertically against the fence or flat on the table with the rebate edge against the fence face.

Having made the first pass, raise the cutter by a similar amount until the full rebate depth is reached.

Shaped workpieces can be rebated or moulded by removing the back fence and using bearing guided cutters or a template set-up. In this case a lead-in point fixed onto the table near the cutter is necessary to give initial support until the cut is established.

Decorative edge mouldings

Decorative mouldings can be run in a similar fashion to rebates, with the workpiece held either vertical against the fence or flat on the table. Depending on the cutter profile, this can often be used to change or reverse the mould profile.

For instance a 60° bit can produce a 30° cut if it is used on edge, or an ogee will cut two different shapes depending whether it is used flat or on its side.

When moulding the full edge of the workpiece, a shaped lead out block should be fitted to the out-feed face of the fence to take up the depth of material removed and prevent any sharp or fine profile detail being damaged as it slides against the fence face.

Always avoid running feather edges against the fence; these are best run using a sliding carriage or a template and guided cutter.

The profile can also be altered by presenting the work at different angles to the cutter, but in this case a workholder should be used to maintain the angle throughout the pass. These workholders offer a safe method of holding the workpiece at a specific angle when guiding it against a straight fence or guide bearing and are usually one of two types:

Carriage: Designed to slide on the table with the workpiece clamped to it. It can be run against the edge of the table or alternatively guided by a slide batten running in the mitre fence groove.

Fixed support: Clamped on the face of the table. This supports the work at an angle while it is run against the table fence.

Composite mouldings

Composite mouldings can be cut using several differently shaped cutters to make up the required profile, but always think ahead and work out the best sequence for cutting each part of the profile.

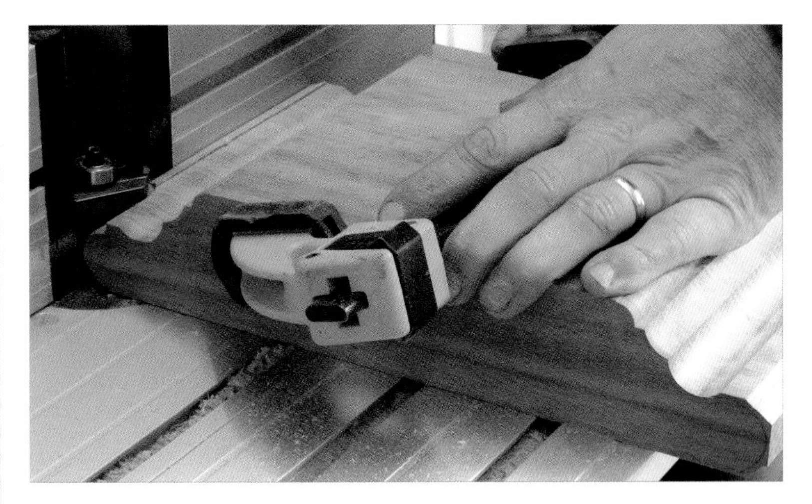

This will enable you to make the best use of the remaining flat faces of the work piece as guide edges before they are finally cut away. In some instances the last cut may leave an inadequate edge that needs a scribed support.

Grooves and dados

These should be cut with the face edge of the workpiece or a square end against the fence.

Set the cutter height for the first pass and make the cut, keeping the face of the work flat against the table and the guide edge square to the fence. If necessary, to avoid break-out at the end of the cut, a scrap batten can be clamped against the rear edge and passed across the cutter with the work.

Alternatively, the sliding mitre fence can be used with a parallel waste batten held firmly against it. There will obviously be some limitation to the width of the workpiece using this method, depending on the distance between the mitre fence face and the cutter. Use the same technique for angled dado cuts as well.

For stopped cuts draw registration marks on the fence to indicate the stopping points, or fix up stops for absolute precision.

Tip

Avoid making dado cuts in wide boards on the inverted table as it is not easy to feed the work accurately enough and it is also difficult to guard the cutter satisfactorily. For this operation, use the router hand-held or on an overhead router table.

Edge planing

For edge planing and trimming operations, a thin false guide strip can be fixed to the out-feed table fence.

This needs to be no-more than 1/16" thick, as this will be the most that should be machined off across the full depth of an edge in one pass. Use a two flute cutter with cutting edges slightly longer than the thickness of the edge, and as big a diameter as possible to minimise chatter.

Fix the packing strip to the fence with double sided tape then use a steel rule held against the face of the packing to set one cutting edge of the cutter against the rule edge, leaving it proud of the in-feed face; this is the depth of cut.

When you are cutting, keep the workpiece tight against the in-feed face until enough material has passed the cutter to sit firmly against the out-feed face.

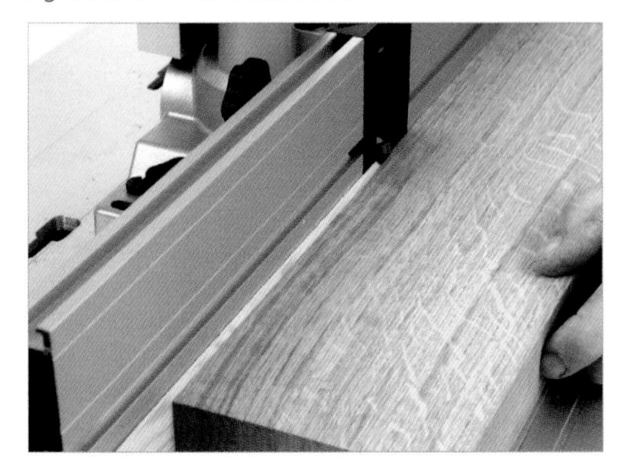

Using jointing cutters

Jointing cutters such as finger joint, comb joint, and tongue and grooving sets, should all be used in the router table rather than in a portable router as they require stability to obtain precise accuracy.

Even when using bearing guided cutters, initially, set them back into the table fence to allow the full depth to be cut in several shallow passes, moving the straight fence to expose more of the cutter on each pass until the full depth is reached. This will always result in a more accurate joint.

Scribing sets and profile scribing cutters

A scribed reverse mould and tenon on a rail or muntin can be cut using a profile scribing cutter with the router mounted in the router table. Available with 8mm and 1/2" shanks they can even be used with medium duty routers if cut in two or three passes, taking a light cut on each run.

Before cutting the finished work, always make several trial cuts to check that the joint is tight and the faces flush.

Having completed a perfect trial joint, keep it available for re-setting the cutter components for future projects.

When cutting the rail or muntin ends, use a work holder to keep it square to the fence and fit a parallel waste batten to prevent break-out on the back of the timber.

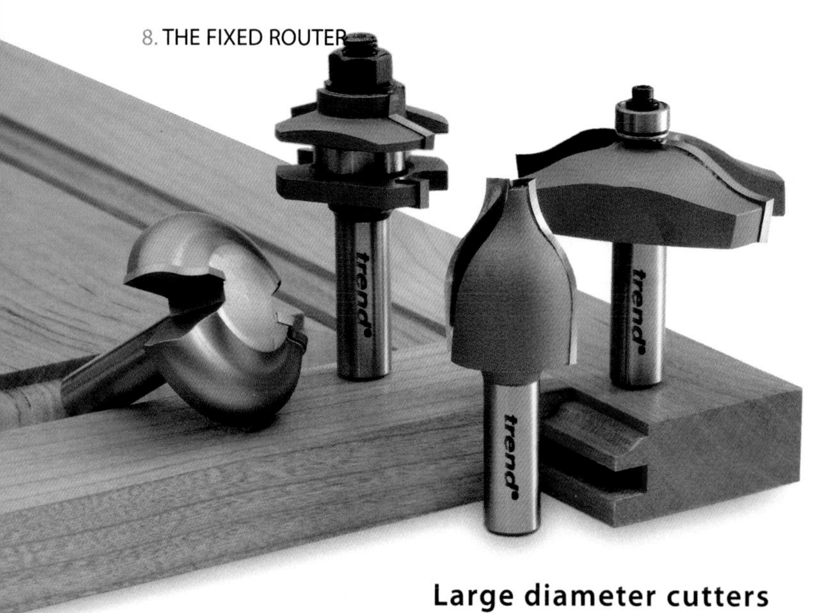

Large diameter cutters

A heavy duty router is needed for the larger diameter cutters and ones that have diameters larger than the cutter opening, like panel raising bits. These can be used in the router table by fitting a temporary MDF facing over the table.

If the existing table fence cannot be used, make up a suitable one and clamp it securely over the MDF. The first cuts should be made across the grain at each end of the panel, as break-out at the ends of the cut will be removed when the panel edges are machined.

Vertical panel raisers

As they have a smaller diameter compared to horizontal panel raising cutters, these cutters can be used in medium duty routers fitted in the router table.

However, it is important that the panel is kept perfectly vertical against the fence throughout the pass. This can be helped by fixing a vertical board to the fence as an additional support.

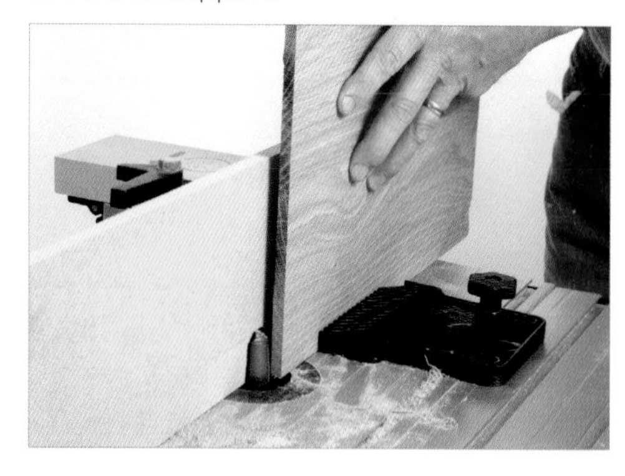

Make the cut in a series of passes, raising the cutter on each until the full width of the mould is achieved.

Halvings and tenons

Halvings and Tenons can be cut using the sliding mitre fence, a work holder, or a slide fitted to the vertical fence. In all cases, use a spelch batten behind the work to prevent break-out.

With the former, where the work is held horizontally, use the largest diameter cutter possible running the rail end against the table fence.

If necessary, then re-position the fence to lengthen the cut from the end of the rail.

If you use a work-holder several rails can be cut at the same time.

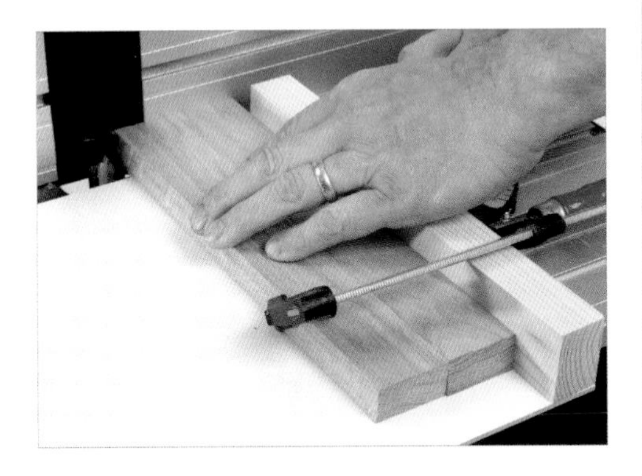

Dovetail dados

It is far easier to cut the dovetail on the edge of a board on the router table, rather than with a hand-held router. However, depending on the size of the workpiece, the opposite often applies when cutting the matching dado. Always cut the dado first as it is easier to adjust the width of the tail to suit.

Run a trial piece across the cutter holding it vertical against the table fence. Turn the piece around and cut the other face. Check that the tail is a tight fit in the dado and adjust as necessary before cutting the first workpiece.

Curved and shaped work

Curved and irregularly shaped work can be guided and machined on the table by using bearing guided cutters or by mounting a bearing directly above a plain cutter. In both cases a guard must be fitted over the cutter and bearing.

Guide bearings can be run against the finished edge of the work itself for edge moulding operations, or against a template for edge trimming or profiling.

If you are machining curved work, always use a lead-in pin or a feed block to minimise the risk of the cutter 'snatching' the workpiece as it is fed into the cutter.

A similar arrangement can be fitted to prevent work from being pulled behind the cutter as it leaves. However, on small radius curved work this may not be possible.

For trimming or moulding edges this way, it is better to allow extra waste at both ends of the workpiece. This will provide a lead-in and lead-out section allowing the work to be fed smoothly onto the cutter. Templates can also be used in a similar way to provide the same effect.

Take care with small or narrow workpieces. Where possible make up a simple work-holder to provide safer control of the work.

Making your own table

You can of course build your own router table and there are several reasons why you might go down this route. Although it will doubtless be cheaper than a shop bought alternative, it is probably more important that you can design it to suit your own particular needs. Mass produced tables are designed as a compromise to suit every router user, and although many of them are extremely versatile, it is unlikely that you will find the 'perfect' table.

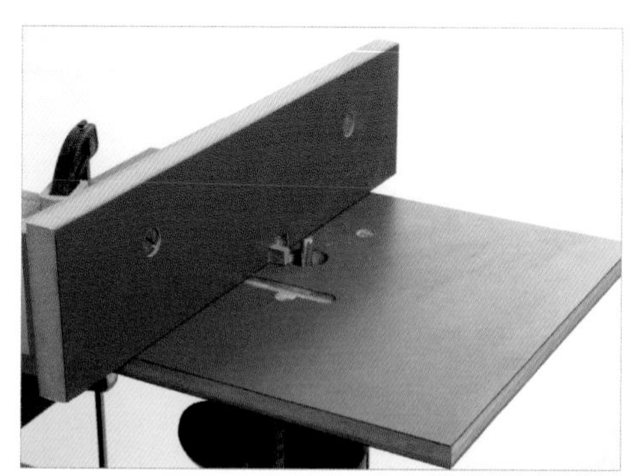

Building your own allows you to incorporate all the features you need, like getting it at a comfortable working height or incorporating a particular accessory, like a box combing jig. You can design the table to be as simple or as complicated as you like. At its simplest, a flat top clamped to the bench with a straight batten as a fence will do an amazing amount of work, provided you guard it properly.

If you are short of space, a fold down table hinged against the wall with swing out supports may be the answer.

Alternatively, if you are into small detailed work a bench top table will probably be ideal.

At the other extreme, you can build a complete routing station, with the table incorporated into a cabinet for storage of all your cutters and accessories and incorporate efficient dust extraction and maybe vacuum clamping as well.

The table top

The prime requirement for the table top is that it is flat, strong and smooth enough to allow the work to slide over it easily. It must also be capable of withstanding and absorbing vibration.

Metal is the ideal answer and you can actually buy ready made tops, but these tend to be rather expensive. So unless you have distinct metal working skills the choice is for some form of wood based material and with the vast range of man made sheet materials, there are various options that are worth considering.

MDF is the most obvious choice as it is cheap, flat and very smooth. However, over time it will sag under the weight of the router so will need some additional stiffening. Although smooth, the surface is easily marked, so cover it with laminate to reduce friction and increase durability. Remember though to laminate both sides to prevent it warping.

Plywood is another alternative, being considerably stronger than MDF but it is often not particularly flat. You can improve this by laminating two pieces together, and again, covering the faces with laminate.

Offcuts of kitchen worktop make excellent router tables although the core is often only chipboard. Their extra thickness gives strength and the laminate covering is extremely durable and friction free, but the thickness will reduce the amount of cutter 'reach'.

You may want to put a mitre guide slot into the table top, but there are pros and cons with this. With a slot you can use the mitre guide for a variety of machining operations, particularly on end grain cuts. You can size it to take the guide off another machine like your circular saw to save cost. The slot will also be useful for a range of other jigs and fittings and to accommodate pressure guards and featherboards.

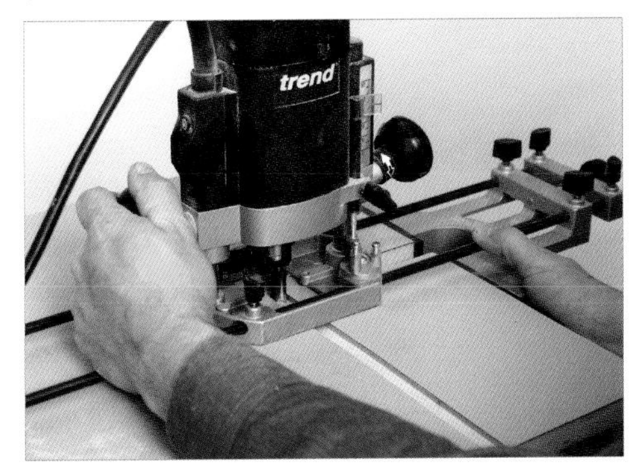

However, unless the top is at least 25–30mm thick, cutting a slot across the table will weaken it severely and may cause it to lose its vital flatness. Also the slot is going to expose the base material, which will probably wear with continual use.

The alternative is to make up cross cut slides and guards that are located along the outer edge of the table, which can be laminated to reduce wear.

Router mounts

The problem with mounting the router to these panels is the thickness needed for adequate stability.

With the router fitted underneath, most of the plunge depth is lost and the table is unusable unless you use a collet extension. Cutting out a rebate to take the router is one option but this will also weaken the top and reduce the necessary rigidity.

The answer is to fix the router to a mounting plate and then rebate this into the table top. This way the most depth you will lose will be about 1/4", probably less if you use a steel plate.

Once again, you can either buy ready made mounting plates or make your own from scratch.

The Trend RTI plate features several insert rings for different cutter diameters and incorporates mounting holes for overhead guards, template guides and lead-in pins.

You may or may not have to drill the fixing holes for the router, but templates are normally supplied to help you with this if yours is a non-standard router base.

These plates drop in from the top of the table, sitting on a machined rebate, and usually stay in place under the weight of the motor though some have retaining clips or corner screws.

Smaller round mounting plates are available that can be left permanently fixed to the router, some being cleverly designed so that they can be inserted into the table from the underneath.

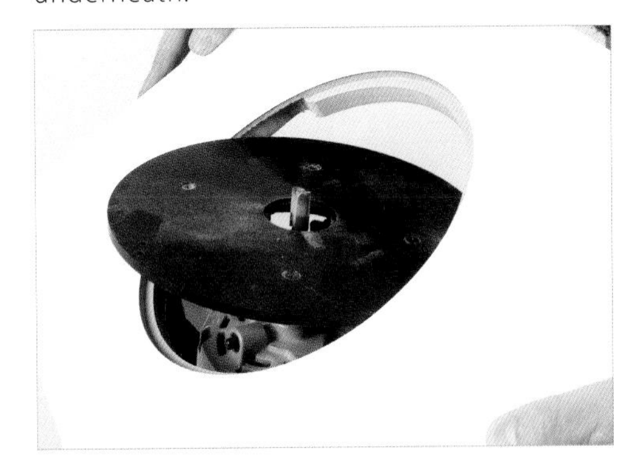

If you want to make your own mounting plate there are, again, various options for suitable materials.

Polycarbonate is relatively cheap, virtually unbreakable but is prone to sag over time.

Acrylic is easy to work and much more rigid.

Phenolic plastic is very strong and rigid though somewhat more expensive.

Whatever material you use, make the mounting plate as small as possible to minimise any sagging and reduce vibration, and make sure it seats flush in the table opening.

Fence

A fence for the table is essential and you will probably find that a simple straight batten, slotted to allow the cutter to protrude, will cover most applications.

However it is quite easy to make up more elaborate fences with features like Tee slots to take guards and sliding faces, or you may even make a split fence that can be shimmed to make planing or full face cuts.

Because table routing generates so much dust, the fence should also incorporate some form of extraction outlet and again you can easily make this. A simple wooden plate with a hole drilled to take the extraction hose works really well!

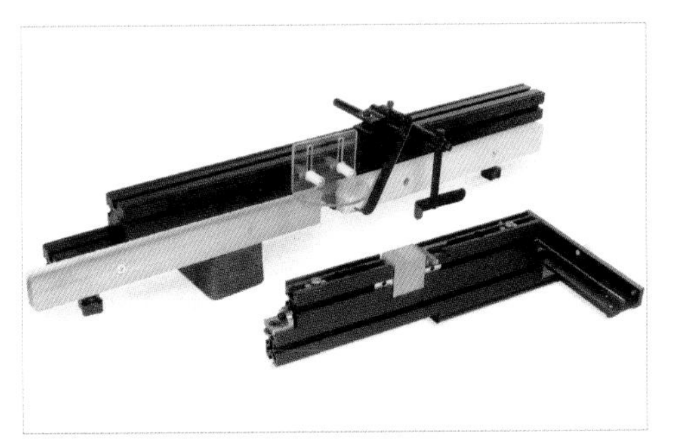

Separate ready made aluminium fences are available to suit home made tables, with all sorts of built in features like micro adjustment, sub-fences and positioning stops as well as spring loaded hold down clamps. Although initially expensive, these fences allow you to make a table that is perfectly customised to your requirements.

Tip

You can make up different fences for specific applications, like one with stops for rebating or a high one for vertical panel raising.

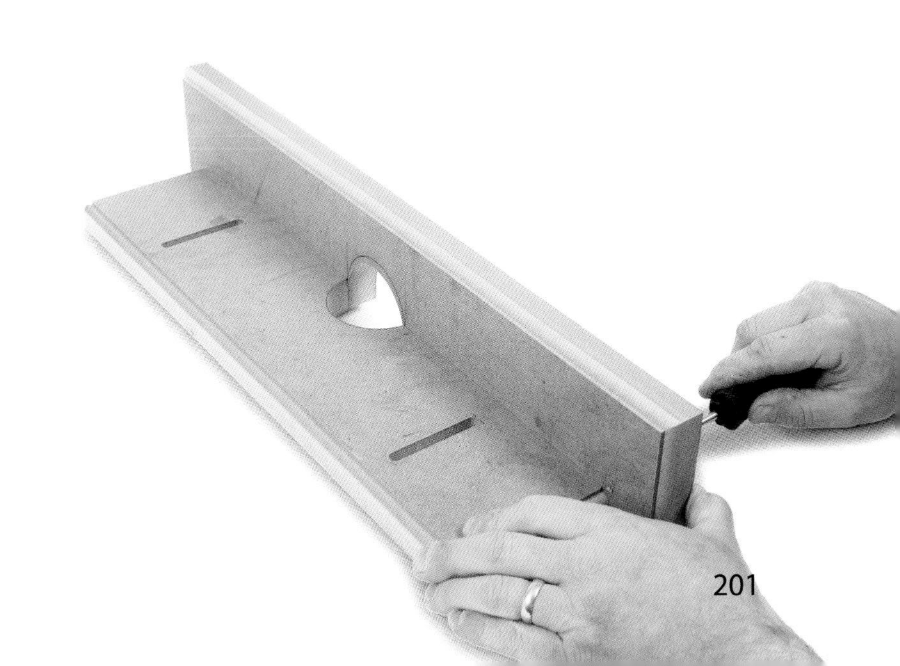

Switch

It is much safer and more convenient if the router can be operated remotely from the tool itself as you do not want to be reaching down underneath the table every time you wish to switch it on or off.

No-volt release switches are available that require no wiring, you just plug the router into them and the whole unit can then be mounted in some convenient location on the table where the buttons are instantly accessible. I would regard these as an essential accessory rather than a luxury, increasing your personal safety for a relatively modest cost.

Overhead router stands

The other way of mounting the router in a fixed position is in an overhead stand.

The main advantage of this set-up is that the cutter always remains plainly visible and the waste material is easily cleared by the cutter, rather than being trapped underneath, which sometimes happens when you are using a router table. It is also very much easier to access and change the cutters.

There are however some disadvantages. Firstly, the entire bit is exposed above the table and is often difficult to guard adequately. Secondly, dust extraction hoods are less easy to arrange around the cutter without it getting in the way.

Extra care also needs to be taken with some hand feeding operations such as internal corner cuts, where the cutter can sometimes grab even when it is being fed correctly. Lastly, the table must be kept scrupulously clean, as just a couple of chippings under the work will affect the cutting depth.

Professional overhead routing stands have now largely been superseded by the CNC type of machine. However, second hand ones are still available and their unique plunge action head, operated via a foot pedal, leaves your hands free to control the workpiece. This makes them ideal for repetition work.

The overhead router lends itself particularly well to producing circular objects. With a pivot point set directly into the support table you can quickly shape platters, wall plaques and discs at some speed and with considerable accuracy.

There are not many proprietary stands available for use by the home craftsman, but some drill stands can be converted to take the small light duty round bodied routers. These have rather limited depth of cut adjustment compared with a professional set-up, so any operations carried out on these stands are usually fed from the edge rather than plunge cut.

If you are mounting a standard router with its base above the work, the cutter is normally guarded by the router's baseplate. However, with light duty routers that can be separated from the baseplate, a separate guard must be fitted.

Remember that the cutter rotation in this mode is opposite to that of the inverted table so when you are feeding across the table, the feed direction must be from left to right.

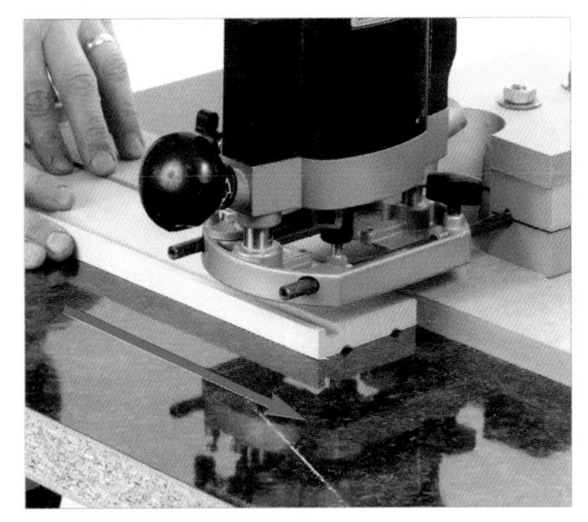

A horizontal clamp or featherboard can be fitted to hold the material firmly against the fence and this can be fitted in a similar way to that used on a router table. However because of the position of the router, vertical hold down clamps need to be positioned either side of the router.

Making a simple overhead router stand

A very simple but effective fixed overhead stand can be made up using a stack of wooden blocks and utilising the two router side fence rods for mounting the router.

Start by machining V slots in two of the blocks to locate the fence rods.

Cut some spare blocks to act as spacers for coarse adjustment to the height of the router.

Drill through the stack of blocks to take the two fixing bolts.

Recess the heads of the coach bolts into the lower block.

Screw the lower block in place onto the base board which can be a piece of MDF or worktop offcut.

Build up the stack to get the required height, pass the router fence rods through the slots and tighten up the locking nuts to fix it in place.

If the router fouls on the blocks, remove the handle and cut out a recess in the upper blocks.

A simple fence can be cut from MDF or similar with a cut-out to accommodate the cutter. A variety of fences can be made to accommodate different sizes or profiles of cutters.

Hold down clamps can either be homemade or bought in, along with other accessories.

Because of the leverage involved, always use the overhead router stand with it clamped firmly to a bench.

Using the overhead router

The overhead router is used in exactly the same way as the inverted router, but bear in mind the opposite direction of cutter rotation, otherwise all the safety precautions apply. Basic techniques ideally suited to the overhead router are:

Straight line work

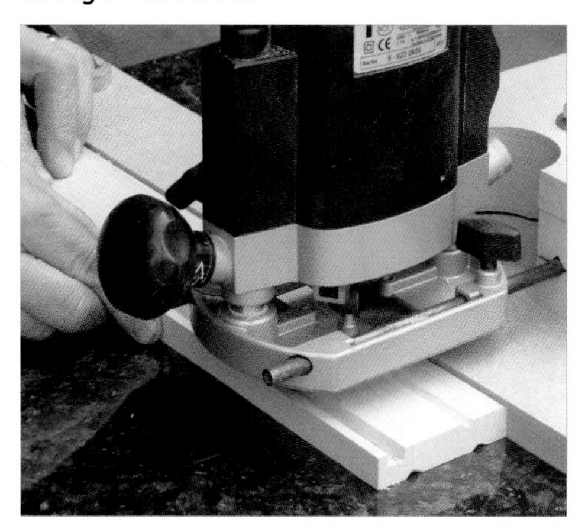

Edge forming with guided bits

Curved work

Pin routing

Edge template work with pin

Internal opening with pin and template

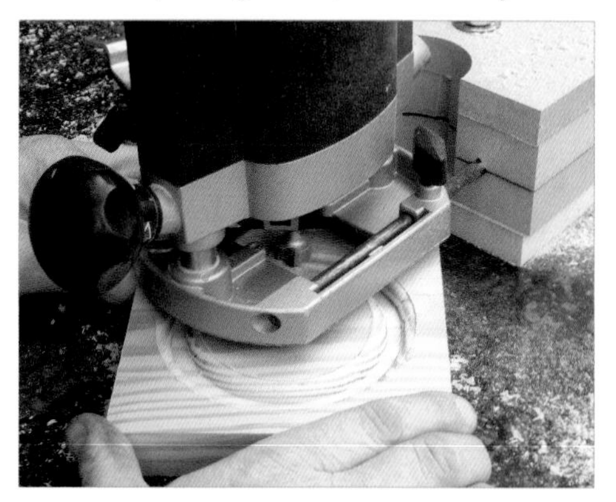

Circular work on pivot pin

Machining centres and other set-ups

There are many other ways of mounting the router and several manufacturers have come up with their own unique solutions. These effectively turn your router into a machining centre, and are usually provided with universal mountings so you can fit any brand of router. Some will also take other types of power tool such as circular saws and jigsaws.

There are two main methods of mounting the router on these machining centres, either with the router fitted to a sliding carriage that passes over the work or with the router mounted overhead and the workpiece clamped to a sliding carriage beneath it.

The main benefit of both of these methods is that the path of the cutter through the work is strictly controlled and therefore far more precise than hand-fed methods.

Sliding router carriage
e.g. Triton

This set-up has the router mounted on twin parallel rails above a fixed table. It is ideal for cutting edge rebates, mouldings, and dados across the grain.

A flip over facility and removable table allows the machine to be set up as an inverted router to make this process easier.

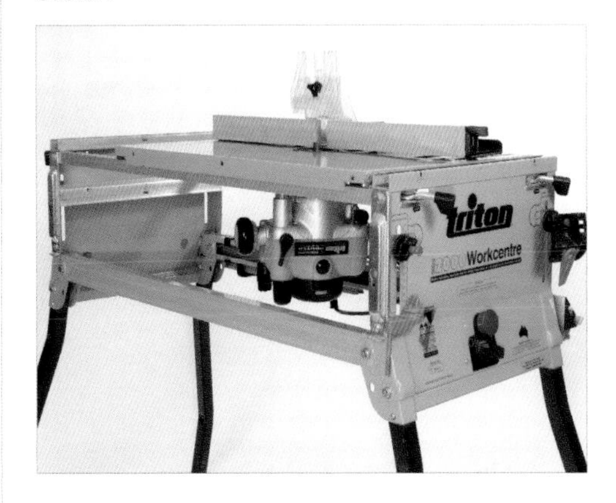

In the sliding carriage mode, the adjustable height table is set up beneath and parallel to the carriage rails. When cutting at 90 degrees, the workpiece is braced against a two piece fence. For other angled cuts, the workpiece is clamped to an adjustable mitre fence.

Vertical clamping machining centre
e.g. Woodrat

In this arrangement, the work is clamped vertically to simplify end routing operations. It is held in place with a cam operated clamp on the face of the sliding carriage.

This carriage is operated via a rotating handle, allowing it to be wound backwards and forwards across the cutter. A key advantage of this is that as the workpiece is being 'power fed' across the cutter, the feed direction can be either against or with the cutter rotation, this latter option virtually eliminating break-out to leave perfectly clean shoulders, not consistently possible with any other routing method.

The router is mounted overhead to slide back and forth on a rigid plate held between precision guides, and can be set at any point across the work to allow the workpiece to be wound across the cutter.

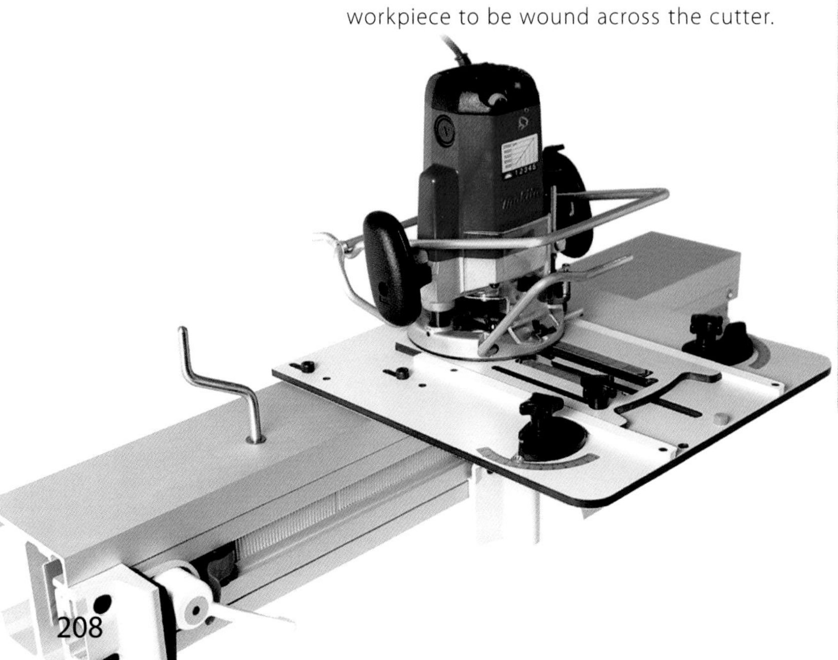

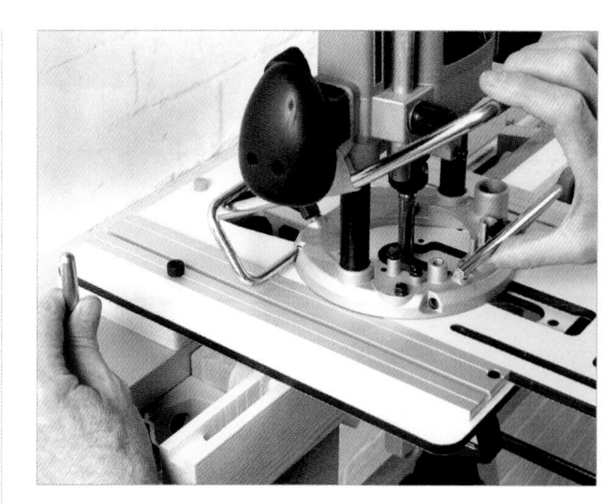

Alternatively, the workpiece can be positioned beneath the router plate by the sliding carriage or clamped beneath the plate when the router is passed back and forth. Used together, the combination of these two feed methods offer numerous variations in the direction of cut and presentation of the cutter to the workpiece, making this a truly universal machining centre.

All types of joint can be cut, using straight, dovetail or other profile cutters.

Another unique feature permits the use of a second clamping position on the sliding carriage which allows each part of a joint or a pattern to be accurately and quickly aligned against its mating component. For production work, batch machining is also possible, allowing several matching components to be cut in one operation.

The carriage clamping facility can be used to hold the workpiece, or simple purpose made jigs can be made to present the workpiece at a specific angle to the cutter. This allows an extensive range of profiles to be machined including dovetail and square tongues, dados, dovetails joints, mortise and tenon joints, slots, grooves, and edge mouldings.

This is only a brief list but other operations such as dowelling joints, spindle end dowels, hinge and lock recesses, raised and fielded panel work can be accommodated on this very versatile machining centre.

Radial arm routing

If you already have a radial arm saw it is usually possible to buy a bracket allowing you to mount a router on the yoke. This, effectively, turns it into a very versatile overhead router with all the associated tilt and travel movements of the sawhead.

The sawblade and guard have to be removed, but once the router is mounted, both the sliding crosscut and ripping facilities of the saw arm can be used for cutting dados, grooves and rebates.

For plunge cutting operations you can use both the router's plunge action and the radial arm saw's rise and fall mechanism, either separately or simultaneously.

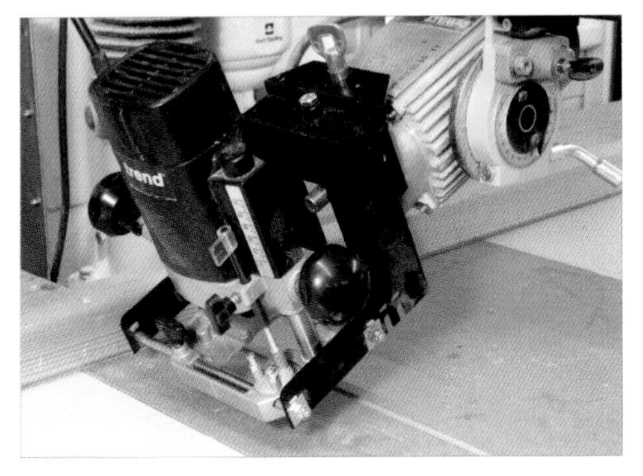

For more elaborate cuts, you can also use the horizontal swivel and tilting facilities of the sawhead yoke. So for instance, the cutter can be set at an angle to the workpiece allowing straight cutters to be used for cutting V grooves (e.g. for plate grooves for display shelves), or to present shaped moulding cutters at different angles to alter the moulding profile. As only the router will be operating and the saw is effectively being used just as a stand, the power supply should be disconnected for safety.

For most routing operations, it is far more convenient to swing the arm at an angle and turn the yoke to face the router towards you. This allows clear access to the router controls without the saw motor or arm getting in the way and it leaves a clear view of the cutting operation.

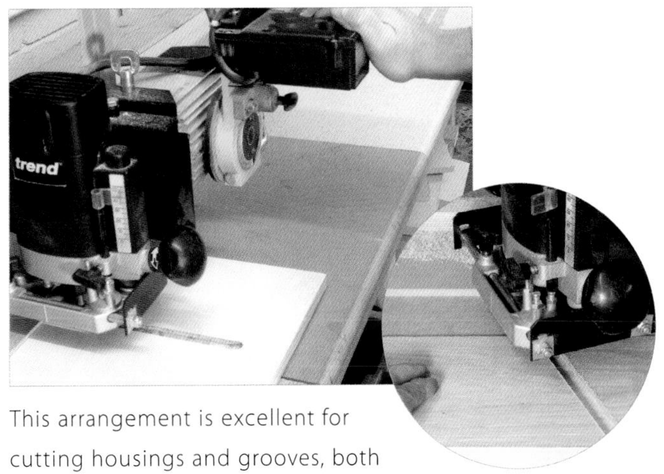

This arrangement is excellent for cutting housings and grooves, both square and angled.

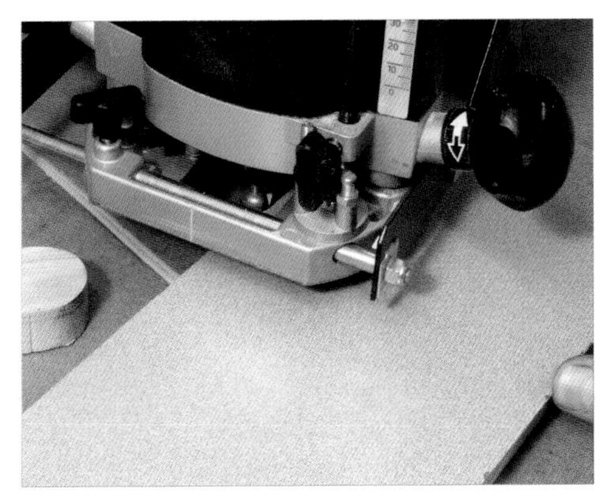

The overhead mode is ideally suited for laminate trimming work as well.

For all 'through' routing operations, a sheet of thin waste material should be fitted to the table to prevent any damage to the table face.

Horizontal routing

A less common routing application is to use the router horizontally.

This is essentially the same as for inverted routing, but with the router lying on its side and the spindle horizontal rather than vertical.

In practice, many operations are much easier with the router mounted laterally. It gives excellent visibility of the cutter, effective waste clearance and more importantly, safe control of the workpiece.

One application is tenoning. This requires precise guiding if you try and do it on a conventional router table, but in horizontal mode with the work passing over the cutter, the table acts as a huge and stable fence.

Unfortunately, there are very few manufacturers who offer a jig or table that allows for horizontal working but it is relatively easy to build your own set-up.

CNC routing

The ultimate in router machining is a CNC machine where the path of the router is controlled by computer. Designed for the industrial user, these machines incorporate all the basic principles of the overhead router but allow fast and precise cutting of intricate shapes with complete repeatability every time. These machines are available in a range of sizes, with the smaller ones being ideal for school or training purposes. These use standard routers as the cutting head, whereas the heavier duty industrial machines use a high frequency motor unit that is quieter, longer lasting and better suited to continuous use. Long life, Polycrystalline diamond coated cutters are often needed to help minimise costly 'down time'.

A range of CAD software is available for either 2 or 3D cutting and modelling, covering applications such as moulding, light engineering in non ferrous metals, plastic engineering, sign making and 3D carving.

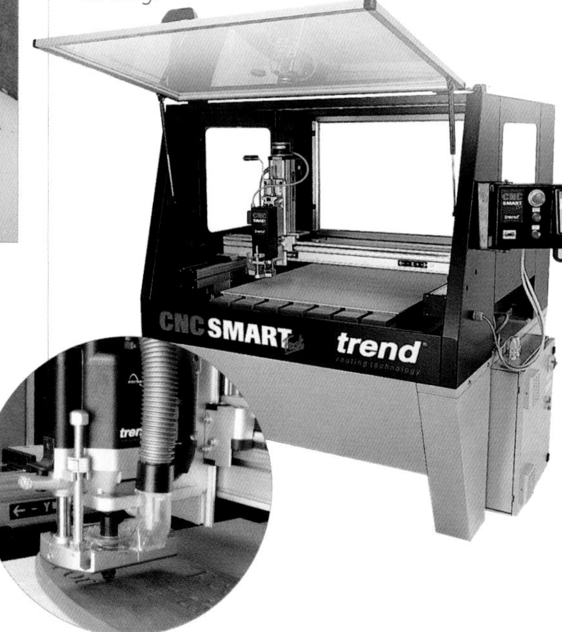

9. JOINTING WITH THE ROUTER

With its limitless versatility, the router can cut a huge range of joints, from the very simple to the highly complex, often requiring little else other than a straight cutter and a few basic self made jigs.

The ability to cut neat and effective joints is one of the most basic woodworking requirements, but often causes difficulty when using hand tools, even to relatively experienced woodworkers. However, using the router guarantees you the necessary accuracy, speed and consistency that is so difficult any other way.

Halving and tenon joints

Halving

Although not the strongest or most elegant of joints, the halving joint is quick and easy to cut and has many uses in basic frame construction.

All types of halving joints such as cross, corner, mitred or angled, can be cut with just a straight router cutter and a simple jig.

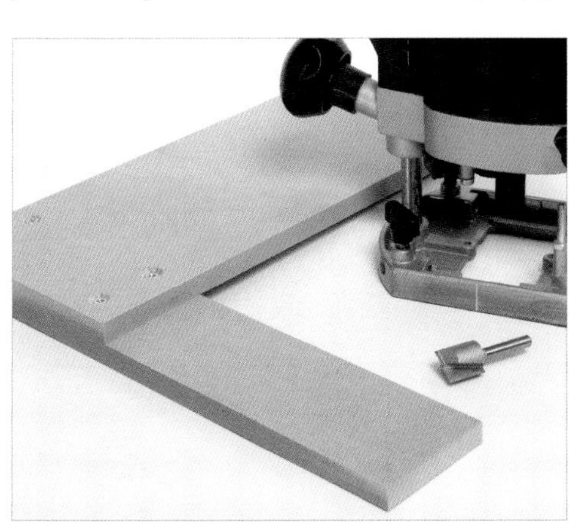

The use of jigs means that if you are producing repetition work e.g. sets of rails of the same size, the components can usually be stacked and clamped together for cutting in one operation, considerably speeding up production and ensuring complete uniformity.

As the name suggests, halving joints are cut to half the thickness of the rail or batten, leaving the face sides of the joint flush. Usually the components are of equal thickness, though this is not always the case and a halving joint is often used to fit intermediate framing members which are lighter than the main framework.

For all halving joints, the router is used with a straight cutter and the depth stop is set to the required depth.

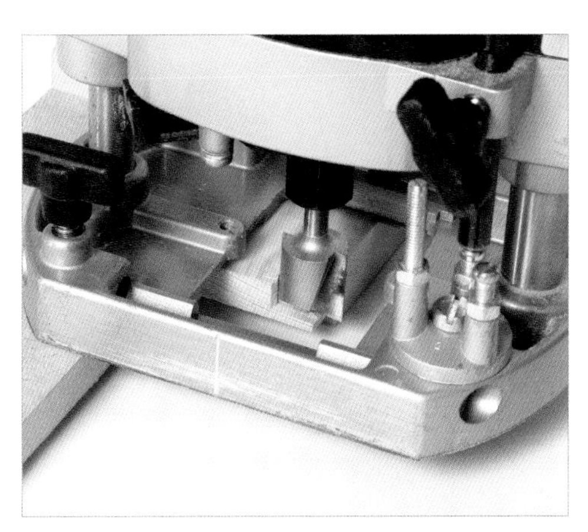

To get this perfect, make some trial cuts from either side of a spare workpiece, adjusting the depth until the two cuts coincide. Always use the largest cutter available to suit the width of the housing and make the cut in a series of shallow passes of no more than 3mm each.

The corner halving joint can be cut with a simple jig made up from two pieces of MDF screwed together at right angles.

Use a pair of these jigs to cut a T-halving joint on a single piece.

Or clamp them to both workpieces to make a cross halving joint.

In use, the jig is clamped across the workpiece, set off from the line of the cut by the distance from the base of the router to the edge of the cutter.

This can be done either by measuring from the guide edge to the cut line, or by positioning the cutter against the cut line and bringing the jig up to the router base.

The jig can easily be modified to make mitred or angled halving joints in exactly the same way.

Alternatively, if you have to cut a halving joint on a regular basis it is worth making up a template jig to be used in conjunction with the guide bush.

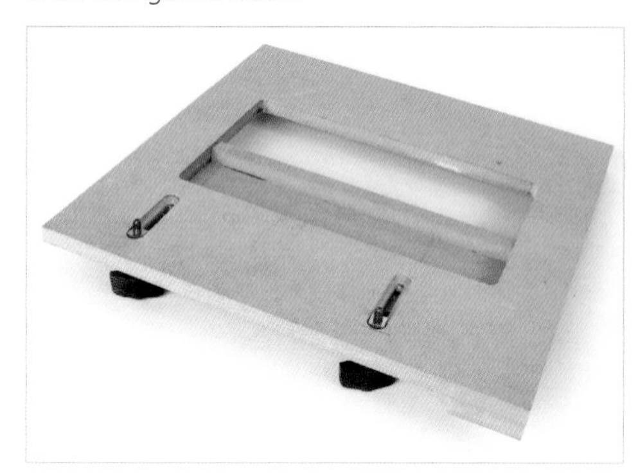

The router table provides the means of cutting the joint, particularly end and mitred variations. The workpiece has to be supported on a sliding carriage or with the mitre guide and must be firmly clamped to it to prevent 'creep'.

The fence can be used as a stop, but as the cutter has to be left exposed, use a suitable guard to cover it if possible. The router depth stop is set to the final cutting depth, but this should be achieved in several shallow passes. The shoulder cut should be made first with a waste batten behind to minimise break-out.

Then the work is slid away from the fence and several passes taken to remove the rest of the waste, repeating the operation until the final depth setting is reached.

Yet another alternative is to use the horizontal router table, which perhaps offers the maximum possible support and therefore produces superb accuracy. As usual, take several shallow passes to reach the required depth.

Tenons

A variation of the halving joint is the tenon, which, when fitted into a corresponding mortise, produces one of the strongest joints for framing and carcassing.

Because of their strength, mortise and tenon joints are used in most forms of furniture construction where the tenon is simply glued into the mortise.

For heavier construction jobs, wedges or dowels are used to pull the joint up tight and to secure it.

A tenon is cut in the same way as a halving joint, cutting one face first then turning it over to cut the second. If you need a haunch, it is probably easier to cut this by hand after the tenon has been machined.

Tenons are generally cut to be a third of the timber thickness, leaving the face sides of the assembled joint flush.

The simplest method of guiding the router for cutting tenon joints is to use one, or a pair, of right angle guides, like those for the halving joint. For repetitive operations, several rails or battens can be clamped together for cutting at the same time.

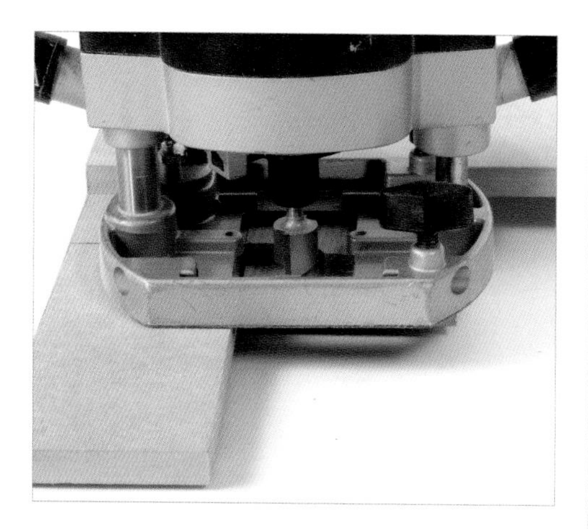

It may be necessary to position a waste batten at the rear of the workpiece to prevent the inevitable break-out.

The same principle can be used for cutting angled tenons, just fix the stock to the top board at the required angle.

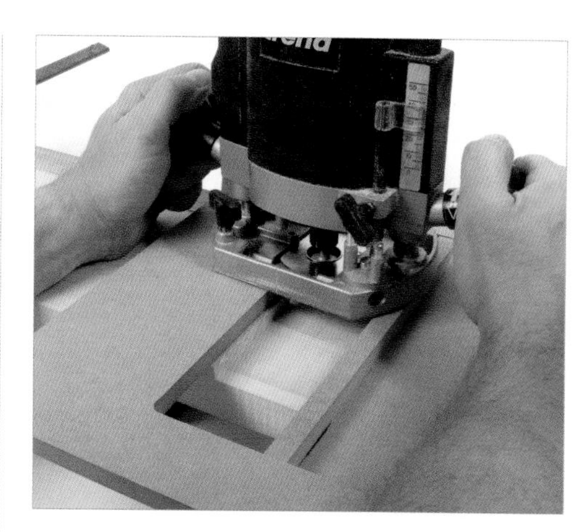

However, with any routing operations inaccuracies can be caused by the router tipping or turning in at the end of the jig or workpiece. To prevent this happening, use a slotted template fitted to the stock in the same way, either at 90° or at any required angle and use a guide bush to control the path of the router.

Remember to take account of the guide bush margin when lining the jig up for a cut.

Routing mortises

As routed mortises are produced with a revolving cutter they will end up with radiused ends.

These can then either be squared out with a chisel, or the edges of the tenon can be rounded over with a chisel or rasp. The normal procedure is to make the mortise first and then cut the tenon to fit, rather than the other way round.

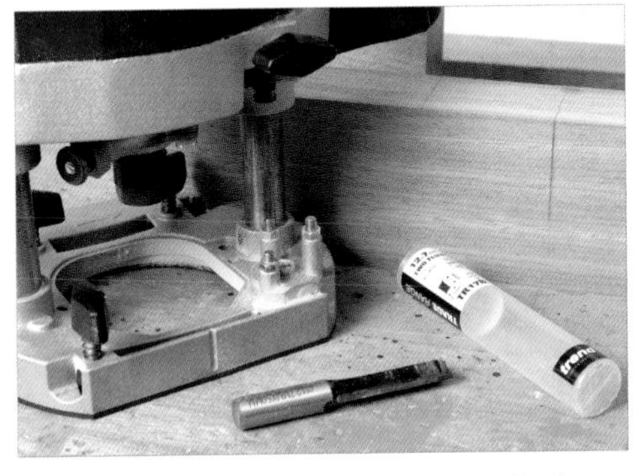

Two flute cutters with a bottom cut facility can be used for morticing, but will require frequent clearing to prevent the waste packing around the flutes.

A better alternative is to choose up-cut spiral cutters as these lift the waste material out of the mortise alternatively staggered tooth cutters, which are used for larger work, again for their speed of cutting and chip clearance.

For small diameter deep mortises, long shank pocket cutters are another option.

Mortises are generally cut on the narrow edge of the workpiece, so providing adequate support for the router base is often an issue. This can be overcome quite easily by temporarily clamping on a wide batten to provide a wider working surface.

Although the router can be guided by a single side-fence for mortise cutting, the addition of a second fence will prevent the cutter from running out of parallel to the rail edge.

Tip

For all morticing work it is important to use only cutters that have good bottom cut and waste clearance characteristics. Single flute cutters are often recommended over two flute ones as they are faster cutting and remove the waste quicker.

For wider rails or workpieces, it may be necessary to exchange the standard fence rods for longer ones.

Ensure that the faces of the workpiece are parallel, as any tapering will cause the fences to jam or wander from side to side. The fences should be set to leave minimal side play but allowing them to slide evenly. The advantage of working with twin fences is that the cutter can be fed in either direction.

To centre a cut precisely across the width of the workpiece, use a cutter slightly smaller in diameter than the width of the mortise. Make the first pass in one direction and then turn the router round making a second pass in the opposite direction.

This can then be repeated for each step until the full depth of the cut is reached. Both stopped and through mortises can be cut with the router depending on the depth, but if you are cutting through mortises, a backing piece should be fitted to prevent breakout. Alternatively, through mortises can be cut from both sides using a jig to accurately locate the cutter.

Twin parallel mortises can also be cut in the same way using the two fences. One mortise is cut to the full depth before turning the router and cutting the second in the opposite direction.

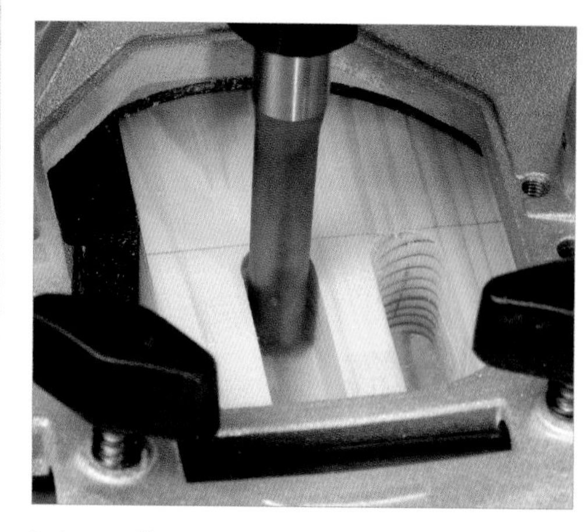

It is usually accurate enough to mark the limits of the mortise on the work and then cut up to them by eye.

However, for accuracy and repeatability try fixing longer faces to the side fence and then fit stops to limit the cutter travel.

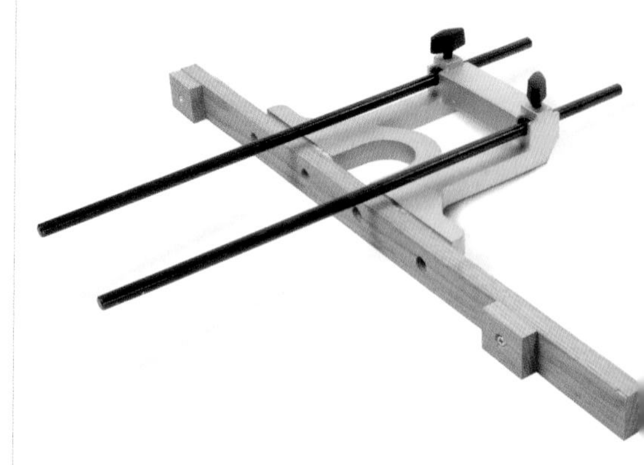

For long workpieces, a stop can be fitted to the front of the fence face to set the starting position and then the length of mortise can be gauged by eye.

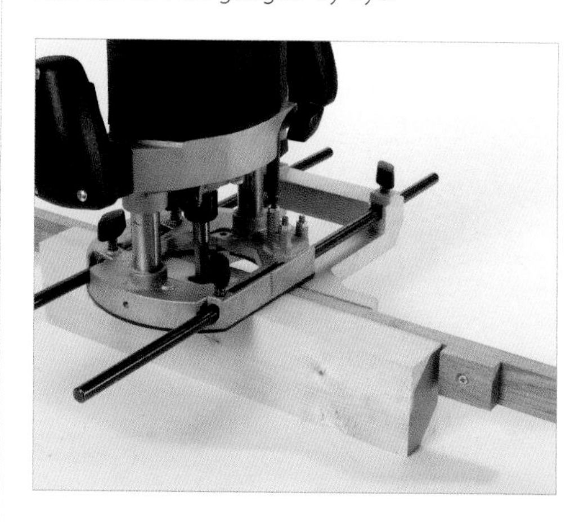

An alternative method of setting the length of a mortise is to use a side batten drilled to take movable dowels or fitted with sliding stops.

The dowel holes are drilled at equal centres and a sliding stop is fitted to set the distance of the mortise from the end of the workpiece.

The batten is clamped in place, flush with the top of the workpiece, ensuring that the clamps will not foul the router. The cutter is centred on the mortise and the side-fence is run against the face of the workpiece.

Haunched mortises can be cut by eye, but are ideal candidates for using a side batten, simply by moving the dowel to shorten the router travel when cutting the deeper part of the mortise.

Another way to guarantee consistent identical mortises is to use a slotted template and the router fitted with an appropriate template. These jigs are usually made for specific jobs, but with a little ingenuity you can make a universal template with adjustable stops and locating fences.

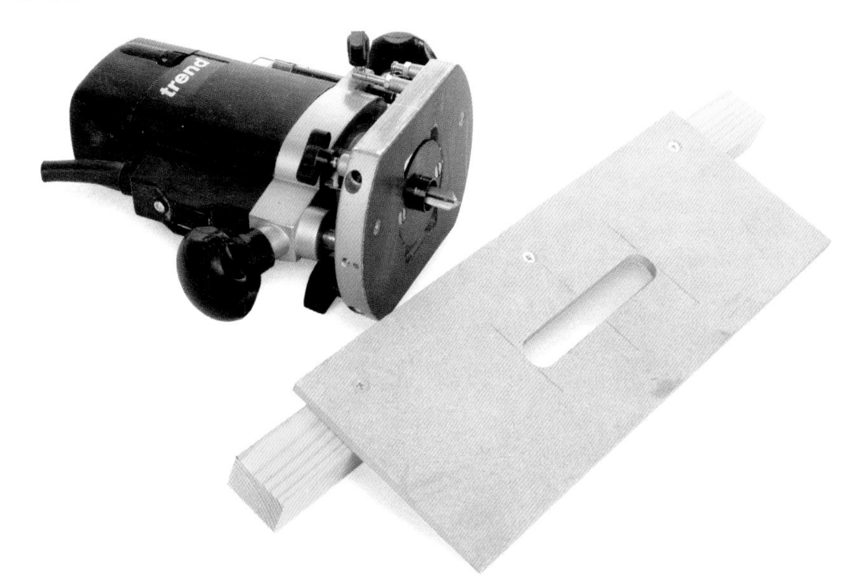

Simple slot templates can be made for use with specific guide bush diameters and to specific mortise lengths.

Remember that the slot in the template has to be routed to a length equal to the mortise length plus twice the guide bush margin. Also, the template should be big enough to support the router over the end of the workpiece with the guide bush having a smooth sliding fit in the slot.

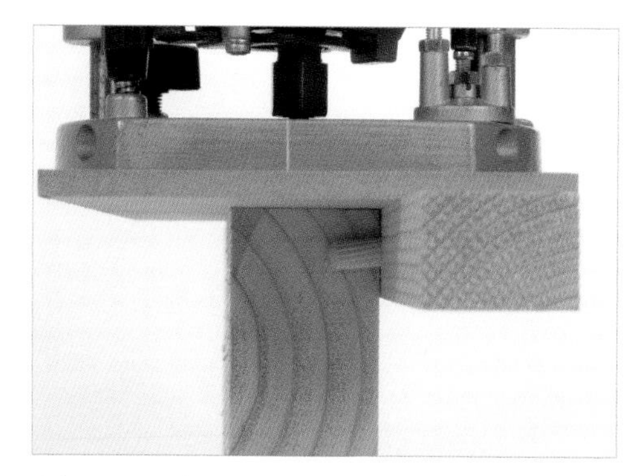

A batten is fixed to the underside of the template, positioned to centre the mortise on the workpiece. This also allows the template to be clamped in a bench vice. A single stop fitted to the underside of the template will position the mortise in exactly the same place each time.

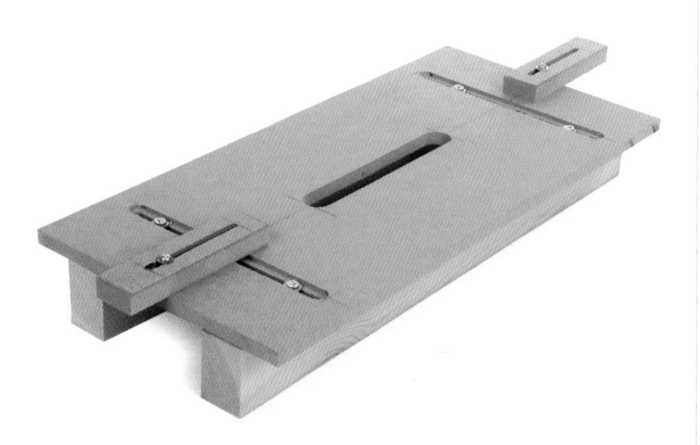

To make the adjustable version, two locating battens are fixed beneath a much longer template which is slotted to allow them to slide in and out to centre and secure the template. To position the guide bush slot, a centre line is scribed at each end of the slot and located over the centreline of the first workpiece. This arrangement is then clamped to the workpiece at a point as close to the mortise as possible.

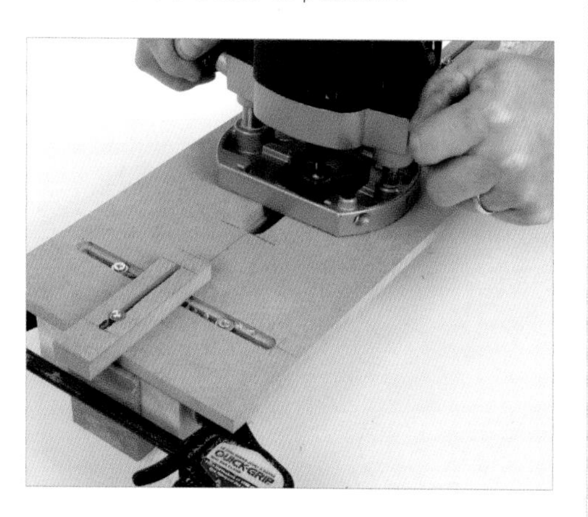

Slotted length stops mounted on the face of the template are used to limit the length of the mortise.

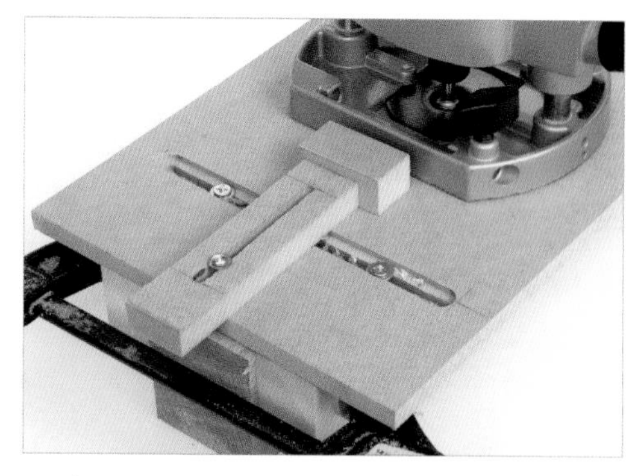

For haunched mortises, a temporary extra stop can be fitted to the front stop, restricting the router travel to the deep section of the mortise.

Mortises can be cut on the router table by lowering the work down onto the cutter, but for both safety and accuracy, it is necessary to fit a second fence parallel to the table fence.

The cutter can then be centred between the two fences. Front and rear stops are useful, as the cut area is obscured from view and you cannot easily work to pencil lines on the workpiece, but note these can be transferred onto the secondary fence to indicate the start and stop points.

You must be very careful during this procedure, particularly with short pieces which should only be lowered onto the cutter with the end firmly up against a rear stop. Slide them forwards until they hit the front stop. Repeat the procedure with each workpiece and then raise the cutter slightly, eventually reaching the full depth in a series of shallow passes.

An easier option, but using the same principle, involves the horizontal router table, where there is much more support for the workpiece and the cut is more visible.

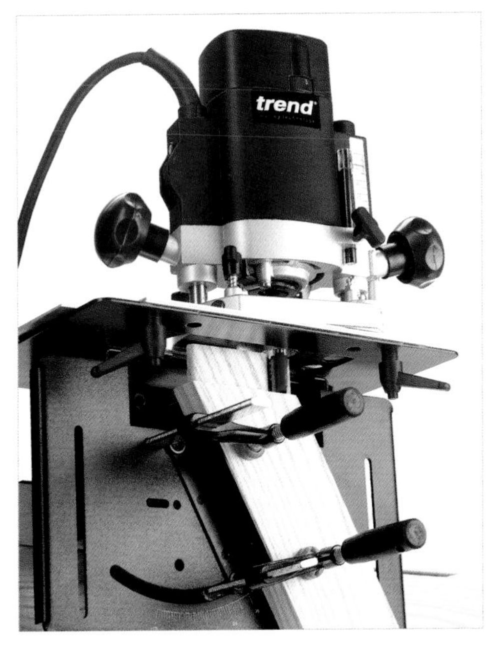

If you are into volume production of small scale mortise and tenons joints, there are specialised jigs available. These allow you to cut both halves of the joint with only the one set-up to ensure it all fits together perfectly. As well as conventional straight joints, such a jig can be set to cut angled or even compound joints that are ideal for cabinet, chair and table construction.

Edge to edge joints

It is often necessary to join boards edge to edge, sometimes trying to make the joint as invisible as possible and at other times, featuring it with some decorative detail.

There are various types of edge to edge joints, the simplest being a form of tongue and groove joint, cutting either an integral tongue to fit in a groove on the next board, or cutting a groove in each piece and then fitting a loose tongue.

Edge grooves and rebates can be cut either with straight cutters, balancing the router vertically on the edge of the workpiece, or with self guiding slotting and grooving cutters on an arbor, which allow the router to be used with the base resting flat on the face of the board or panel.

If you are using a straight cutter the workpiece must be clamped on edge in a vice, or against the edge of the bench. With long workpieces, suitable support must be provided at the ends and along their length to prevent bowing.

Make sure that any clamps will not get in the way of the router and that there is enough clearance for the side-fence over the vice or any other supports.

For thin workpieces, you can increase the stability of the router by clamping a thick batten alongside the workpiece with the top edges flush. The batten should extend beyond the ends of the workpiece to allow the router to be fed smoothly onto and off the edge.

To form a groove, mark out its position and width on the end of the workpiece. Choose a cutter the same width as the groove, hold the router in place and adjust the side-fence to position it accurately. A fine fence adjuster is a real help here.

Make the cut in a series of shallow passes, feeding the router against the rotation of the cutter to help to keep the side-fence firmly against the face of the workpiece.

As with mortising, the process is more accurate if you can mount a second side-fence but this does require the work to be accurately thicknessed and dead straight.

Special slotting and grooving cutters mounted on a threaded arbor provide another alternative for grooving and in many ways this is a much easier way of doing the job, as the router has much better support when used flat on the face of the work.

The arbors are long enough to allow you to use a combination of cutters so you can build up wider cuts or use several cutters spaced apart to produce multiple grooves or tongues.

Tip

To centre a groove perfectly along the edge of a board you can use a cutter that is smaller in diameter than the required groove width, but keep turning the router round to make successive passes in each direction, cutting to the full depth in a series of steps.

The depth of cut is set by mounting a guide bearing above or below the cutter and can therefore be altered by using different diameter guide bearings.

As before, running the cut from either face will ensure that the groove is perfectly centred.

Most operations using these cutters allow the work to be cut in a single pass, but with hard or difficult timbers, the side-fence or a larger diameter guide bearing will limit the depth of the initial cut.

For short lengths of board or small panels, it is much easier and safer to cut edge grooves on the router table. Again, you can use both straight or arbor mounted cutters, but with straight cutters the work must be held perfectly vertical. To achieve this, it helps to fit a taller face board to the table fence.

Some form of side pressure guard is also useful to keep the work pushed hard up against the fence and keep the groove straight.

Cutting the groove is only half of the joint and you then have to cut the matching tongue.

In some cases, you can groove both edges then insert a loose tongue which can either be cut from plywood for maximum strength, or alternatively cut from timber that has been accurately thicknessed to the groove width. In this case, it is normal practice to cut the tongue across the end grain if possible.

Integral tongues can be formed by cutting a rebate along both edges of the workpiece either using the router handheld or in a table.

Tip

To help avoid splitting out the edge of the board, avoid cutting rebates whose width is more than half the cutter diameter.

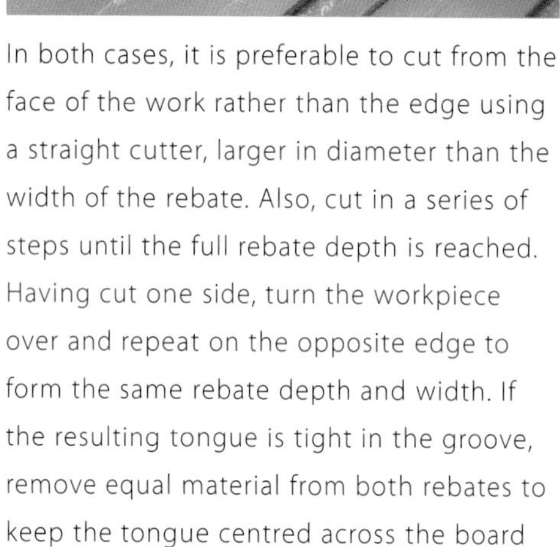

In both cases, it is preferable to cut from the face of the work rather than the edge using a straight cutter, larger in diameter than the width of the rebate. Also, cut in a series of steps until the full rebate depth is reached. Having cut one side, turn the workpiece over and repeat on the opposite edge to form the same rebate depth and width. If the resulting tongue is tight in the groove, remove equal material from both rebates to keep the tongue centred across the board edge.

Self guiding rebate cutters can be used either in the router, hand held, or with it mounted under the router table, but the dimensions of the rebate will be restricted to the standard cutter and bearing diameters.

Arbor mounted groovers are another very effective way of cutting a tongue by using two identical cutters mounted on the same arbor. This allows you to form it in one operation by cutting both rebates at the same time.

The cutters are separated by a suitably sized guide bearing and shims to make up the required tongue thickness, the depth of the tongue being determined by the diameter of the guide bearing.

To form the classic V joint tongue and groove effect, 'Match-lining' cutter sets are available. These comprise of three interchangeable cutters of two different diameters, with one of them being ground to a stepped chamfer profile.

Two different diameter guide bearings are used to vary the depth of cut for the joint profiles. In use, the cutters are assembled to cut one side of the joint before being re-assembled in a different sequence to cut the matching reverse profile.

For smaller one-off jobs, the same effect is obtained by cutting a standard tongue and groove profile and then adding the V chamfer as another operation using a V groove cutter.

For a more decorative effect, you can use other shapes of moulding cutters for this final operation or even a profile scribing cutter which will do the whole job in one go, though you will then have to machine this in a router table.

The object of most edge to edge joints is to increase the surface area available for gluing and this is epitomised by the finger joint which effectively increases the glue line by a factor of three.

A dedicated cutter is fitted with a series of shaped cutters to produce the profile, the exact arrangement being varied to suit the timber thickness. Ideally the cut is made with the router under a table but it can also be made freehand.

Another variation of the standard tongue and groove joint is the 'bead joint', which is cut with a matched pair of specialised cutters such as the sunk and staff bead.

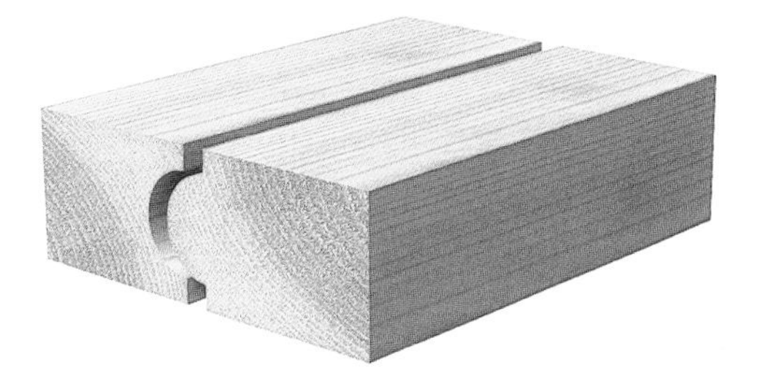

These can again be used either handheld or in the router table, but note that the staff bead cutter does remove material from the guide edge, so the outfeed fence must be shimmed out accordingly.

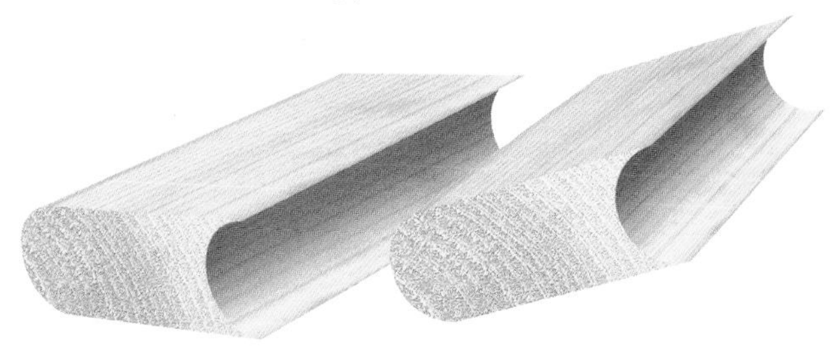

The same joint on a bigger scale is the 'cove joint', again, cut with a matched pair of cutters. A useful feature of this joint is that it allows you to join up several narrow strips edge to edge, to make curved panels.

Dovetails

The dovetail is the classic woodworking joint combining pleasing visual appearance with superb strength, but it is difficult to produce accurately by hand unless you are experienced and highly skilled. Fortunately, there are a number of jigs available that can be used with the router to cut identical dovetails both quickly and consistently.

The simplest of the jigs has a fixed finger template matched to a specific size dovetail cutter and guide bush combination, which cuts a regular pattern of lap dovetails that, is rather obviously, machine cut.

However, there are more expensive and sophisticated versions that allow you to mimic the appearance of a hand cut joint, with variable spacing of the pins and tails in both lap and through dovetail styles.

Tip

To ensure accurate setting of the cutter height when using any dovetail jig, always use a fine height adjuster

The more advanced jigs even allow you to cut really exotic looking joints that are impossible to produce any other way.

They all work on the same basic principle using a precision template, either fixed or adjustable. This ensures the spacing of the pins and tails is perfect and the cutter itself will ensure that the size and pitch remains the same.

The more elaborate machining centres allow for the greatest differences in tail width and spacing. They can be used for complicated variations of the joint. Their inherent rigidity and control also allows the use of finer pitch cutters, which makes the cut appear more like a hand cut one.

Basic Operation

The workpieces are clamped in the jig aligned at right angles to each other but offset by half the template spacing (pitch).

During the cutting operation the router is controlled by a guide bush running in a fixed finger template, both parts of the joint being cut in one operation.

The normal capacity of the jig is 300mm but there are larger versions taking material up to 600mm wide.

Fixed finger templates are matched to a specific size of dovetail cutter and guide bush combination. This produces the characteristic equal width and equally spaced pins and tails. Most jigs are supplied with an appropriate guide bush to match the template spacing, but if it doesn't fit your router, you can use a sub-base. Jigs supplied with bearing guided cutters make this unnecessary as they can be used with any router.

The spacing or pitch on fixed finger templates is always equal, so it is essential that the workpiece is a multiple of that spacing e.g. spacing = 21.5mm, therefore width of material = 43mm, 64.5mm, 86mm, 107.5mm etc. As both parts of the joint are cut in the jig at the same time, they need to be offset by half of this spacing i.e. 21.5 ÷ 2 = 10.75.

This offset is determined by either adjustable stops or fixed pins fitted to the jig. Adjustable end stops vary on different makes of jig, but those consisting of stepped metal plates are the easiest to set and by allowing some adjustment to the joint, slight variations in material width and appearance are then possible.

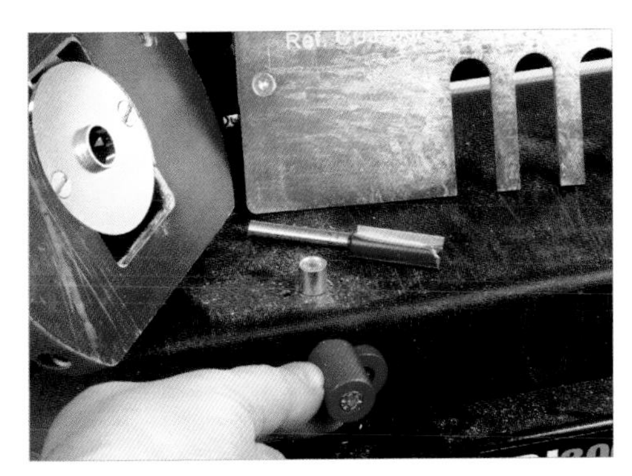

Separately adjustable stops may also be used to cut rebated drawer fronts. This enhances the look of the finished joint by allowing extra width to be added to the outer pins.

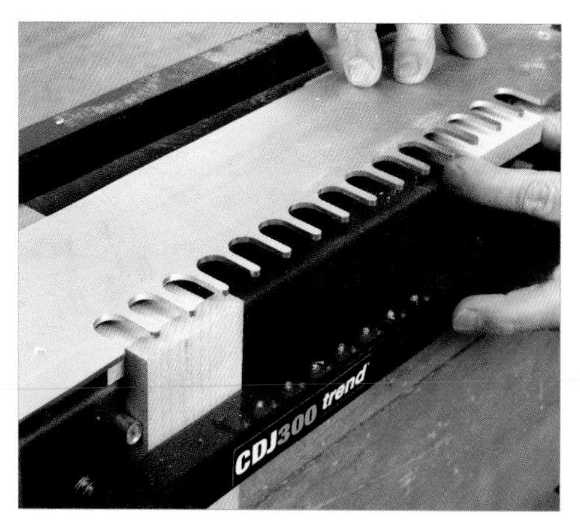

The exact method of clamping the work varies from jig to jig, but it is vital that the two pieces are held securely and in line during the cut. Threaded screw or cam clamps are the most common, although the latter are far quicker and easier to use, but in both cases narrow workpieces may require extra clamping, or spacers at the other end, to prevent them moving.

Using dovetail jigs

Before using any dovetail jig, it is essential that you spend time cutting trial joints, as the only way to produce the exact spacings and depths is by trial and error. So remember to machine up a few odd sections of material to practice on before you do it for real. This initial set-up may take some time but once achieved, you can cut each joint quickly and consistently. As every jig is slightly different, read the setting instructions carefully before you start, but the following gives a general guide to the procedures involved using a bush guided jig.

For drawer components, one end of each piece will be cut on the right hand side of the jig, the other end on the left hand side.

When both stops are accurately set, the bottom edges of the drawer will assemble flush, but do remember to mark the orientation of each piece carefully.

The stops should be set with the vertical pair centred on the first or second slot, whilst the horizontal stops should be centred on half the width of a finger from the edge of the first slot.

Fit the timber into the jig with the drawer side vertical and face side inwards. Then fit the drawer front in horizontally, with the face side down, butting it up against the vertical piece, making sure they are flush.

Fit the finger template in place, adjusting it backwards and forwards with the spacing nuts until the sight line corresponds to the join between the two components. Once set, these spacer nuts allow the template to be removed and refitted perfectly.

With all bush guided cutter templates, the length of the tails and pins is governed by the length of the template slot.

The cutter depth is set initially to about 17mm for the standard 12.7mm dovetail jigs (a setting gauge is usually supplied for this).

A scoring cut is made by first traversing lightly across the work from right to left to minimise break-out.

The cutter is then fed between each finger working from left to right. Make sure the guide bush bottoms into the comb and keep the router level at all times. Do not force the cutter into the wood as this will cause it to snatch and lift, resulting in a poor and loose fitting joint.

As it is very difficult to realign workpieces back into a dovetail jig once they have been removed, always check that the joints are fully cut before removing them from

the jig. If all is well, unclamp them and rotate one through 180° to mate them together. It is unlikely that they will fit perfectly first time and you may need to make some small adjustments.

If the joint is too loose, increase the cutting depth slightly. If the joint is too tight, raise the cutter a fraction. If the sockets are too deep, bring the finger template forward on its adjusters. Move it backwards if the tails don't go fully home.

Lap dovetail jigs

Most simple dovetail jigs are fitted with a standard template to cut lap dovetails of a specific size and pitch, but alternative sized templates may be available and even templates for comb jointing and dowelling. These router cut lap dovetails are generally used in the construction of drawers, in particular for modular unit furniture.

Through dovetail jigs

Through dovetails can also be cut with the router using fixed or adjustable finger templates. In this case, two matched cutters have to be used, a dovetail cutter for the tails and a straight cutter for the pins.

Unlike the lap dovetail jig, each part of the joint is held vertically in turn for cutting either the tails or pins, with a piece of waste material behind to minimise break-out.

Various versions of this type of jig are available, either with fixed or adjustable finger templates. For fixed finger templates the width of material being jointed must still be a multiple of the pitch.

Adjustable finger templates, as found on the Trend DC400 multi functional dovetail jig, can be set up to suit any width of timber and allow you to vary the pin and tail positions and spacings with ease.

Both through and lap (half blind) dovetails can be cut on the more sophisticated adjustable dovetail jigs such as the Leigh jig. This jig features excellent adjustability and has a complete range of guide bushes available for virtually all makes of router.

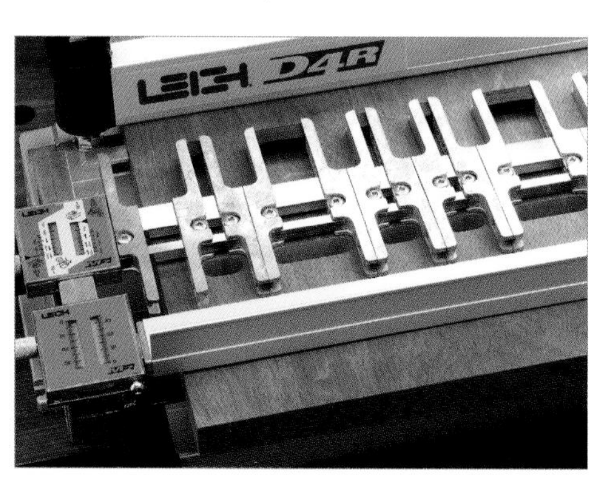

With additional accessories and templates, it can also be used to cut mortise and tenon, finger or comb joints, Isoloc joints and sliding and oblique dovetails.

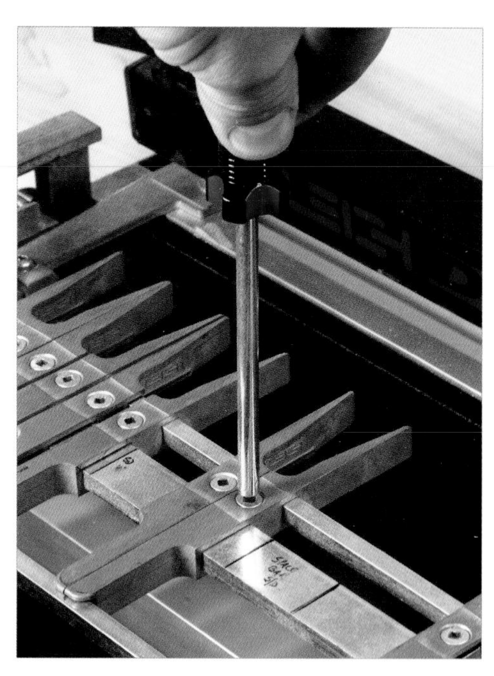

The standard dovetail template consists of separate fingers mounted on a solid bar. Their positioning is adjustable to allow variations in the width and spacing of individual dovetails and their pins. This also means that a range of cutter lengths and angles can be used with the same template.

By setting the fingers to the required pin spacing and then rotating the template through 180 degrees, this automatically sets the reverse ends of the finger for cutting the tails and ensures a precise fit of pins and tails.

In use, the timber is held in the jig by quick release bar clamps. For through dovetails, both workpieces are alternately held vertically in the front bar clamp. For half blind (lap) dovetails, the tail board is held vertically in the front bar clamp and the pin board is held horizontally under the top bar clamp.

The edges of the workpieces are automatically aligned by pre-set stops and the fit of the joint is set precisely using colour coded graduated scales incorporated into each end of the template. As before, matched dovetail and straight cutters are used for cutting through dovetails, whilst half-blind dovetails are formed using the same cutter for both joint profiles.

Machining centres

These machining centres with their sliding carriages are truly universal and allow you to cut virtually any type of dovetail joint without additional templates.

Their main advantage is that the pin and tail spacings can be set by eye and several components can be cut at once. Also they are not cutter specific and you can use any suitable dovetail cutter without having to worry about matching it up to a suitable guide bush.

As the timber size is not limited by the jig or template, dovetails can be cut in narrow boards as well as rail ends and other carcassing and frame components. Not only does this set up allow variations in spacing and pitch, it also allows the workpiece to be canted at any angle so mitre and secret mitred dovetails, exhibition case joints and other complex joints can be machined very precisely.

With such precise and rigid control of the cutter, afforded by the combination of the sliding work carriage, traversing plate and variable clamping facility, the benefits of using HSS fine pitch cutters can be realised, with minimal risk of breakage. Unlike template cut dovetails, fine pitch dovetails can be cut on machines such as the Woodrat, producing far more elegant dovetails than is possible with template cut joints.

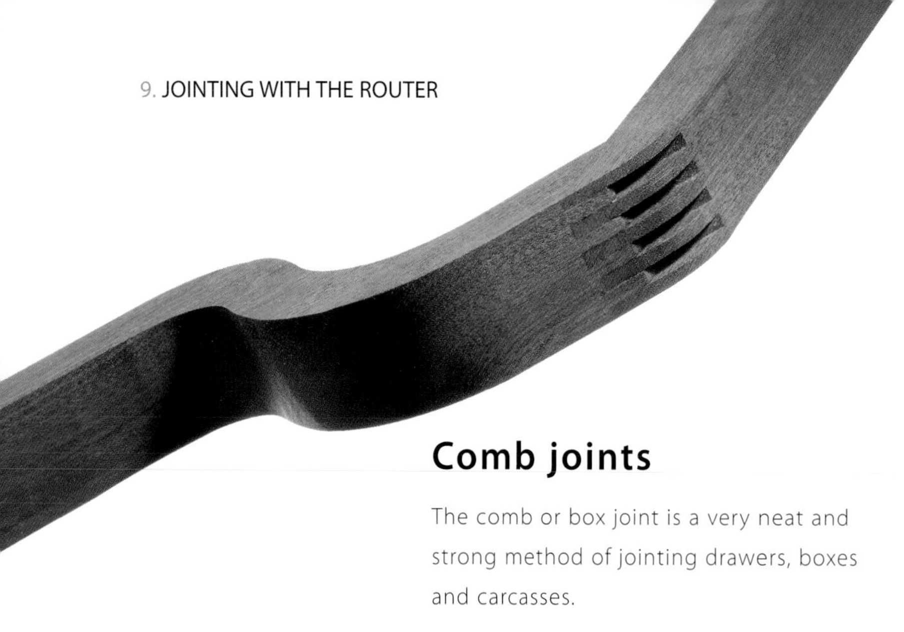

Comb joints

The comb or box joint is a very neat and strong method of jointing drawers, boxes and carcasses.

Although not as decorative or as inherently strong as the dovetail, it does however provide a huge surface area for gluing which is what gives it strength.

It is usually used for more functional pieces, though it makes a nice feature if contrasting timbers are used for opposing pieces.

Traditionally comb joints were cut on a circular saw fitted with a wobble saw or a dado blade, but this practice is now illegal as it requires the removal of the crown guard. The router is an eminently suitable replacement as the cutter produces a perfectly square and flat bottomed cut.

Like the dovetail, the comb joint relies on the use of a jig of some sort for accurate and consistent cutting. Fortunately many of

the proprietary dovetail jigs can also be used for comb jointing, you just have to change the template to a suitable box jointing one and then use a straight two flute cutter.

Whilst these jigs are ideal for cutting comb joints on bigger workpieces, smaller work can be cut more quickly and in one operation. A dedicated comb cutter is fitted in a heavy duty router in a fixed position under the router table. These cutters consist of a set of five 4mm wide groovers mounted on an arbor with a selection of bearings to control the length of the fingers.

Once set up, a comb cutter system is the ideal way of mass producing small boxes, although the maximum capacity is 40mm.

With a little ingenuity, you can even turn the comb joint into a decorative hinge. Round over either end of the work before you cut the joint, then drill through and insert a fine pin as the pivot point.

Dowel joints

Dowels are a very effective way of reinforcing a straight butt joint and are mainly used for jointing wide pieces of natural timber, particle board or fibre boards.

They can also be used to form framing and carcassing joints as an alternative to mortise and tenon joints. As well as strengthening the joint, the dowel also ensures perfect positioning of mating pieces but it does obviously rely on accurate alignment.

The dowel holes must mate perfectly on each piece to ensure that faces, edges and corners are flush on assembly.

Ready made packs of dowels are generally available in diameters of 6, 8 and 10mm. The holes are formed with special router dowel drills designed to cope with high rotation speeds.

These have a slow spiral to help waste clearance, a pointed centre tip for easy alignment and sharp side spurs for a clean entry. Standard single and two flute cutters can also be used, as long as they have end cutting flutes, but they are not as easy to plunge accurately.

On flat panels, the holes can be cut by eye, aligning the drill centre spur on a pre-marked point.

On a panel edge, twin side fences can be used on the router to position and centre the drill.

For repetitive work, the drilling process can be speeded up by using a spacing jig or side batten, or for even better accuracy, by using a guide bush and template.

Dowel spacing jig

The dowel spacing jig consists of two battens joined at right angles. The required dowel spacing can be marked off along the edge of the top piece, but to avoid confusion, spacing marks can be set out on a strip of masking tape stuck to the jig.

This tape can then be removed to allow different spacings to be set out for future projects. An added refinement is some form of stop to align the jig in the same place for each workpiece.

Mark a centre line along the top edge of the workpiece and clamp it upright in the bench vice, then clamp the spacing jig flush to the edge of the work and adjust the router side-fence to align the centre point of the cutter onto the centre line of the workpiece.

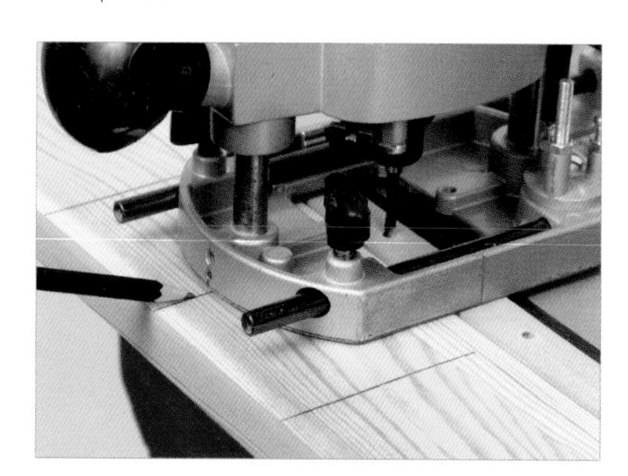

Scribe the centre line of the cutter on the edge of the router baseplate. (A vertical line is often engraved by the manufacturer).

Set the depth stop to allow the cutter to plunge cut to a fraction more (1.5mm) than half the dowel length.

Align the baseplate centre line at each dowel position in turn and plunge cut to the full depth. It may be necessary to cut in shallow steps if you are using a standard cutter and waste clearance is slow. However, take care to relocate the cutter precisely if it is lifted completely clear of the hole during the boring operation.

Template dowelling

A quicker and more accurate method of dowelling is to use a template of some sort. These are available ready made in limited form but it is often more practical to make your own to suit a particular job.

Ideally the dowel template should be cut from clear polycarbonate, acrylic or thin MDF, but make it big enough to provide adequate support for the router and leave room for fitting the spacing bars.

Scribe a centre line along the template face and mark off the dowel hole positions at the required intervals. Carefully indent each hole centre to align the drill precisely and bore a hole to perfectly match a suitable guide bush; one around 12mm diameter is ideal, as it allows plenty of clearance around even the largest of dowel drills. Use a pillar drill to ensure that the holes are drilled at right angles to the template face.

Cut a couple of narrow slots across the template at each end and recess these on the top face to take the screws that hold the locating battens.

The battens themselves can be made from any suitable timber but make sure they are straight and true. Use pan head or countersunk screws to fix the battens to the underside of the template, and make sure the router slides freely over the top of them.

Edge dowelling with the template

Line up the template centre line with the centre line of the board, slide in the locating battens and tighten up securely. A single clamp will normally provide enough pressure to stop the jig sliding out of position.

Fit the appropriate guide bush to the router and set the depth stop to allow the cutter to plunge cut to a fraction more than half the dowel length, but remember to allow for the thickness of the template.

Locate the guide bush into the selected template holes and plunge cut to the full depth. To avoid boring in the wrong place cover any unwanted holes on the template with masking tape.

Corner dowelling

Bore the holes in the end panel as above, then remove one of the locating battens and slide the template up until the remaining batten butts up against the end of the other workpiece, holding it firmly with a clamp or double sided tape.

Face dowelling

Mark the centre line of the dowel holes across the full width of the work. Remove both of the battens and clamp the template in position, aligning the centre line on the template over the centre line on the work piece. Use double sided tape to hold the template on wide boards if it is difficult to reach in with clamps. Locate the guide bush into the template holes and plunge cut to the full depth as before.

Drilling rail ends and edges

Rail ends and edges are best bored for dowelling using a smaller version of the guide bush template.

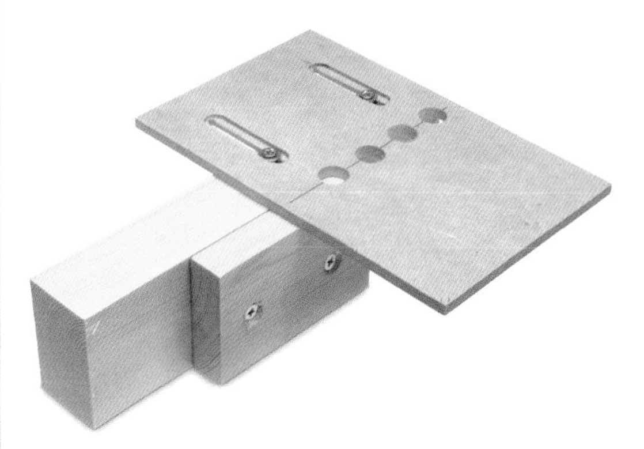

Three or more holes can be drilled in the template in the same way but at a closer spacing.

A right angle bracket fitted to the template allows it to be clamped to the workpiece, and you can add side stops for centring the dowel holes across its width.

Proprietary dowelling jig

Some dovetail jigs can also be fitted with a dowelling template that replaces the dovetail finger template. These are used with a guide bush to locate the router at the required dowel positions.

Wide boards up to 610mm can be accommodated on some jigs but if you have a smaller jig, wider boards can be drilled by clamping the jig to the bench and sliding the work past it.

Biscuit jointing

Another way of reinforcing a joint is to use a 'biscuit' which is essentially just a flat dowel. The main advantage of biscuit jointing is that the process doesn't require the same degree of precision that is needed with standard dowels, and whilst the joint is immensely strong, there is a small amount of 'give' available at the assembly stage.

There are biscuit jointers available as a dedicated power tool to cut the necessary recesses, but it is a process that can be carried out equally well with the router.

A biscuit joint is ideal for edge to edge joints, butt joints and corner butt joints. It can even be used to reinforce tricky mitre joints, and works well in either solid timber or manmade boards.

The biscuits are made from compressed hardwood chips, usually beech, and are set into semi-circular recesses cut into the mating faces of the joint.

When assembled, the flat face of the dowel offers a large surface area for gluing, far more than is possible with round dowels. Because the pockets are relatively short, unlike the grooves in loose tongued edge joints, the edges are not left weak and the joint is very strong. The glue causes the compressed fibres of the biscuits to swell slightly and this helps tighten the biscuit in its recess. However, it is unlikely to distort the face of the work, unless it is particularly thin.

Biscuits are commonly available in three sizes.

No-0, to suit board between 10 to 12mm thick, No-10, for 13 to 18mm board and No-20, for board over 19mm thick, but they are all 4mm thick. The recommended minimum thickness of material is 10mm, to maintain the strength of the finished construction.

Spare biscuits should be kept in a sealed container or bag to prevent them swelling before use, particularly if your workshop is damp.

As well as being structural they are also locational, holding components in place and stopping them sliding about as you clamp up. For wide workpieces, use two parallel rows of biscuits.

For edge work, you can use a biscuit jointer set which consists of a 4mm flat slotting cutter fitted to a threaded arbor with a selection of three different diameter bearings, 15mm, 19mm, and 23mm to vary the depth of cut for each size of biscuit.

For face work, the arbor mounted cutter cannot be used so you will also need a 4mm diameter straight cutter. The depth of cut for this straight cutter is set from the router's depth gauge and stop, allowing 1.5mm extra depth as a gap for gluing.

Whilst proper biscuit jointing tools use a 4mm wide blade, whose radius matches that of the biscuit, a smaller diameter cutter is used in a plunge router system. This means you have to move the router forwards to form the required length of groove and the end radius will not match that of the biscuit, so it is theoretically not as strong, but this is rarely a problem in practice.

Edge jointing

Biscuit dowel recesses are cut on the edge of boards and rails using the arbor mounted grooving cutter.

Fit the required diameter guide bearing before fitting the arbor in the router.

With a marking gauge, scribe a short centre line along the edge of the workpiece. Position the router on the face of the workpiece and centre the grooving cutter on it (i.e. 2mm either side of the line). This setting is not critical and you can do it by eye, provided you make all the cuts from the face side.

Hold the two joint edges together with the face sides uppermost and the face edges together. Mark out the centreline for each biscuit, as well as the end points and square these across both boards.

Then clamp the edge of one board, face side up, overhanging the bench and centre the arbor on the first dowel position.

Cut sideways into the edge of the board to full depth, then move the router backwards and forwards to create the required length of groove. It helps at the assembly stage to make these grooves fractionally longer than necessary to allow a little positioning room. Repeat the procedure at each dowel position and on each board.

Corner joints

Groove the edge of the first component as above, and then if the length permits, clamp the other one end up in the vice. (If this is not possible it will need to be clamped on the bench face side up and the router held horizontally.)

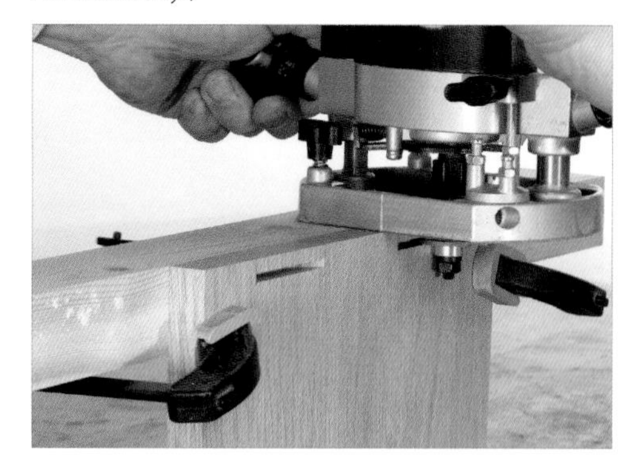

Keep the grooving cutter depth set as for the edge component. Clamp a parallel squared batten flush along the edge of the second board to provide a wider edge to support the router. Cut the recesses as before.

T-joints

As the grooving cutter cannot be used in the middle of the face of the workpiece, replace it with the 4mm straight cutter and set the depth of cut depending on the biscuit size to be used. Draw the centre line across the face of the board marking out the position of the biscuit slots using the already grooved component as a template

Mark off half the width of the router base plate from one side of the line at both ends and clamp a straight batten across in this position. Use this as a guide to cut each slot to the full depth in a series of 2mm steps.

Mitred joints can be reinforced with biscuits using the router handheld and guided with a template jig, or for heavy duty applications a jig on the router table can be used.

Corner joints

A right angled corner joint is probably the most common woodworking requirement if you are making boxes, cabinets, drawers, chests etc. Although you can use the router to make elaborate joints like dovetails, there are a whole range of other options. The router can be fitted with a straight cutter and side-fence, or alternatively mounted in the router table. For more complicated joints, you can make up simple jigs or buy specialised cutters for a particular application.

The simplest corner joint is the rebate joint, where one piece is rebated into the other. This provides a more positive location than a simple butt joint and also increases the gluing area. As with all these corner joints, it is essential that the ends of the workpieces are all cut perfectly square and true.

The grooved rebate joint is a stronger version of the joint, providing a definite registration for each piece. The groove usually extends to half the thickness of the work, with the tongue one third the thickness of the piece, though nothing is critical and you can juggle the dimensions particularly if you are jointing different thickness pieces.

The corner locking joint is a further refinement with a double interlocking rebate resulting in another very strong joint. It is best cut on the router table but a very simple jig makes it foolproof if you use a slotting cutter. A real advantage is that it can be used for joints where one component overlaps the other as in a drawer front.

If you are a more experienced user, there are dedicated cutters that can produce more elaborate corner joints such as mitred types for a really neat finish.

These cutters will more than repay their cost in a mass production situation, though they usually have to be used in a router table. The simplest variation is the mitre corner joint that has to be cut with two separate cutters.

The mitre lock joint is cut with a single cutter making a separate pass on each piece.

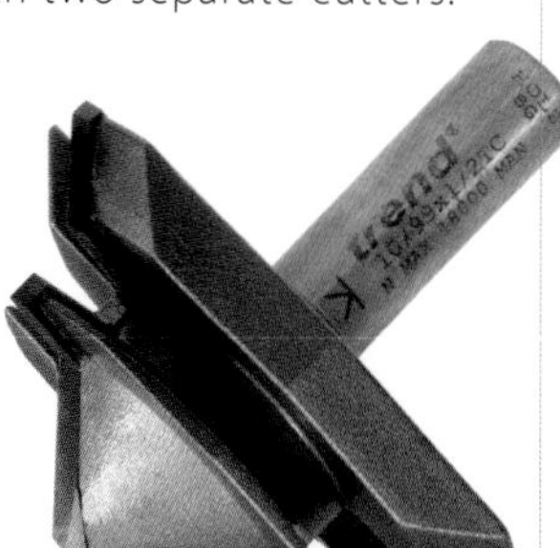

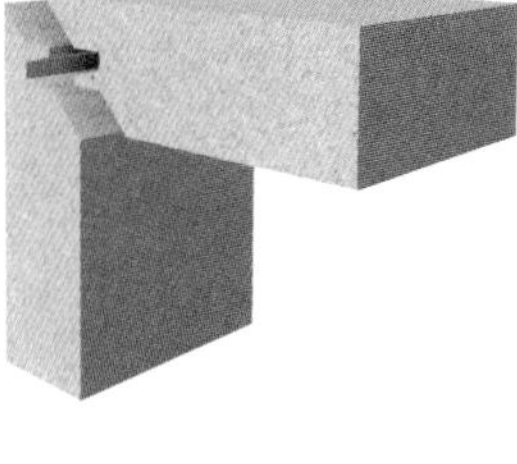

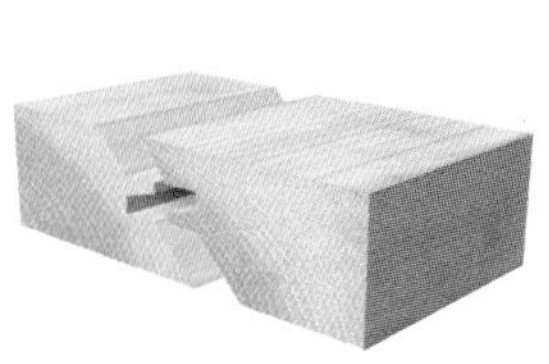

Drawers can be cut and assembled very quickly using the special drawer lock joint cutter which maximises the glue line for a really strong joint.

Housing joints

Housings are shallow slots cut across the width of the workpiece, usually to accommodate a shelf or divider. There are various alternatives, all of which are easily cut with the router.

The simplest is the through housing which is just a slot of just the right width to make the shelf a tight fit.

For a neater appearance, the stopped housing is better as the groove doesn't come through onto the edge.

However, the front end of the housing is best squared out by hand with a chisel to minimise the amount of overhang, or the edge of the shelf can be radiused to match.

The dovetail housing is an extremely strong way of joining a shelf into a carcass side and is effectively one long sliding dovetail joint.

It doesn't involve any complicated or expensive jigs. It produces a very neat joint that holds the shelf securely and prevents it from warping but can still be left unglued to allow for any shrinkage across the width.

Dovetail housings which are cut across the ends of the workpiece can be guided using a side-fence. The distance in from the board end being limited by the length of the standard side-fence rods. Longer fence rods can be used, but may reduce the accuracy due to flexing.

In either case, a longer face should be fitted to the fence to prevent the side-fence turning-in at the start and finish of the pass. A batten, equal in thickness to the workpiece, should be used to prevent break-out on the rear edge of the workpiece.

Dovetail housings which are cut across the width of the workpiece can be routed using a straight edge, a tee-square, clamp guide or even a homemade slot jig used with a router and fitted guide bush.

This jig can be fitted with a stop if the slot doesn't go right across the board. Parallel housings can be spaced using a plunger dropped into each successive housing.

The dovetail housing has to be cut in one pass; you cannot vary the depth, although you can make a second pass to widen it.

If the initial cut is going to be too heavy for your router, remove the bulk of the waste with a straight cutter and then follow up with a dovetail one to produce the undercut.

For the mating half of the joint, the tail can be cut in several ways but is ideally cut on the router table.

This is easier, safer and more accurate than doing it freehand. For maximum support, the timber is held securely against the router table fence which is fitted with a flat sub face. A cutter aperture in the bottom edge, leaves enough space around the cutter for waste clearance.

Tip

Always cut a trial piece to check that the width of the finished tongue will be a precise fit in the housing.

If the tongue is too thick to fit the housing, set the fence to cut deeper on both sides of the workpiece. Always take equal amounts from both edges to ensure that the tongue remains central.

With stopped joints the end of the tongue has to be cut back to hide the rounded end of the housing.

In many instances, the length of the workpiece will make it impossible to cut the dovetail tongue on the router table, so you will need to do it with the router handheld. It is important that the router is given plenty of support to prevent it tipping by clamping a batten flush to the inside edge, or by making a simple L jig and a guide bush.

To minimise break-out, make a shallow back cut across the face of the joint from right to left first, before finishing off the full depth cut from left to right.

Other joints

Rule joint

This joint is traditionally used on table tops where one leaf drops down to leave a decorative edge. It effectively disguises both the hinge and the gap between the two folding edges.

Two matched cutters are needed and the timber edges must be perfectly straight and true if the finished joint is to be even along the entire length of the tabletop.

The convex edge is cut with a standard ovolo cutter and the mating half is cut with a cove cutter, but the radii must match perfectly. The cutters may be plain or self guided, provided the thickness of the board allows support for the bearing.

For accuracy, the joint is best cut on the router table to make sure the cutter stays square to the work as any discrepancies will stop the joint hinging over properly. However, this may not be practical with large tops and you will need to use the side-fence. Also use a fine height adjuster to make sure the relative depths of cut are perfectly matched.

Knuckle joint

When two components have to fold against each other, a very neat alternative is the knuckle joint that can be cut with another dedicated cutter.

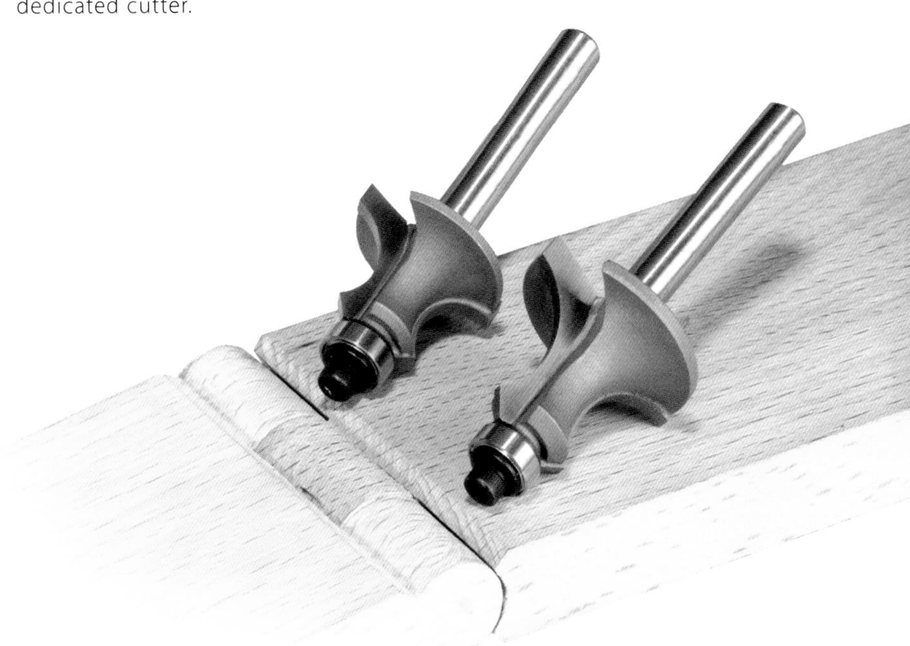

10. ROUTING OTHER MATERIALS

Not only is the router a superb tool for use with solid wood and timber based products, it can also cut and shape a variety of other materials.

Plastics

Most forms of plastic such as Perspex, PVC, ABS and Tufnol can be machined with the router. The composition of these materials varies enormously so a good start to assess their machining characteristics is to refer to the trade name on the particular manufacturer's website as they usually publish all the cutting data there.

Plastics are either cast or extruded, the thinner sections of the latter generally being more brittle and difficult to work.

As you would imagine, the harder and denser materials tend to machine more cleanly. For instance Tufnol is an excellent template making material that routs cleanly and easily.

The main problem when machining plastics such as PVC with its low melting point is the phenomenon of 'weld back' where the waste material does not clear properly behind the cutter. The friction heat melts the material which then adheres to the cutter and/or the cut surface. In an industrial situation, this is minimised by using a jet of compressed air to cool the cutter.

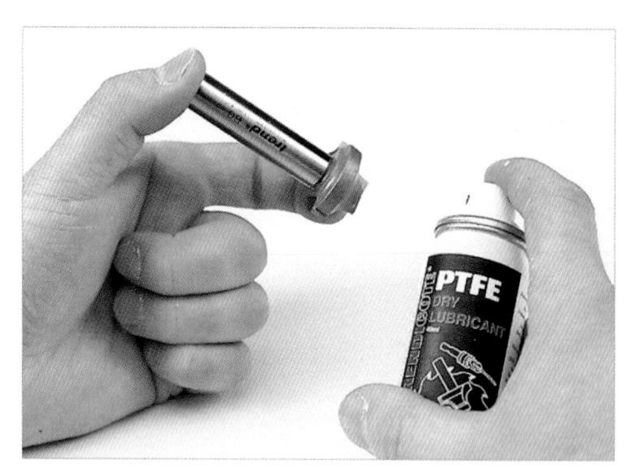

Alternatively, you can use a suitable specialised lubricant such as Trendicote, though this has to be applied to the tooling only and not to the work. Effective extraction is also more important when machining plastics.

On the non abrasive plastics, high speed tooling generally cuts cleaner than TCT, and although you can use standard cutters, there are specialised ones for machining plastics that have different clearance angles to minimise weld back.

Spiral cutters are particularly effective as they remove more of the swarf from the cutting area.

Speed is another factor that you can vary in the pursuit of a cleaner cut. Both feed speed and rotational speed need to be reduced on plastics with low melting points.

Cast resins

There is now a variety of cast resin materials made to simulate granite for use as kitchen and bathroom worktops. Such expensive materials are better known under their trade names, such as Corian®.

Although the material will work with standard cutters, there is a range specially designed for them, ranging from simple straight ones to elaborate edge moulding profiles. They have been designed around the special techniques involved in fabricating sections of these materials in kitchen worktop construction.

Sections are edge moulded after they have been glued together. The bearing guided cutters are fitted with plastic sleeves to prevent them marking the surface.

Although resin boards machine easily, they do produce clouds of fine powdery dust so extraction is vital.

Laminates and veneers

Laminate overlays are commonly used to provide a hard wearing surface on table and worktops, whilst veneers are used to cover manmade sheet materials to give the impression of solid timber.

Although widely used, both these materials are very difficult to trim neatly by hand as they chip and splinter very easily.

However, with its fast revolving cutter, the router will leave a clean cut edge that requires no further attention.

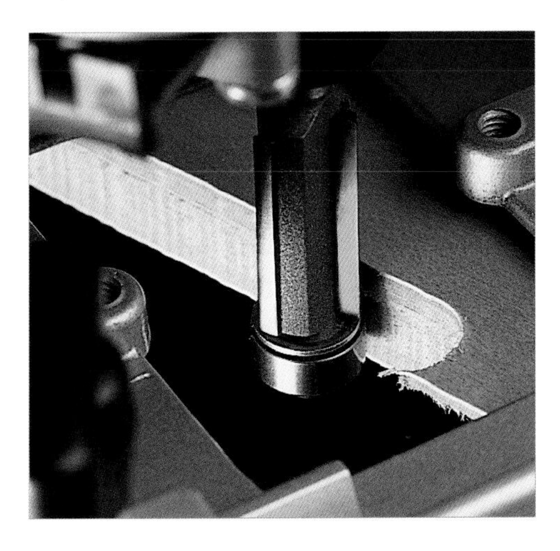

The secret is not to try and trim off too much in one pass; as a general rule never leave more than 3mm of overhang to trim back. With real wood veneer, a better result is obtained using a down cut spiral cutter that prevents the surface lifting.

A large range of dedicated cutters are available that will trim laminate or veneer flush to an edge. These vary from very simple straight cutters that require the use of a side-fence, self guiding cutters or combination trimmers.

Double trimmers designed for professional use allow you to cut both faces at once, either finishing the laminate flush or with a chamfered edge. For heavy duty use, it is worth considering using a cutter with replaceable blades, as they are usually made from a longer lasting grade of tungsten carbide.

For trimming back to an internal profile, a 'pierce and trim' cutter is ideal as this cuts the laminate back to the aperture. For instance when you are laminating over a sink opening. Their small diameter allows you to work right into a tight corner. Once again, double trim versions are also available to trim the two faces simultaneously.

Flat bottomed trimming cutters with 3 cutting edges are designed for flushing off hardwood lippings or plastic edging. They have bevelled corners to prevent scoring and leave a super-fine finish. For perfect results these need to be used with a fine depth adjuster on the router, and you will also need to lift the router base slightly with a stepped sub-base jig to provide enough clearance over the upstanding edge.

The laminate trimmer router

If you need to trim laminates on a regular basis there is scaled down router available for just this purpose. It will take most of the smaller cutters as well as a roller guide for curved work. The main advantage over a standard router being that it is lighter and easier to handle.

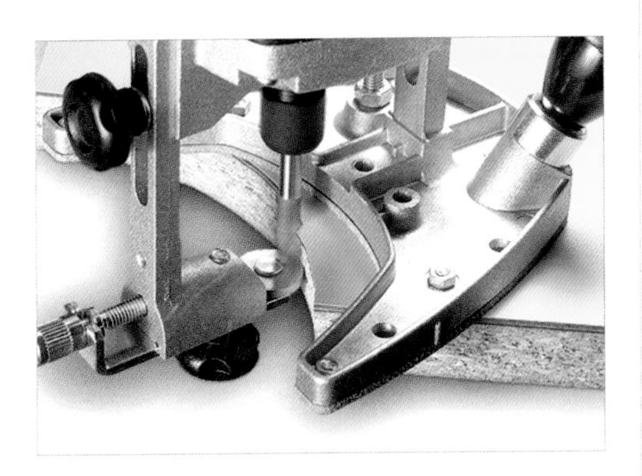

Working with laminates

If you are covering the edge and face of a board, the normal procedure is to stick on the edge lippings first and then trim them back before fitting the face. This prevents the face surface being marked or damaged by the lower edge of the cutter if you do it the other way round.

Set the trimmer up on its stepped base and fit a bottom flush trimming cutter, adjusting the depth of cut with the fine adjuster until it just skims the uncovered top surface. To make the cut, now move the router in a clockwise direction, which is contrary to normal practice, as the rotation of the cutter will then push the laminate back against the edge and prevent it chipping off.

Once the lippings have been trimmed flush with the top, the faces can be covered. Cut the laminate big enough to leave a 3mm overhang all round. Any glue squeezing out needs to be removed promptly as it can interfere with the cutter and clog it, particularly the bearing guided type.

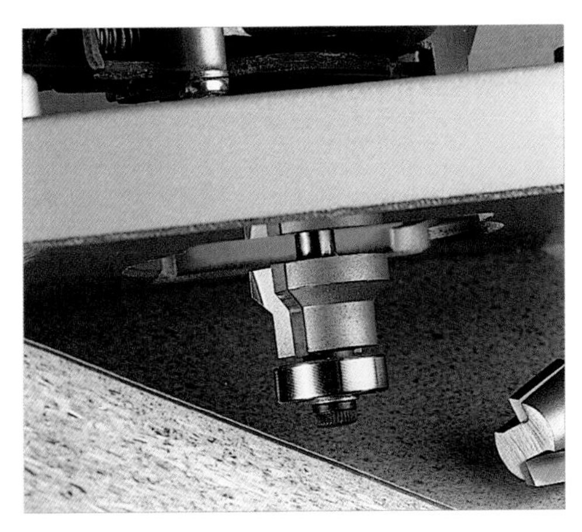

When the glue is properly dry, use a straight or angled trimmer to cut back the excess and leave a neat and professional looking edge. To minimise the risk of marring the edge when trimming back the top, make sure the bearings are in good condition, or if you are using an integral pilot guided bit, use wax or Vaseline as a lubricant.

Sometimes it is necessary to butt joint two pieces of laminate together if there is a large area to cover. The only sure way to make the two edges mate up perfectly, is to overlap them slightly and then cut through both simultaneously using the router guided with a straightedge.

Set a small diameter straight TCT bit so that it just cuts through into the supporting material. Any slight deviations will be mirrored on each edge and the fit should be perfect.

Laminate is an extremely abrasive material, even for TCT cutters and will soon wear the cutting edges. To maximise the cutter life always limit the amount of overhang for trimming back to about 3mm. Just a small increase on this will raise the cutter wear by as much as 400%.

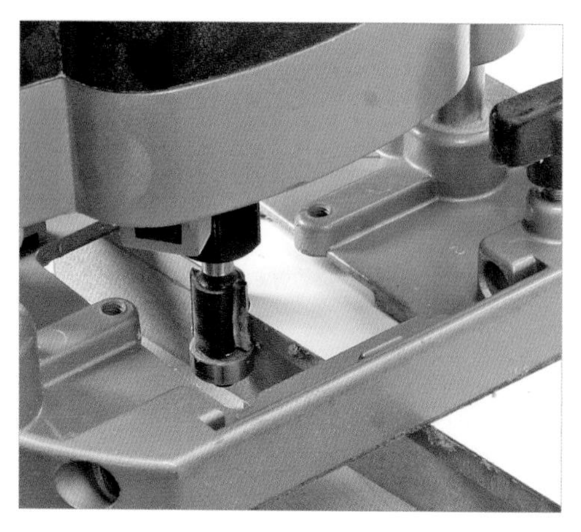

Also, vary the depth of cut to spread the wear along the whole cutting edge rather than concentrating it in one spot.

Cutting and jointing post formed worktops

Anyone involved in kitchen fitting will know that cutting and joining worktops at right angles is one of the most difficult operations, particularly if you wish to end up with a seamless joint.

One alternative is to insert a metal connecting strip that covers the join but this spoils the continuity of the flat surface.

With their brittle laminate surfaces, kitchen worktops can be tricky to cut with a saw without chipping and it is almost impossible to get an accurate and clean enough cut for jointing using hand tools. However, the router is capable of producing the necessary accuracy for both cutting and jointing.

The main cut is made using a saw, leaving the cut slightly over length and then trimming it back to final size using the router and a straightedge.

Use a heavy duty router and fit a long straight 1/2" diameter cutter and make a single pass.

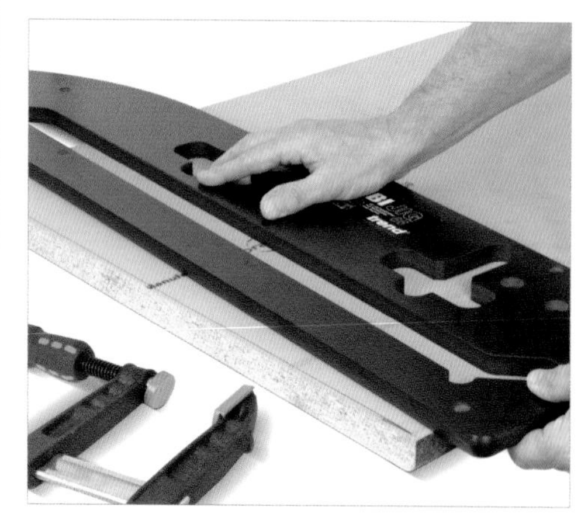

Remember that the rotating action of the cutter could chip the laminate away on the edge of the worktop, but you can avoid this by cutting the right hand ends with the laminate face up and the left hand ends with the laminate face down. Feeding from the front edge both times.

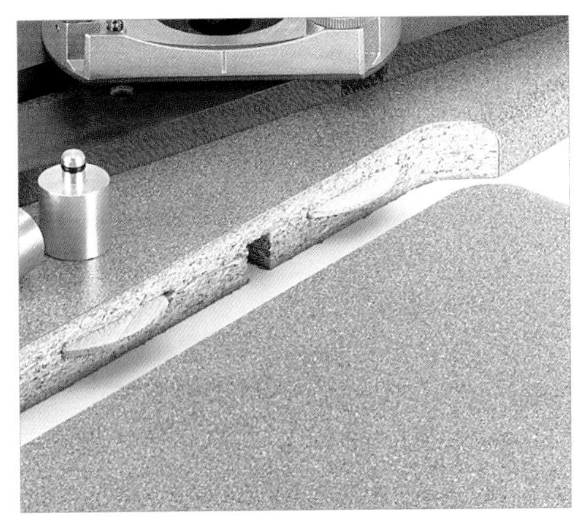

Although you could join the two worktops at right angles using a long mitre joint, it is more conventional to just butt them together, but this requires a small mitre to be cut to accommodate the bull nosed sections.

If you are likely to be jointing tops on a regular basis, there are specialised jigs to help you cut the joint perfectly each time. These also incorporate templates for cutting the recesses for the connecting bolts that hold the finished joint together. It is rare that walls will meet at a perfect 90° so some jigs allow you to cut the joint slightly off square.

However, although very efficient for the regular user, these jigs are not really cost effective for a one-off job, although they can be hired from good tool shops.

Fortunately, you can make a simple but less sophisticated jig that allows you to cut a perfect butt joint every time, and you can also build templates in to it for the connecting bolt recesses. All you need is an offcut of thin MDF, a long reach straight two flute cutter and a guide bush with a suitable diameter. You could also make the jig suitable for using a top-bearing guided cutter, but a guide bush working in an enclosed slot will give much more positive guidance.

The jig consists of a long slot slightly longer than the width of the worktop but with a short return at 45° on one end. This allows you to cut the mating halves of the worktop perfectly straight and with the 45 degree angle accounting for the rounded shape on the front of the worktop.

Using the jig

The jig is easy to use, but it does rely on some careful alignment. You need to clamp it securely onto the top, and as you are usually working on site, I prefer to work with the top securely supported on trestles. This provides a comfortable working height and allows good access for the clamps and better visibility of the cut. For extra security also use a couple of strips of double sided tape to prevent any 'creep' as you tighten up the clamps.

Start by first cutting the male part of the joint, measuring accurately to get the jig positioned so that the rounded post formed edge will be cut away. You can also make any minute alteration to the alignment at this time to compensate for the joint not being true if the walls are out of square.

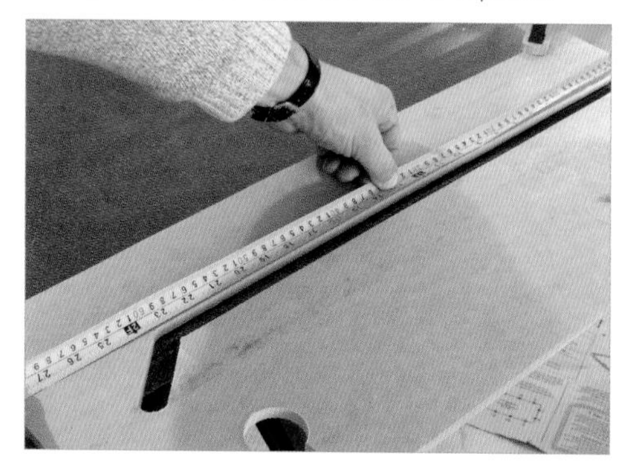

Make the cut in a series of passes, going slightly deeper with each one, rather than trying to make a heavy cut. Notice that this part of the joint is cut from the top surface, so that the revolving cutter is working into the top and there is then no danger of chipping away any of the laminate as it enters.

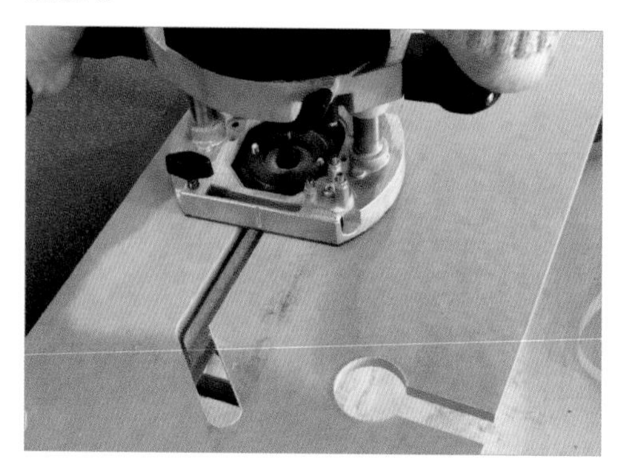

Position the jig very carefully so that the finished cut is perfectly straight and clean as it is difficult to make alterations later.

The next stage is to cut the other work top to match, a relatively easy process if it is free at one end. However, in most kitchen situations the worktops bridge between two walls and the cutting operation is a little more involved.

Start by cutting the second worktop a couple of inches longer than you need and then place it in position, laying it in place over the top of the routed cut you have just made. Scribe the far end to match the wall surface, and cut this accordingly. Laminate tops will usually mark quite easily with a pencil but with the dark coloured ones you may find pencil lines difficult to see. In this case, use a white crayon or chinagraph pencil to make sure lines are clearly visible.

With the end of the top now neatly scribed and up against the wall, lay your first cut over the top of the other end and mark the position for the matching half. Trim this to within 2 or 3 mm off the line using a jigsaw, but cut from the underside to minimize any splintering of the laminate.

Now position the jig to clean up the cut back to the line, but this time it is fixed to the underside of the to. This is so the revolving cutter is, once again, spinning into the work on entry to help minimise chipping. It is also easier to just pin the jig

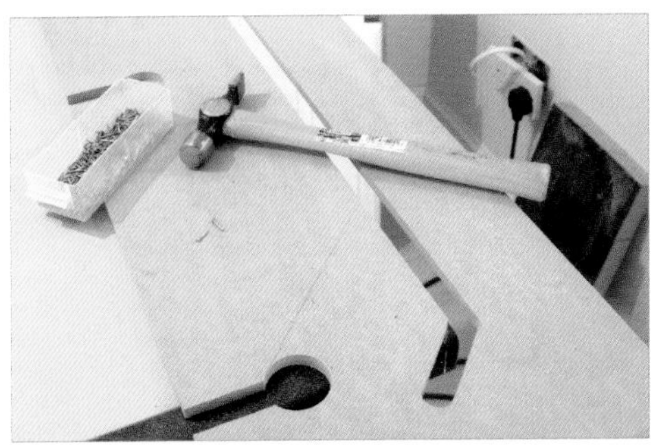

in place when you're working on the underside, rather than having to fiddle about with clamps. If you have trimmed accurately enough with a jigsaw, there should only be a few millimetres to cut away with the router and is usually possible to complete the cut in one pass, to leave another perfectly straight cut with the tiny 45 degree return to accommodate the postformed shape.

The joint should fit together perfectly, though in theory there is always a minute discrepancy as the guide bush cannot be exactly the same diameter as the cutter. In reality, this difference is insignificant provided you match them as closely as possible.

All you have to do now is cut the recesses for the fixing bolts that hold the two halves together. These are cut on the underside of the top, but mark them while the tops are in place on the base units so you can position them such that the bolts can be tightened up later with a spanner. There is often a base unit cross rail in the way that will interfere with the spanner's movement, so work accordingly. Once again, the jig can be just pinned in position, and the same cutter and guide bush arrangement is used to cut the recesses.

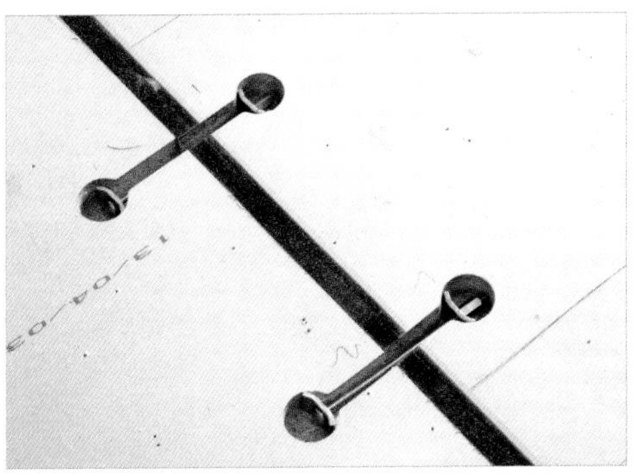

Make sure these are deep enough to fully accommodate the bolt, but not so deep that you weaken the top. Two bolts per joint are all that is normally needed but spaced as far apart as possible.

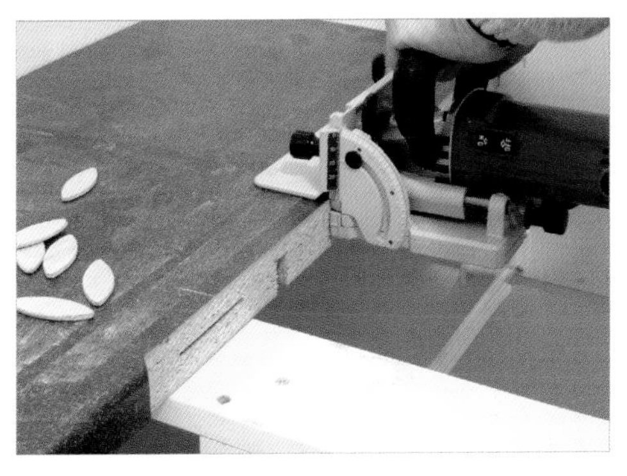

You could rely on just these two bolts alone to complete the joint, but it is then very difficult to keep the two halves of the joint perfectly level as you tighten up the bolts. It is far better to firm up the joint using two or three biscuits, which will keep everything in line as you tighten up.

Although the joint will be very tight when it is pulled together you must always remember that worktops will often get wet and even the slightest gap will allow water to penetrate. As the substrate under the laminate is chipboard, any dampness will cause it to swell and the joint will very quickly disintegrate. To help minimise any ingress of water, run a bead of mastic along the top edges of the joint with plenty of waterproof glue over the rest of it. Then you can tighten up the bolts to pull the two tops up together securely, and leave what is hopefully, a perfectly impermeable and virtually invisible joint.

Routing metals

Most non-ferrous metals can be machined with a router and standard cutters, with materials like brass and copper being the easiest to work as they are self lubricating.

Aluminium is a little more difficult as there are so many different grades, all with their own working characteristics. Some of the cheaper, softer grades are more difficult to work than the harder better quality ones.

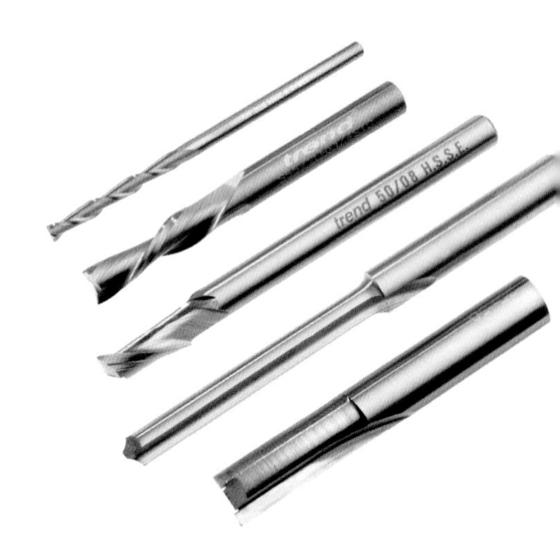

Special HSS or HSSE cutters are available, although standard ones can be used. TCT cutters do not give such a clean finish as the HSS variety.

Specialised tooling used in the window industry has been developed from end mill tools used in engineering and is made from high grade HSS with added cobalt to make it tougher.

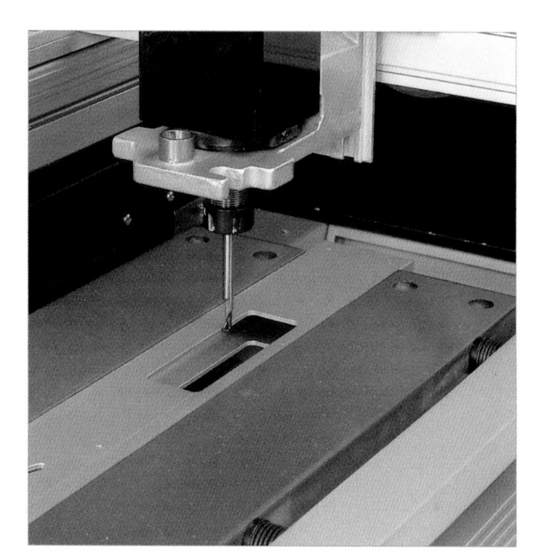

HSSE cutters have a relieved cutting edge to help waste clearance and the cutting angle is shallower to resist the abrasive properties of the hard coating of anodised aluminium. These cutters will plunge-drill and mill lateral slots in extruded sections for door and window making. Upcut spirals are better as they lift the waste material away, because like plastic, aluminium is subject to weld back.

Some form of lubricant is a must and on industrial machines a mist spray of water soluble oil is used to maintain low cutting temperatures to minimise this problem.

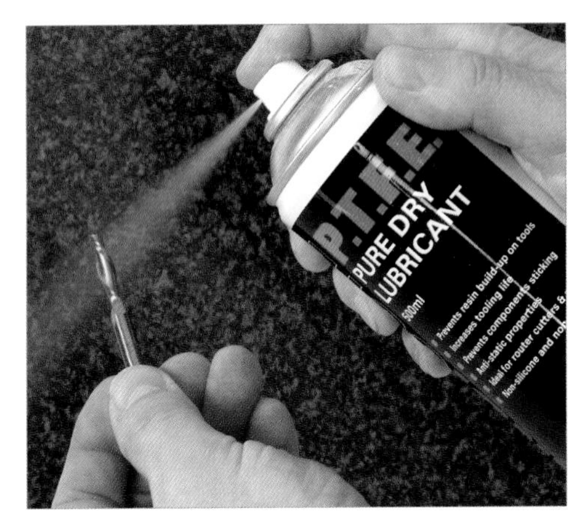

This is obviously not feasible on a hand router, so you need to use PTFE spray or lubricating wax on the tooling.

It is not safe to machine metals with a router mounted in a table as the metal swarf will fall into the router's manifold and damage the interior workings of the router.

It is also essential that the work is securely clamped as there is much more likelihood of it being snatched by the cutter. Rotational speed should be set around 10-12,000 rpm and feed speed reduced to a maximum of 1.5m per minute. Only very shallow passes should be attempted and some experimentation will be needed to find the best combination.

Despite all these precautions, the working life of a cutter used on metal is greatly reduced, and they will need to be renewed on a regular basis.

Other materials

Fibreglass (GRP) is another material that can be worked with a router, the normal application being to trim off the 'flash' around the edge of mouldings. As this material is effectively just strands of glass it is highly abrasive and special solid tungsten coarse cut rasps are used in preference to conventional cutters.

The coarseness of the burr does vary and they are available with end cut and bearing guides for template work. Others are suitable for carving and grinding work in a variety of materials, but all must be used at the recommended speeds, which can vary between 10-30,000 rpm.

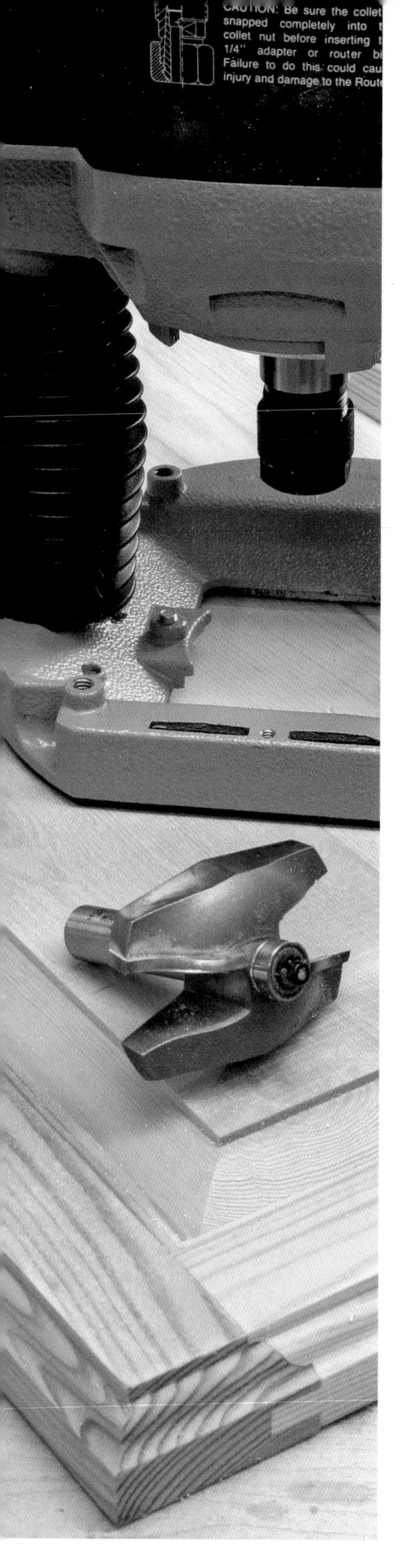

11. REALISING THE POTENTIAL

So far we have looked in detail at the router, its cutters and their general functions. This chapter considers how this incredible potential can be utilised for specific projects.

Obviously, with such amazing versatility, the router has a vast range of applications, but a quick look at some of the more popular ones will hopefully inspire you to try some of the techniques to extend your own ambitions, and produce projects of a quality that has previously been unobtainable.

Door construction

The router can be used to make traditional interior and exterior doors, incorporating all the conventional joints, glazing bar sections and weather sealing options. It is also particularly suited to making panelled cabinet doors in a variety of styles.

Panelled doors are made up with a solid frame consisting of two vertical stiles and two or more horizontal rails. Intermediate support is provided on wide panels with additional uprights called muntins. The inside edge of the stiles and rails are grooved to accept the panel, which can either be of solid timber or veneered board.

Traditional frame and panel styles

Rectangular frame and panel doors

Simple rectangular frames can be fitted with flat panels, usually of plywood or solid timber. Additional decoration may be added in the form of planted on mouldings.

Raised and fielded panel doors

Traditional raised and fielded panels are cut from solid timber and edge moulded to fit into a grooved frame.

Multi-panel doors

Both flat and raised and fielded panels can be divided up by the addition of vertical muntins and horizontal rails.

Arched or radius top frame and panel doors

Arched panel doors are produced using a radius template cut with a trammel or ellipse jig.

Cambrio or cathedral top doors

These are produced using a template to cut both the rails and the matching panel edges, which can then be profiled using bearing guided cutters and panel raisers.

Simulated frame and panel doors

Simulated panel mouldings can be cut into the face of sheet material using a template and guide bush, or a bearing guided moulding cutter. Because the moulding will expose the core of the panel material, this type of construction is only suitable for solid timber or on MDF panels that are to be painted.

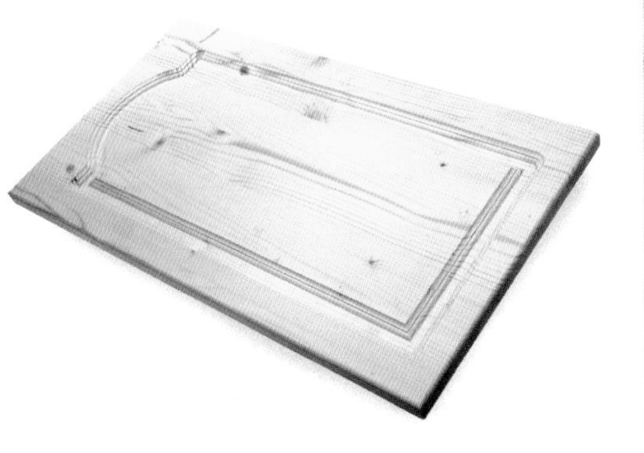

Cutting simulated panel cabinet doors

Rectangular simulated panel mouldings can be cut directly into the door blank, using the router side-fence as a guide, but for accuracy, length stops should be positioned to ensure that the corners meet precisely.

A much better method is to use a template and guide bush, which will be much more accurate, particularly for repetition work or if the panel is curved.

Templates can be either internal or external and are best cut from thin MDF. Internal templates are actually easier to use as they control the router better at the corners. Make sure that all the curves flow cleanly and that the template edges are finished smooth and square.

Cut the template surround larger than the actual door panel, to allow locating battens to be fitted underneath.

To prevent the router tipping, use double sided tape to fix a piece of spare template material within the template if you are using an internal shape.

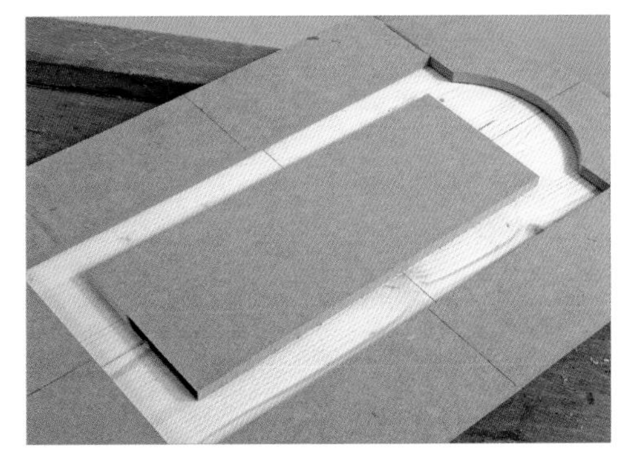

However, leave adequate space between the template guide edge and the spare piece to allow clearance for the guide bush or cutter bearing.

If you are using an external template, stick a piece of template material to the router base to serve the same purpose.

Use a shank mounted bearing guided cutter, or fit a suitable diameter guide bush to follow the template edge, cutting the profile in a series of shallow cuts to reach the full moulding depth.

Remember that the final depth should allow for any surface sanding when finishing the door.

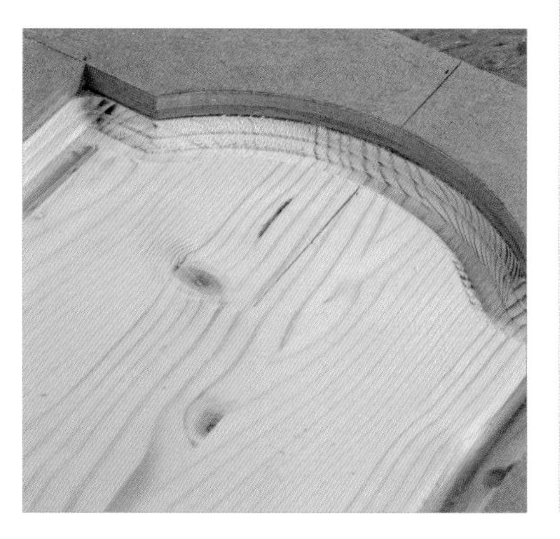

The outer edges of the door can then be moulded in the conventional way using bearing guided cutters or the router's side fence.

Matching drawer fronts can also be produced in the same way.

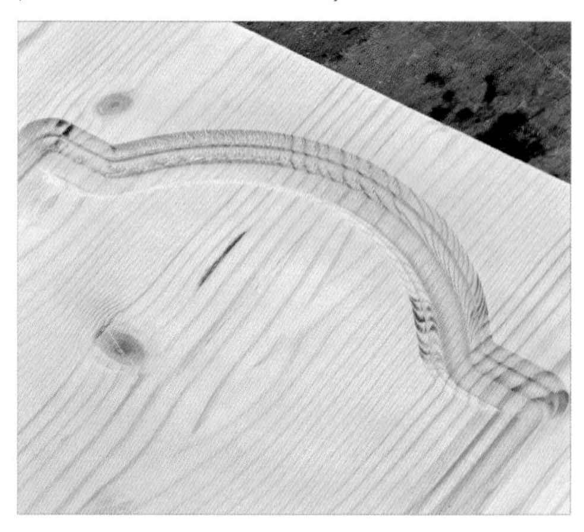

Framed cabinet doors

Cabinet door frames can be made up in a variety of ways using mortise and tenon joints, bridle joints, biscuit or dowel joints.

However, special tooling is available for the router to produce profile scribed joints, for instance where the ends of the rails are cut to simultaneously form both the jointing tenon and the reverse of the stile edge moulding.

The thickness of the rails and stiles needs to be in proportion to the overall door size, so frames for larger or heavier doors should be between 20-22 mm reducing to 18 mm for smaller doors. Check on the manufacturer's specification for the material thickness before buying a particular cutter, as they are normally quite size specific.

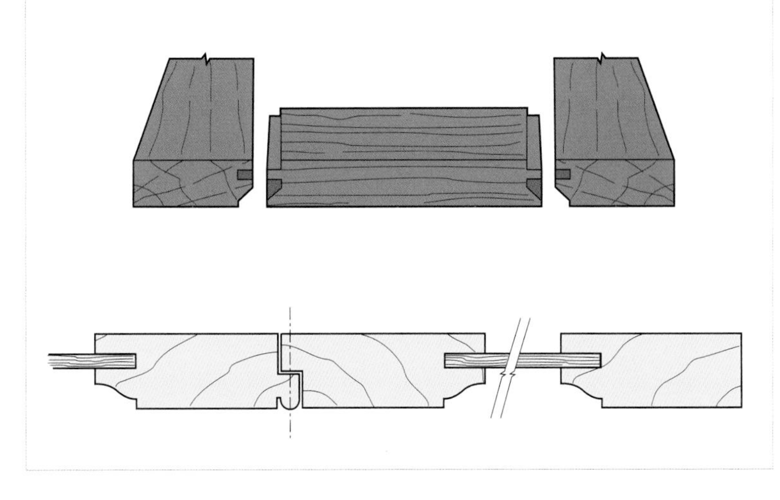

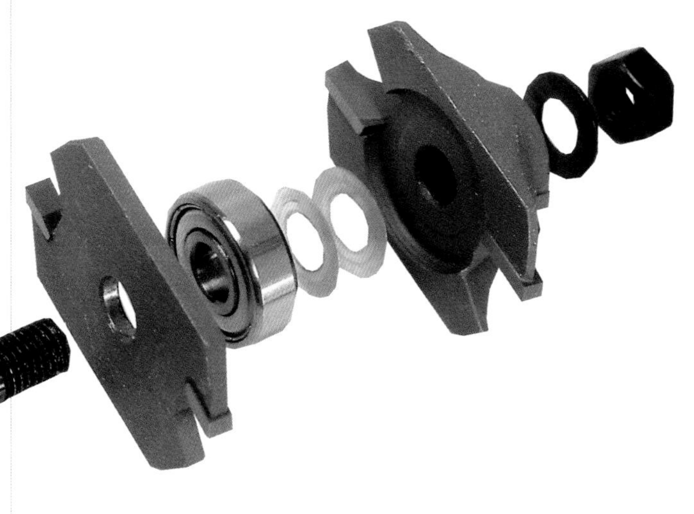

Profile scribing

Profile scribing operations should only be carried out with a router of at least 900 watts and fitted under a table or to an overhead stand. They cannot be cut safely and accurately using the router freehand.

Although some cutter sets are available with 1/4" shanks there is a more extensive range on 1/2" shanks. As the two cuts have to be matched precisely, it is also essential to fit a fine height adjuster to the router.

To get the best results, only use good quality timber which is straight grained and free of knots. Carefully match the material for the frames and panels for both grain pattern and colour. The timber must be properly dried, to minimise possible shrinkage problems.

Prepare enough material to complete the job and allow for some extra to use for making trial cuts when you are setting up the cutters.

It is sometimes a good idea to leave the stiles slightly over-length to form horns that will protect the ends of the door. These are trimmed off later when the door has been finally assembled. Mark all the components clearly with a face side and edge, as it is so easy to machine the wrong profile when you have to make several different cuts on similar pieces.

Try and set aside enough space to put them down into clearly separate piles to minimise the chance of confusion!

The procedure for cutting a scribed joint is to first cut the tenon and scribe on the rail ends and then cut the groove and moulding on the rail and stile edges.

If you do it the other way round, there will be significant break-out on the previously formed end profiles.

For all profile scribing operations, it is advisable to adjust the fence faces to close the gap either side of the cutter.

There are two variations of profile scribing cutters:

Combination sets

A single profile cutter, groover and bearing are mounted on a threaded arbor, but the order of the components has to be re-arranged each time to change from profile to scribing cuts.

Shims are provided to allow fine adjustments to the fit and to compensate for loss of size due to sharpening.

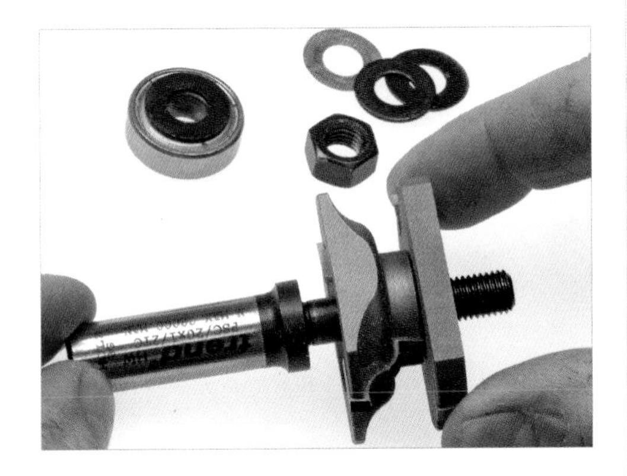

East Set™ cutter sets

This is a combination system. It comprises a single grooving cutter, twin moulding cutters and bearings pre-mounted on the arbor. This allows both the profile and scribe to be cut simply by adjusting the height of the cutter in the table. No other adjustments have to be made.

Tip

When building up compound cutters on an arbor always stagger the cutting edges, i.e. two cutters at 90°, three cutters at 60° to each other.

Before you start work on your finished workpieces, it is essential to make a trial joint on some spare material of the same dimensions. This allows the settings to be fine tuned for a perfect fit, as trial and error is the only way to perfection.

Cutting the scribe

To ensure a safe and accurate cut, the timber of the rails or muntins should be cut dead square and to exact length.

It should then be mounted face up in a workholder or held firmly against the mitre guide, making sure it is at a perfect 90° to the fence. The workholder can be a simple affair with the work held in place with a clamp.

If you are making panels on a regular basis, it is worth making up a more elaborate workholder with an integral toggle clamp for quick changeover, or buying a dedicated jig.

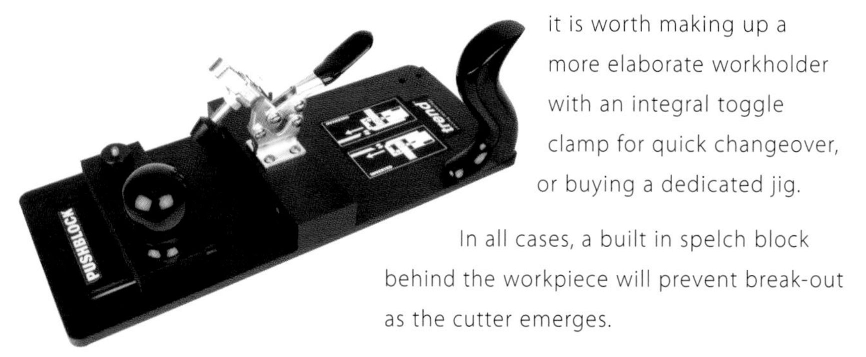

In all cases, a built in spelch block behind the workpiece will prevent break-out as the cutter emerges.

The table fence itself must be set in line with the bearing using a straightedge, as this sets the correct depth of cut.

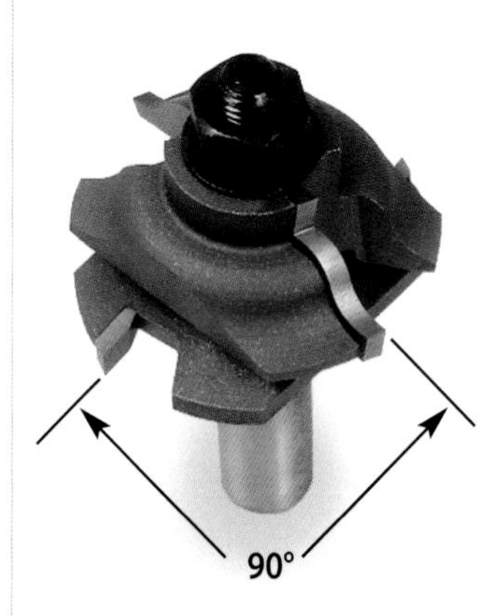

If you are using an adjustable cutter, start by setting it up in the scribe configuration, with the two cutters at 90 degrees to each other, and check that the arbor nut is tight.

Fit the cutter assembly into the router ensuring that at least three quarters of the shank length is gripped in the collet. Set the height of the cutter above the table so that the bottom edge of the groover cuts slightly into the baseboard of the workholder. The cutter height needs to be adjusted to leave an adequate depth of top quirk on the moulding. This should be at least 1.5mm, as any less will leave a weak and poorly defined edge that will be lost when the finished door is sanded or painted.

Clamp the rail in the workholder, aligning one end against the fence. Feed the work past the cutter in a smooth continuous movement, keeping the rail end tight to the fence and the workholder baseboard flat on the table.

Cutting the profile

Re-assemble the cutters in the correct order for cutting the edge profile, fitting shims between the components if necessary to get the required spacing.

Use the scribed rails ends as a guide for this. Once again, arrange the cutters at 90 degrees to each other.

Lay the pre-cut scribed rail face down on the table and adjust the cutter height in the table to reproduce the original profile depth. Check this by aligning the groover with the stub tenon of the rail end.

With the cutter running at full speed, cut the profile along the stile keeping it firmly against the fence face with a suitable push block. Make several lighter cuts if you are using 1/4" shanked cutters or if the mould is very deep.

Don't forget to mould all of the pieces including those already pre-cut with the scribe profile.

Fit the rail end into the stile profile, check that the faces are flush and that the joint is a sliding fit into the edge profile. If they are not, re-set the cutter height or re-arrange the shims to tighten or loosen the joint before making a second trail cut and check again.

A well fitting joint should leave a perfect corner with no break-out. When you get to this stage, keep a sample joint as a reference for quickly resetting the cutters again in the future.

Shaped rails

Profile scribing cutters can also be used to construct framed doors with shaped top and/or bottom rails, but for safety and accuracy, it is worth making up a combined template and workholder. It is also easier to cut the scribed end joint before shaping the rail, as a straight piece is always easier to hold than a curved one.

The rail shape is initially cut slightly oversize with a jigsaw or a bandsaw and then trimmed back using a template/workholder. A straight bearing guided cutter is fitted in the router table. If necessary, the template can be fitted with handles to keep hands well clear of the cutter.

The work is held securely in place with a rear locating batten and end blocks, which also work as lead-in and lead-outs. Use some double sided tape for extra security as well to make sure the rail is gripped tight. It is also necessary to fit a lead-in pin on the table to prevent the end of the workpiece being snatched as you start the cut.

Once all the curved rails have been cut, they can be profiled to match the other components. Replace the trimming cutter with the profile scriber and set the height using the pre-cut rail end as a guide.

Remember to fit the work in the holder face side down. Feed the work smoothly into the cutter, starting initially with the lead-in block of the holder against the lead-in pin of the table. Check that this joint fits properly before cutting the rest of the rails.

Plain flat panels
Cut from Medium Density Fibreboard (MDF), plywood or other timber based sheet material. These materials can either be veneered to match the frame timber or left plain for painting.

Tongue and groove match boarding
Either v-jointed or with a bead profile, the boarding can be cut to length and if thicker than the groove, rebated to fit.

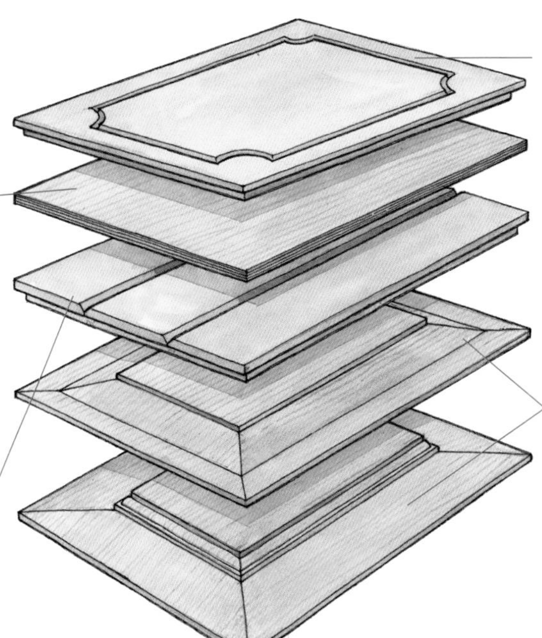

Relief moulded Panels
Cut from MDF sheet, these have a decorative relief moulding cut into the surface, either to form a border parallel to the edges or as a pattern across the panel surface. Panel moulding cutters are used to machine the moulding, guided by a template and guide bush, straightedge or the side-fence.

Raised, fielded and moulded panels
These traditional panel boarders can be simply cut using the router fitted with a panel raising cutter selected from the Trend range.

Panels

The door frame can be fitted with either a plain or decorative panel made from solid timber of sheet material. However the panels must be made from a stable material that won't shrink or twist in the frame.

The finished thickness needs to be a sliding fit in the door groove, but not so tight that it causes the weak rear edge of the panel groove to break away.

Where the panel material is much thicker than the door groove it can either be rebated on one or both faces, or reduced in thickness with a large decorative mould to form the classic raised and fielded effect.

Calculating the panel sizes

The most reliable way to determine the panel size is to temporarily clamp the door frame together and measure the actual inside groove dimensions.

Depending on the panel material, some allowance must be made for movement as large panels are rarely dimensionally stable. Timber will always shrink significantly more across its width, than along the length. So for solid timber frames and panels, reduce the measured width by 6mm and the length by 2mm to get the ideal panel dimension. The panels are always left loose in the frames to allow this movement to occur. If you do glue them in place, the panel will probably split or warp the door as the movement is restrained.

Frames and panels made from MDF or plywood can theoretically be cut to dead size as these are unlikely to move, but in reality, it is easier to assemble them if there is a 1mm allowance all round.

Making a template for a shaped panel

Curved and shaped panels can be cut and moulded using a template cut to fit into the frame, in much the same way as cutting the rails. Create the outline for the template by drawing round the inside of the dry assembled frame and then adding on the required groove width, less the shrinkage allowance. Cut this out carefully, where possible using the router with a trammel, to get the necessary smooth and square edged curved outline.

You can then use this template to mark out each panel before cutting them slightly oversize.

They can be trimmed to match the template using a bearing guided template profiling cutter.

For repetition work, it is worth making a simple combined jig using a pair of matched templates mounted on a base board, as this allows you to cut both the rails and matching shaped panels.

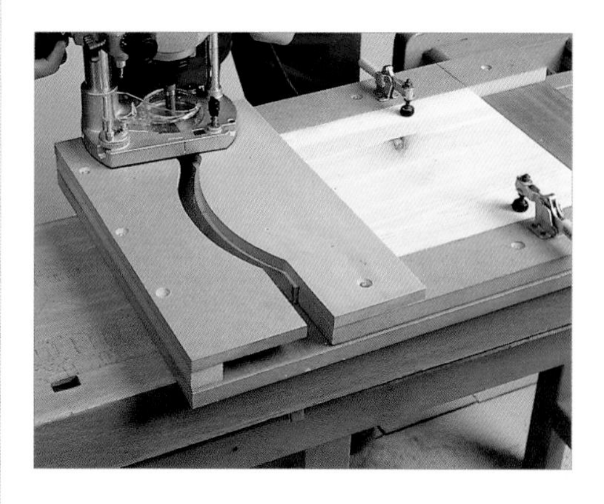

Raised panels

Rectangular or shaped panels are formed using either horizontal or vertical raised panel cutters which are available in a range of styles.

They are guided by either the table fence, a guide bearing or a template. The large diameter horizontal panel raising cutters should only be used with the router mounted in or over a table, whereas the vertical cutters can be used in hand-held machines with suitable additional support, although it is preferable to use a table. However, it is not possible to use the vertical panel raising cutters for producing shaped panels.

Vertical panel raising cutters

Being smaller in diameter, some of these cutters are available with 8mm shanks and can therefore be used in lighter duty routers without a variable speed facility.

Ideally, they are used on a router table with an additional taller sub fence to provide some extra vertical support. A horizontal pressure guard of some type is also needed to keep the bottom edge of the panel pressed flat against the fence, otherwise the panel edge thickness will vary. If you want to use these cutters in a handheld router, the panel needs to be clamped vertically, with some extra horizontal support to prevent the router wobbling.

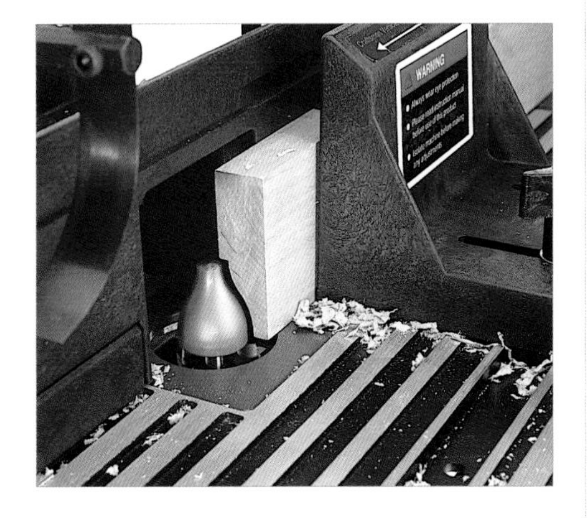

Horizontal panel raising cutters

Large diameter horizontal panel raising cutters can be used for moulding either straight or shaped panels, the latter requiring a bearing guided version.

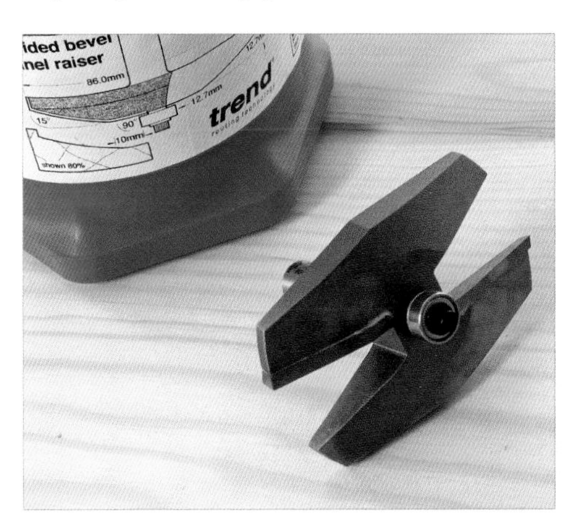

Because of their extreme size, care must be exercised with these cutters and they must only be used in a fixed router and at the recommended speed. Cutters above 50 mm in diameter should not be used at speeds over 18,000 rpm. Above 67 mm diameter, the maximum speed is 16,000 rpm and above 80mm diameter, the limitation is 12,000 rpm.

Some router tables may not have an aperture big enough to accept the cutter, in which case fit a false table top which will allow the cutter to be set slightly lower than the surface.

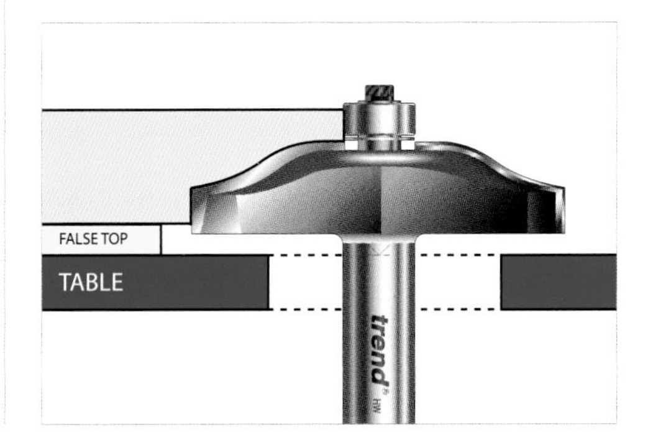

Never try and cut to the full depth in one pass with these large diameter cutters, the router will struggle to maintain the rpm and the cutter may snatch. Instead, take several shallow passes, finishing off with a really light one which will be at full router speed and therefore leave the best possible finish.

Wider mouldings can be produced by resetting the fence to allow the cutter to cut in a series of passes.

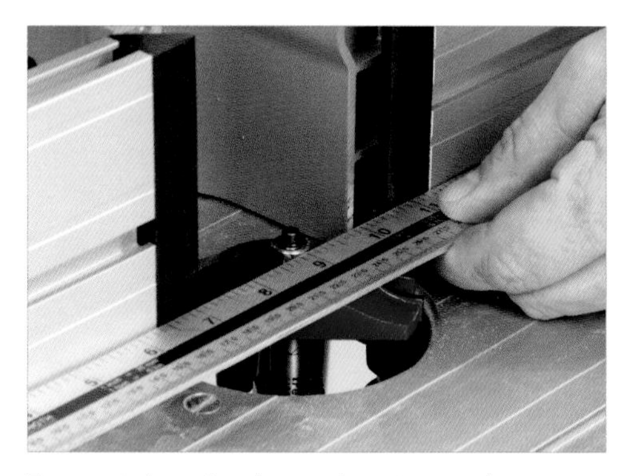

For straight edged panels, it is usual to use the table fence, even with bearing guided cutters, setting the bearing in line with the fence.

With curved panels and a full sized template, you can just use the bearing guided cutter, but there must be some form of lead-in fitted to the table. This lead-in should be fixed securely to the table as close as possible to the cutter to provide a rest, so that the work can be steadied against it as it is fed into the cutter.

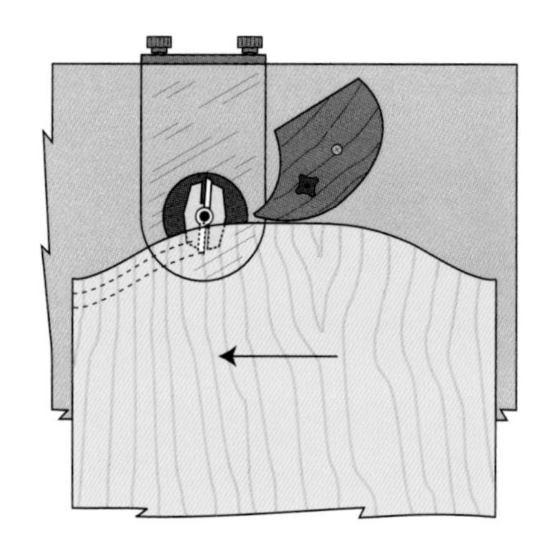

Always make the cross grain cuts first as any break-out will then be removed by the long grain cuts.

If you have a problem with the cutter tearing the grain, try pre-scoring the edge of the cut with a sharp knife first.

Simple panel raising

Whilst the various proprietary panel raising cutters are very effective, the majority of them are extremely large in diameter, which in turn necessitates the use of a router table and a heavy-duty router. All this becomes very expensive, even ignoring the not insignificant cost of the cutters themselves. This may be fine if you are making panels for a living, as the initial investment is soon recouped in terms of the amount of production time saved and the quality of the finished job.

However, on a smaller workshop scale, where fielded panel production is a relatively rare event, a less expensive alternative is available.

You can produce plain chamfered fielded panels using just a small router fitted with a straight bottom cut bit and a suitable guide bush.

You will however need to make a jig to hold the panel at a suitable angle to cut the necessary large chamfer and there are several alternative designs for such a jig.

The profile of the fielding is obviously just a straight taper and whilst this is probably fine for some jobs, it may be that you want a small flat tongue on the panel where it enters the surrounding rails.

If this is the case, cut an initial rebate round the panel using the router with the side-fence in the conventional way and then use your jig to form the rest of the slope.

If the fielding is deep, it also becomes more obvious that the edge of the raised section is angled in slightly, since the cutter is not at right angles to the surface. Whilst this may not be too apparent on shallow cuts, it is much more obvious and may not be acceptable on deep ones. In this case, again use the router and side fence and run around the raised section to straighten up the cut.

Another way of making up the panels is to plant routed centre pieces onto a flat panel.

This is often applied when the raised section needs to be particularly high or the flat section is especially wide. Planted-on panels are fine for work that is to be painted but for high quality work the lack of grain continuity is usually obvious and may detract from the finished appearance of the door.

If you are making glass doors, the frames are made up in exactly the same way, replacing the panel with a sheet of glass. Some of the profile scribe sets are available with 4mm groovers to take thinner glass for smaller doors.

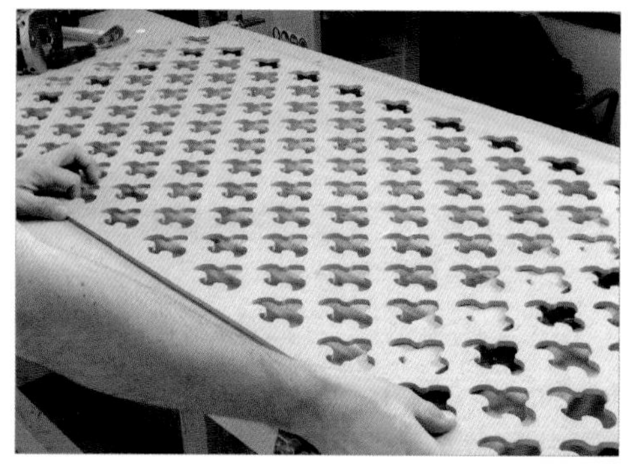

Similarly, there are now a vast range of grille patterns available in metal and MDF, all of which can be used to make very effective door panels.

Assembling panel doors

Having taken so much care machining the components of the door, it is important that they are assembled equally carefully to keep the door square and true.

Start with a dry assembly to make sure everything fits together easily without needing force, otherwise weak edges will be split away. Mark each piece for easy reference and do as much sanding as possible before assembly as it is much more difficult to do it later.

Avoid applying excess glue as this will squeeze up into the panel groove, sticking the panel tight and restricting its movement. Man-made panels can be safely glued into the frame, but timber ones should be secured with a couple of fine veneer pins at the centre of each rail. This still allows for movement but stops the panels rattling in their frame if they do shrink.

Cramp the door using packing pieces on the cramp jaws to protect the edges and check it is all properly square by measuring the diagonals, ensuring it is not bowed. Remove any excess glue before it dries, particularly in the detailed corner mouldings but avoid spreading it into the surface of the grain as this may affect subsequent staining and polishing.

If you have left the stiles over-length the horns can be trimmed back carefully when the glue has set.

If the doors are to be fitted to the face of a carcass or frame, they look more aesthetically pleasing if you rout a

decorative mould around the outside edge. Choose a moulding cutter of a similar size and style to the profile moulding, ideally one with a bearing guide. If the panel is raised higher than the surrounding frame, fit a packing piece to the base of the router to provide additional support to stop the router tipping.

On cabinets with no centre partition to act as a stop between the meeting stiles of double doors, the edges are usually rebated. However, this makes the width across the face of the two stiles appear to be uneven so balance them up by routing a bead on the face of the widest stile to equalise the gap. The bead diameter must equal the width of the rebate.

Door panels can be decorated further using the Trend Router Carver system that allows you to carve a range of designs. Pre-formed templates guide the router both horizontally and vertically to produce variable depths of cut.

Fitting hinges

Cabinet doors are generally hung using either flap hinges set into a rectangular recess, or concealed Blum® or circular type hinges set into a circular recess on the back of the door. These latter ones are usually used on kitchen doors and are spring loaded so that the door doesn't require a catch.

Flap hinge recesses

Rectangular recesses can be cut using a simple template and guide bush combination. For small cabinet hinges, a small diameter straight flute cutter can be used but as it is cutting in from the edge; it will not require a bottom cut. Although not strictly needed, there is a dedicated hinge recessing cutter which is ideal for shallow lateral cuts, the two flute TCT cutting edges giving excellent chip clearance.

However, the cutter will leave rounded corners, requiring the corner to be finished with a sharp chisel or a dedicated corner chisel such as Trend's.

You can set the depth of cut on the stop using the actual hinge flap as a spacer.

Round recesses

These can either be cut with the router or in a vertical drill press using a dedicated hinge sinking bit. If the router is chosen, make sure you use only the dedicated router bits as these are designed for use at high speeds with scribers that ensure a very clean hole. For accurate repetitive boring, make up a suitable template and use it with a guide bush on the router.

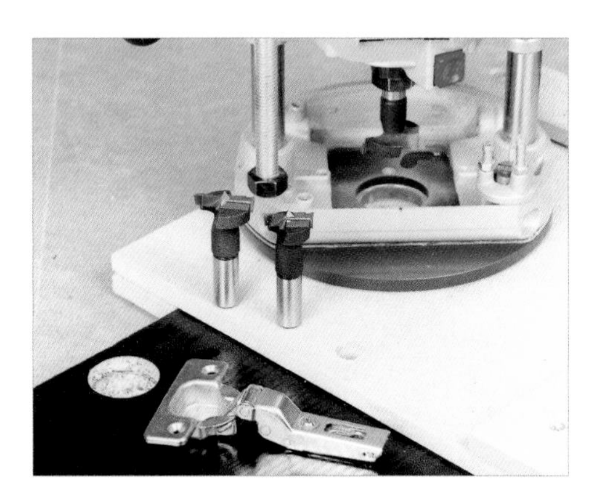

Larger doors

Interior and exterior doors are often built on the same principles using a frame and panel construction, the only difference being that the material is thicker.

The amazing strength of modern glues means that a lot of commercial timber constructions like doors, do not now need the mechanical strength of large joints.

On an interior door with a frame construction, it is often enough to rely on an ovolo scribe and profile to form the joint, but for more demanding applications, and certainly for exterior use, the joints need to be supplemented with a mortise and tenon for additional strength.

A simpler more traditional approach is to make up a grooved frame with square edged timber using standard jointing techniques and then decorate it by machining a separate mouldings round the edges of the panel.

Such mouldings can either sit within the frame edges or overlap slightly, i.e. the so called Bolection mould.

A variation of this technique is to make up the frame first and then run the router round it to apply the mould.

This inevitably leaves rounded corners between the stile and rail, which may or may not be acceptable.

Of course there are many other styles of door which can all be enhanced with a little router work. For instance the standard ledged and braced door is greatly improved if the joints are decorated with a simple bead mould or even just a plain V profile.

Louvre doors are easily made using a simple angled template and guide bush set-up.

Some doors used in both domestic and industrial situations may be subject to fire regulations that rely on the fitting of an intumescent strip as a smoke seal which has to be recessed into the door itself. This can be achieved with a standard 10mm cutter using one, or preferably two side-fences on the router.

Alternatively, dedicated cutters are available that allow you to work from the face of the door, or from the face of the frame if the strip is to be fitted into the door rebate.

A door can be cut to length very cleanly using the router working against a suitable straightedge. The cut must be made in several passes to avoid overloading the router, and it may help to scribe the line with a sharp knife first to prevent the cross grain areas from feathering. Use the same procedure if you need to cut a rebate on the

bottom of an external door. Special cutters are available to cut the slight leading angle on the underside of the door.

Simple hinge sinking jigs can be used to hang these larger doors but for trade users there are several larger jigs that allow you to cut the recesses in the door and the linings with one set up.

Similarly locks and other hardware can also be recessed with the router. For standard locks, there is a jig that uses a set of interchangeable templates to cut both the mortise and face plate recess.

Cutting a neat letterbox opening in the door is always difficult, a jigsaw will not cut straight and square in such deep material. The router will ensure a perfectly clean and square cut provided you use a template. You can either make your own or use one of the proprietary adjustable ones if you have many different sized openings to cut.

Drawers

While traditional drawer construction using blind or through dovetails can be achieved using a dovetail jig, the router is ideal for some much simpler methods of drawer construction.

Use it to make simple or bare faced lap joints, or even using one of the specialised drawer jointing cutters designed for this purpose.

Inset drawers slide in to finish flush with the carcass, with only the front normally being made of decorative material. The rest of the drawer is normally made from plainer, less expensive material. Overlapping drawers are made by screwing a larger false front onto a simple box construction. In either case, the front can be decorated with edge mouldings or routed on the face.

Drawer slides

Drawers can be allowed to just slide into their recess in the cabinet, running on the bottom edge of the drawer sides.

This is fine for most applications but the use of some form of drawer slide will make the drawer close more smoothly. The simplest slides are formed by cutting a wide square section groove centrally along the face of each side. This then slides over a batten, preferably of hardwood, screwed to the inside faces of the cabinet.

Alternatively, proprietary metal or plastic slides can be used. For these, the drawer needs to be constructed smaller than the inside width of the cabinet to allow for the thickness of the slides on either side. These have many advantages, the principal one being that they are very smooth running, don't wear and incorporate automatic stops to prevent the drawer being pulled out too far.

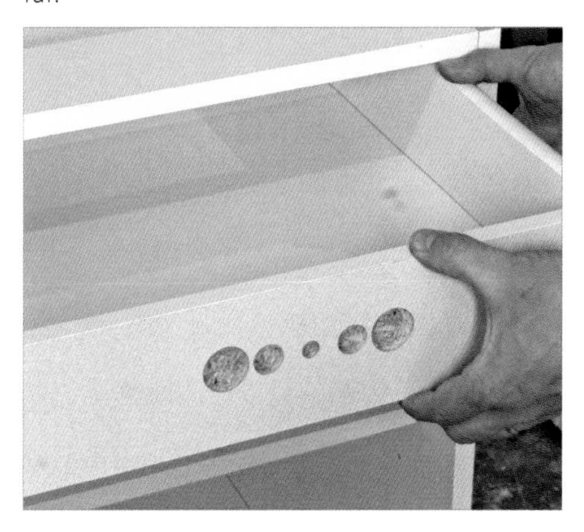

Storage and furniture construction

Every room in the house, and even the garage has need for storage, whether it be simple open shelves, wall hung units or free standing cabinets. Whatever their construction, these all require accurate and neatly cut components. A task that the router with its range of accessories and cutters can perform with relative ease and minimum of operator skill. The range of possible designs is limitless but the following few pages illustrate some of the basic principles and techniques.

At its simplest, furniture can be constructed from a series of standard base units as found in kitchens. These can be modified to take drawers, cupboards, or a mixture of both. They will also house built-in appliances and to support a continuous run of worktop.

These base units are essentially boxes made from sheet material and jointed at the corners. They are inherently weak but are greatly strengthened by adding a back which normally slides into a groove in the sides.

A stronger unit is obtained if you can stiffen the carcass with a shallow frame at the top and bottom, but in reality this is often simplified down to some deep top and bottom rails, with the bottom one set back to locate a kickboard.

If you use vertical frames to stiffen the structure, you can use the router to put in some decorative detail like fluting to add more style to the unit and personalise the basic construction.

Base units for modular construction are normally based around standard dimensions. These are 900mm tall, 600mm deep and then 300, 400, 500 or 600mm wide. Double units are 1000 or 1200mm wide.

These dimensions are more or less universal and allow you to buy ready made doors or drawer fronts to suit your own carcass units.

This form of base unit is normally constructed from standard veneered panels; either timber or melamine faced, and are assembled with biscuits, housing joints or with standard knock down fittings.

Wall units are made in a similar way although they are standardised at 300mm deep. You can either make them to fill the gap to the ceiling, or leave a gap for fitting a cornice moulding to the top of the unit.

The same construction principles are used for solid timber work, with much of the emphasis on biscuits and housing joints, but there is now more scope for moulding edges and adding other decorative detail. Refinements like corner beads and some of the other classic profiles greatly add to the finished appearance.

The alternative to routing decorative profiles

direct onto the components themselves, is to add separate trims to enhance the appearance. You can use a moulding cut in a single or multiple passes, or build up a composite using several separate profiles. This latter approach is perfect for the heavy section mouldings found on longcase clocks for instance.

Cornices can be built up in a similar way if you only have a small router, although there are specialist cutters to machine it in one pass, but they require the use of a heavy duty router and suitable table.

Shelving units are another useful item of furniture that can be made to a professional looking standard with the aid of a little simple router work. A housing jig will speed up the process of making the necessary stopped grooves, using either a guide bush or a straight cutter with a bearing mounted on the shank.

Alternatively shelves can be made adjustable using a template to rout a series of shelf support holes.

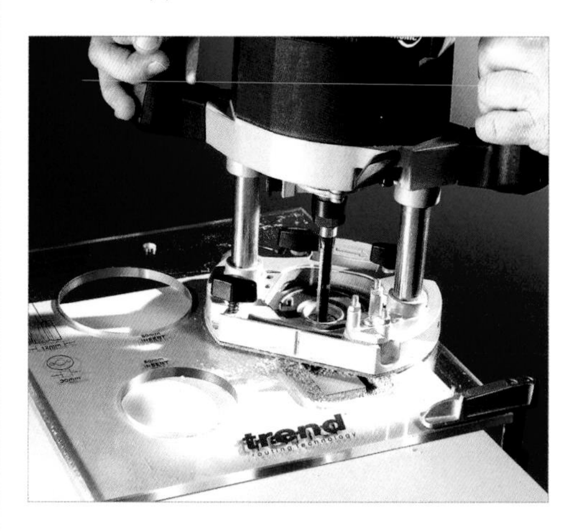

If you are making desks then the router can be used for fitting a range of cable management inserts which are available in a variety of styles. A corner template ensures the corners of the top are all radiused identical.

Wooden worktops for kitchen use may require water channels which can be cut with a standard radius cutter or a dedicated radiused rebate cutter.

Although there is a vast array of cabinet furniture available off the shelf, it may be that your design requires some bespoke touches such as drawer pulls and special cutters are available for just this purpose.

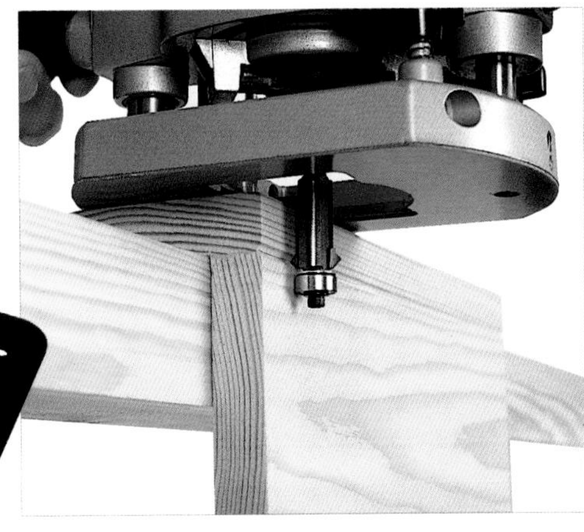

Specialist groovers allow you to make decorative cuts in panels and frames to disguise glue lines or to form a fluting effect.

If you need to hang a picture flush to the wall, a keyhole cutter can be used to cut the necessary shaped recess that ensures secure hanging.

A variation of this cutter is the T slot version that cuts either round or square slots for concealing electric cables. These special cutters require a 6mm slot to be cut first with a straight groover.

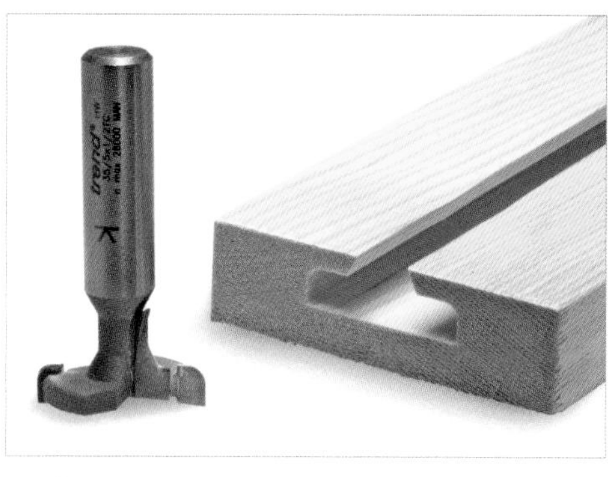

Modern merchandising units use hanging pegs that fit into a slatted back and a variety of cutters are available to cut the necessary profiles.

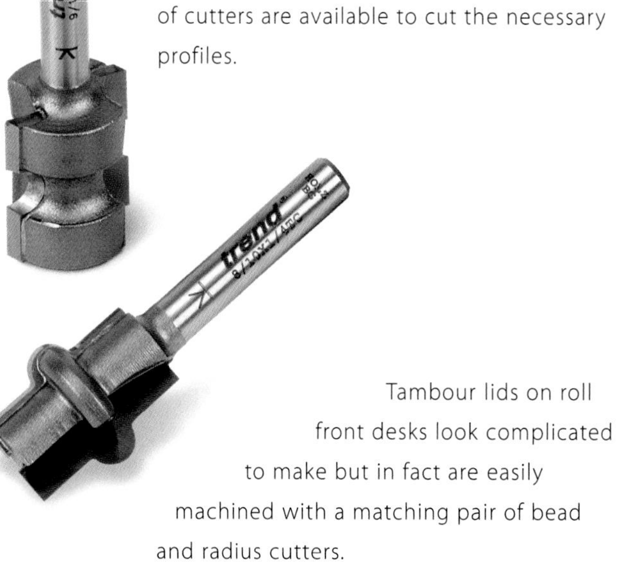

Tambour lids on roll front desks look complicated to make but in fact are easily machined with a matching pair of bead and radius cutters.

Joinery construction

Windows

Replacing a window frame is easier than would appear at first and is well within the capability of a small or medium duty router. The frame can be made up in a similar way as for making a door and in fact uses many of the same cutters.

However, although you can do much of the work with standard cutters, there are special sets of matched glazing bar cutters that cut the sash bar profile and simultaneously form the scribed joint between them.

There are a variety of different profiles, but most of the simpler ones require the glass rebate to be cut separately.

The window board is easily machined with either a rounding over or a staff bead cutter.

An existing window with single glazed units can be upgraded to take double glazing by using the router to deepen the rebates.

Older windows showing signs of rot can often be salvaged by routing out the damaged area and splicing in a new piece. Make a simple template and pin it in place then use a straight cutter and a guide bush to remove the rot. Rout well into the surrounding area to be sure of removing the damaged wood, and if possible, avoid routing close to stile and rail joints.

Widow frames benefit greatly from having a draught proofing strip fitted, and whilst the necessary housing for this is best cut during the manufacturing stage, it can be made in situ to improve an existing window. In practice, the corners of the frame will cause an obstruction, so a small amount of handwork with a chisel will be necessary to complete the job.

Mouldings

Skirting boards, architraves, picture rails and dados can all be formed with the router, but although you can make them with several passes using smaller cutters there are specialised cutters designed to cut the whole profile in one pass.

Obviously, because of their size these cutters need a heavy duty router and machining is usually more efficient if it is used under a router table. Because the profiles are so deep it may be necessary to fit shims to the outfeed fence to provide suitable support for the work as it is fed through the cutter.

Inevitably, there are going to be long pieces, so make sure there is plenty of support both at the cutter and on the outfeed side of the table. Don't let the ends waggle about as this will cause a ripple effect. A roller stand is essential if you are working on your own, as even the slightest movement at the tip of the work will ruin the length of moulding. Find a helper if there are many long pieces to be worked and feed steadily to get a smooth finish.

The available range of cutters covers most of the 'standard' profiles, which have changed little over the years. However, the router is ideally suited for making up smaller runs of moulding to match some existing non standard profile.

More ornate effects can be obtained by fitting corner blocks which could be carving them using the Router Carver system or possibly applying some standard decorative moulding.

Architraves for curved top doors or windows can be formed using the router fitted with a beam trammel, and the technique can be extended even to make a fully circular window frame.

It is sometimes necessary to make up large columns either for support or to conceal some existing feature such as steelwork or piping. A simple box construction with tongue and groove or biscuit joints can form the main structure, but the joints can be concealed and the structure lightened in appearance by adding decorative fluting or other moulding. The sharp corners will also benefit from some routing work, usually by introducing a stopped chamfer.

For multiple fluting profiles, make a pass from each side with each fence setting to minimise the amount of resetting between cuts.

Radiator covers are another popular project for the router and they are extremely simple and quick to make up. The main carcass can be made from either MDF, or solid timber.

Simple mouldings are all that you need and there is a good range of grilles available in a range of wood based and metal materials, allowing you to create either contemporary or traditional effects.

Most of these decorative mouldings can be fixed discreetly using fine pins or adhesives.

However, it is sometimes necessary to screw them in place so use a plug cutter to make suitable pellets to conceal the screw holes,

but take care to set the correct speed on the router for this work.

Decorative detail doesn't need to be restricted to the edge of furniture and joinery work. Cut through detailing can be used for numerous applications but is typified by decorative bargeboards.

These use a repeating pattern which is easily cut using a template, moving along the length for each successive cut. The bulk of the material is removed with a jigsaw and the final profile is trimmed back to the template with the router. Once the shape has been formed, further routing can be carried out to profile the edges using bearing guided cutters.

Similarly pierced cut outs in furniture can be enhanced with a chamfer cutter or similar.

Hand rails for staircase work are now easily produced using the router as there is a large range of standard profiles available, though these usually have to be used in conjunction with another cutter to produce the rounded top profile.

However, as with skirtings and architraves you can use a combination of individual cutters to match up to an existing profile. As they are mostly bearing guided, handrail cutters can also be used to machine up simple curved sections as well.

The Routabout system produces a very neat solution to the problem of forming access holes in flooring. The jig cuts out a perfect circle that is then replaced into the floor with a suitable spacer ring to provide instant access to pipes or cables.

Miniature work

If you are involved with small fine work and in particular dolls house making, there is a good selection of 1:12 scale cutters available to produce all the mouldings you need to replicate full sized joinery and furniture work.

Making your own mouldings is considerably cheaper than buying prepared stock and it allows you to produce consistent and uniform material in a range of different profiles.

The material needs to be good quality and straight grained with a fine texture. Reclaimed Brazilian Mahogany, Lime and Jelutong are ideal as they can be machined with tiny detail.

Apart from the specialised cutters you do not require anything else for miniature work, though a light duty router is obviously easier to handle than something bulky and powerful. It is also much easier to machine with the router under a table. With such small cutters you do need high speed to produce clean cuts and for regular miniature work it might be worth considering buying a specialised miniature router and table.

This features higher speeds and the table has smaller openings than a standard table to give much better support to small sections. However, you could quite easily make your own miniature table and fence to overcome these problems.

The problem with a lot of miniature work is actually holding the material and a better finish is often obtained by routing the edge of a wider board and then slicing off the moulding strip.

The components for the dolls house itself can be cut using a standard router using a range of templates for operations such as cutting the widow and door openings.

Inspiration

All of these routing techniques can be applied to making a range of simple furniture and other household objects.

Use the panel door principles for assembling planters or storage boxes or even mirror or picture frames.

Tables are always useful and you can use the router to create all the necessary joints for contemporary or traditional styled pieces.

Routing applications are not limited to inside furniture either and you can soon fit out your garden with some very stylish outdoor seating.

The ability to make drawers easily with the router opens up a whole range of possibilities for storage projects made in timber and MDF.

Storage is always at a premium in any household, but with a router you can make shelving units in a variety of styles.

Don't forget the kitchen as well, plenty of scope here for useful projects.

Glossary

A

acrylic

Plastic type of material, often with trade names e.g. Perspex, Plexiglas and Oroglass. Used as alternative to glass. TC cutters should be used to machine acrylic materials as they tend to be abrasive.

aperture

A hole in the centre of something.

arbor

A spindle onto which a variety of slotting, slitting and grooving cutters can be mounted along with various spacers and a locking nut. A ball bearing may also slide on the spindle to act as a guide as an alternative to a side-fence.

architrave

A moulded framework surround for doors, archways, etc. Architraves can be machined with a router or spindle moulder.

armature

Found on commutator (carbon brush) motors. Includes the rotor, windings and commutator. In a router, the armature has a thread on one end which holds the collet and nut assembly.

arris

A sharp edge produced where two surfaces meet at an angle.

automatic feed

A powered device for feeding timber through a machine.

B

back-cutting

Feeding the workpiece in the same direction as the cutter. This should generally be avoided as it tends to lead to 'snatching ' of the workpiece and reduced quality of finish. A notable exception being the use of a suitably constructed jig, for example a dovetailing jig.

barley twist moulding

A spiral pattern resembling a twisted rope. This type of turning can only be produced easily with the Trend Routerlathe or similar devices.

barrel moulding

A moulding with a convex or bellied profile. Also called a 'pulvenated' moulding.

batten

Any straight-edged piece of timber or material used as a guide against which the router or portable saw passes.

bead

A small rounded (convex) profile or moulding. Available in numerous variations and sizes.

beam trammel

A flat bar with a pivot point onto which the router is mounted to cut curves and circles.

bevel

A surface or edge cut at an angle. A 45 degree bevel is called a chamfer.

biscuit dowel

These are dowels compressed in the form of an oval biscuit with roughened surfaces to give a key for PVA glue to adhere to.

biscuit jointing

Means of jointing timber and composite boards using dowels shaped like oval biscuits. Special 'biscuit' jointing power tools are available but the techniques are easily carried out using a conventional router.

bit
Term used in the USA and sometimes in the UK, meaning a router cutter (all grades). Available in straight form, helical shaped, or with a multitude of mould profiles.

blockboard
A board made from cores of timber bonded together and covered with veneer on both sides.

bolection
A raised and rebated moulding which projects beyond the face of the frame into which it is inserted.

bottom cut
A straight bit with cutting edges on the end to allow plunge cutting.

box corner joint
Another term for a comb joint. Grooves for comb-jointing are usually cut by a series of stacked groovers mounted on an arbor. Box corner joints can also be produced with a straight router cutter in conjunction with a suitable jig.

box jig
A guiding device which involves the workpiece being held within a box structure for machining or drilling to a pattern.

brazing
A form of welding that secures a carbide cutting edge to the steel body of a router cutter.

break-out
Term used for describing the splitting out of the edge of material being machined.

bridle joint
A joint similar to a mortise and tenon but with the positions of the mortise and tenon reversed.

built-up cornice
A cornice produced by joining several sections together.

built-up timber
This refers to timber which has been jointed from smaller sections.

burning
This occurs generally when routing at too slow a feed rate, taking too deep a cut, or when the non-cutting part of the tool is rubbing the workpiece. It can also indicate that a router cutter may need resharpening.

burrs
Small multi-fluted rasps used for deburring, cleaning welds, and woodcarving. Normally used in portable hand grinders or light-duty hand routers.

butt-joint
A joint made when two pieces of wood are joined together with no overlap, shoulders, or tenons.

C

cambrio
A particular arched shape formed on the top of raised panel doors.

cam clamp
A simple means of clamping a workpiece by using an eccentric shaped component, which is pivoted round to exert pressure.

capillary cutter
A cutter which produces a radiused groove in window and door joinery, for the purpose of draining off water.

carbide
Tungsten carbide, a very hard and durable compound used to make router cutters. This is either brazed onto steel shoulders or produced as an integral solid carbide cutter. Carbide requires careful handling and storage as it is brittle.

carbon brushes

Found in a commutator motor. The brushes feed current to the windings on the rotor and bear on the metal segments (commutator) on the rotor.

carbon steel

Used for twist drills and machine bits and has 0.6 to 1.8 % carbon content.

carcass

The body part of a box-like piece of furniture without the doors and fittings.

casement

A glazed frame or sash which is either hinged or pivoted.

cavetto

A quarter-round concave moulding, with a quirk shoulder.

chamfer

A bevelled edge made on a corner of a workpiece between 30 and 60 degrees.

chatter marks

A series of ripples left on the cut surface caused by feeding too fast or using a blunt cutter.

cheek

A strip of timber or plastic often used to extend the bearing surface of a fence to prevent router or timber running off course when feeding-in.

chipboard

Manmade wood particle board used in cupboards and shelf units, usually faced with a veneer, plastic laminate or melamine foil. TCT cutters should be used with this abrasive material.

chip limiting

The space between the surface of the cut and the bit body that controls the size of the cut and the speed of feeding.

chuck

Usually refers to the holding device at the end of a power drill or lathe. Serves a similar purpose to that of a collet on a router.

clearance angle

The angle of the cutter edge relative to the body of the bit.

cnc

Computer numerical control. The technique where a cutting head such as a router is controlled by a computer through a program defining the cutting path to be followed.

collet

A chuck or gripping device which fits on the end of a routing machine spindle to hold the shank of the cutters.

collet capacity

The size of cutter shank that will fit a particular collet. Common sizes are 1/4", 3/8", 1/2", 8mm and 12mm.

collet nut

The hexagonal nut that retains the collet in place on the spindle of a router.

comb joint

A joint usually consisting of parallel cut fingers which interlock. Often called a corner box joint.

combination cutter

A cutter which can perform more than one profiling or shaping operation, usually by applying it at different depths and angles.

concentric

One or more circles within each other, having the same centre point.

contour

The profile or section of a moulding, denoting shape and size.

copy router

A router which has the facility to cut or profile when working from a template or guide.

core box

A groove with a rounded concave bottom. A core box cutter is often termed a radius cutter or a veining bit.

Corian®

A 'marble-like' solid surface plastic material with a dense structure used in luxury kitchens and bathrooms. Can be cut to a wide variety of shapes and designs with router cutters. (Corian is a trademark of Du Pont)

counterboring

A method of recessing the head of a screw or bolt into material. Tools which drill and cut the recess simultaneously are called counterborers.

countersinks

Similar to counterboring, but these tools cut countersink recesses to receive bolts and screws with countersunk heads.

cove

A round concave moulding, normally produced by a radius cutter, used mainly for edging purposes.

cramp

Equivalent term to 'clamp'.

cutter blocks

Usually refers to the main body of a spindle cutter head into which cutters are inserted and locked. The term is also used to refer to the body of router cutters which have replaceable cutting edges.

cutter creep

Movement of the cutter shank within the collet during use, caused by insufficient tightening or collet wear.

cutting diameter

The maximum width of the path made by any router cutter in one pass.

cutting length

The maximum length of the full cutting edge of a router cutter.

D

dado

Square or rectangular recessed channels cut into a wood surface against the grain of the wood.

'dead man' switch

On/off switch without a lock so it must be held 'on' at all times when using the router.

depth gauge

A means of limiting the amount of plunge on the router to cut to a predetermined depth.

depth of cut

Length of cutting edge of a router cutter or, depending on how the cutter is set-up in the router, the depth of cut the tool has been set-up to produce.

depth stop

A device on a routing machine which is adjusted to set the depth of cut the plunge action will reach.

dial gauge

An engineering tool designed to make minute measurements.

disposable tip cutter

A type of cutter used in industrial or heavier duty applications. The tips of the cutter can be removed when blunt and replaced with new ones. This type of tooling can increase productivity by reducing down time on CNC machines.

dovetail

A joint in which one part is tapered in shape (the 'dove's tail') and fits in a socket shaped to correspond. As a result of its design, it produces a strong joint to resists any outward pull. A strong reliable means of jointing timber.

dowel

A headless pin of wood or composite used with an adhesive, to hold a joint together.

dowel drilling bits

Accurately sized cutters for drilling holes to receive dowels. Also used for cutting holes to receive plugs. For use in plunge routers or drilling machines. Often called lip and spur bits.

dowelling jig

A jig enabling a series of exactly spaced holes to be bored accurately in both members to be joined. Specially useful for dowelling door frames, mitres, and similar work. Can usually be used with a plunge router or power drill.

down-cut shear

A straight bit with the cutting edges slightly inclined so that they push down on the surface of the cut.

downtime

Non-productive time such as when changing cutters or repairing machines.

drop leaf table

Sometimes called a 'flag table', drop leaf tables use a rule joint system for hinging. This involves routing an ovolo mould on a table with a radius profile on the leaf to match.

E

eccentric

One or more circles within each other not having the same centre point.

eccentric chuck

Chuck to hold eccentric router cutters. The chuck has a hole which is bored off centre.

eccentric cutter

Cutters which cut 'off centre' with cutting edge being proud of the body, giving a larger cutting diameter

edge planing

Using a straight cutter to make a very light cleaning cut along the edge of a workpiece.

edge trimming

Cutting back the edge of a workpiece or overlay to a pre-determined size.

edging

Length of solid wood used to edge composite boards, such as plywood, chipboard and MDF to give an attractive appearance and provide a stronger fixing base for screws, etc.

electronic

Referring to the current generation of routers which have a variable speed motor (8000-25000rpm) for soft start, and speed selection for different diameter cutters (the larger the diameter the slower the speed). Full wave electronics prevent any drop-off in speed underload so ensuring an accurate finish.

ellipse

The technical description is 'the cross section of a cone at any angle other than at right angles with the axis.' Ellipse routing jigs are available for fitting to portable routers.

end grain

The view of an end grain, as seen when timber is cut approximately 90 degrees to the grain direction (traverse).

escutcheon plate

A metal plate around a keyhole, which

protects the surrounding surface; or the metal lining of the keyhole itself.

F

face edge
This is the 'master edge' from which other measurement and markings are made. The face edge must be planed and finished absolutely square.

face side
The surface of a flat, planed piece of timber that is used for the first marks and measurements, and from which all other measurements are taken.

false base
This is usually a sub-base or adjustable base fitted to a router or jig to support it or guide it.

false fence
An additional thin fence made from hardwood or plastic, which is fixed to the metal face of the fence on a router table either to prevent splintering-out (break-out) or to give more support when machining long lengths of board.

featherboard
A special holding device designed to push the work up against the fence on a router table.

feather edge
The end of a section of wood cut to a wedge, or tapered point. Used also for wedge clamping.

feed direction
The direction in which the router is moved in relation to the grain of the workpiece. On a router table, the direction in which the workpiece is advanced in relation to the rotation of the bit. (This should always be opposite).

feed rate
The speed at which the router is advanced by the operator. When the router is fixed, it is the speed at which the timber is fed.

fence
A guide fence is a ledge against which timber is passed to keep it on an even path.

fielded panel
A decorative panel used in a framework or door. It consists of a panel with a wide chamfered rebate worked around the edges. Often a small moulding is worked at the inner side of the rebate. The cross grain should be worked first.

fillet
A small strip of wood used to support shelves, but also loosely applied to a narrow strip of timber fastened to the surface of the workpiece to act as a fence when the router is working beyond the capacity of its own fence.

fine adjuster
Most plunge routers have a feed in device for the fine feeding of the router head or side-fence.

fine height adjuster
A screw mechanism allowing you to make precise adjustments to the cutter height.

finger joint
A corner joint consisting of a series of interlocking projections like a dovetail but without the tapers.

fixed base router
A router that remains in one fixed vertical position throughout the operation. A plunge router fully compressed and locked serves the same purpose.

fixed head routing
The router is mounted in a fixed position, either above or below the worktable.

flute

A straight or spiral groove behind the cutting edge of a router cutter that permits the chips to be expelled from the cut. Good fluting is necessary to clear the chips efficiently.

forstner bit

A special bit which is guided by its circular rim rather than its centre point. The advantage of this tool is that it bores a neat, cleanly-cut hole with a flat bottom, its centre point serves only to ensure accuracy for the starting cut. Not for use with abrasive materials unless TCT grade is used.

frame jig

A device for guiding a router along or within a frame of narrow battens. Usually adjustable to accept different size workpieces

framing

An assembly of pieces serving as an enclosure or a support for a decorative skin.

G

g-clamps

G shaped clamp made from solid metal, with screw thread turn handle.

g-codes

The ISO standard control codes for CNC routers. For example G01 X50 Y50 is a straight line movement 50 mm diagonally from the origin.

glazing bar

Bar with two rebates to hold glass at each side, and usually but not invariably moulded. Used widely in windows and glazed doors etc.

glazing bead

Small wood bead used to hold a glass pane in its rebate.

glue gun

A hot-melt glue method. Instant bonding, ideal for temporary bonds, eg. fixing work to bench, etc.

gripper clamps

Term for quick-action sliding clamps used in woodworking.

groove

Recessed channel, usually of rectangular section, intended to receive a panel, sliding door, or part of a joint such a a tongue.

grounding

Removing the background of a design which has to be carved.

guide bush

A round ring or bush which is mounted on the base of a router, with a space for the cutter to pass through it. It acts as a guidance device for following templates and board edges.

guide pattern

A template of some sort that guides the router to form a particular shape, used in conjunction with a bearing guided cutter or guide bush.

H

halving joint

Joint where both halves of wood joined together are of equal thickness, used for framing.

hardwood

Deciduous trees generally give hardwood. Note that certain hardwoods do not necessarily have a hard consistency.

haunched

The small projection left by reducing the width of a tenon.

heartwood

The more durable wood (although this varies according to age and type) from the centre of the tree. The dead wood as opposed to the sapwood, which is the growing wood close to the bark of the tree and which carries the sap.

HSS

High-speed steel, hardened and treated high carbon content steel, used to make router cutters giving maximum sharpness. Suitable for non-abrasive materials.

hones and honing

Hones come in many shapes and sizes and in a variety of materials. They are usually applied for honing or touching-up (sharpening) cutting tools, chisels, etc.

horizontal routing

Using the router mounted horizontally in a special table or guiding jig.

housing

A wide trench cut along the grain to house a shelf or similar, also called a 'dado'.

I

inlay

A piece of wood, metal or other material glued into a pre-cut groove or hollow and smoothed flush with the surrounding surface; to insert such a piece.

intumescent strip

Intumescent strip and smoke seal systems provide fire barriers around doors and windows. Specially designed router cutters are available to recess the strips into timber frames.

J

jig

A general term for a device used as a holding and guiding mechanism for a router cutter.

K

kerf

The thickness of cut made by a saw or a slotting tool such as a biscuit jointer router cutter. The terms is also used to refer to the thickness of the blade of the tool.

keyhole cutter

A router cutter that produces a special slotted groove on the backs of picture frames, etc allowing objects to be wall hung.

kick back

The jump back made by a power tool when its cutter or blade jams; or the jump back made by a workpiece when thrown by a machine cutter or blade.

knot

A very hard mass in a piece of timber formed at the junction of a branch. There are two kinds of knot: the 'dead' knot which is loose and generally falls out, and the 'live' knot which is firmly a part of the wood.

L

laminate trim cutter

A router cutter for trimming plastic laminate which trims the overlay or vertical mounted edge strip.

lap joint

A joint where one piece overlaps another.

ledged and braced doors

Consist of vertical boards and horizontal bars or ledges strengthened by diagonal braces.

M

man-made material

Reconstituted materials such as MDF, chipboard, blockboard and plywood.

MDF

Medium-density fibreboard, a versatile man-made board used widely in the woodworking industry. It is smoother than hardboard and denser than chipboard. It has excellent machining characteristics when cut with a router. MDF boards may be veneered or laminated.

mitre

The joining together of two pieces of wood usually but not necessarily 45 degree. A picture frame is a typical example.

mortise

A rectangular hole or slot cut into wood that will receive another member (called a tenon) to make a right-angle joint, or to receive ironmongery such as a lock.

moulding

A wood surface profile, or a narrow strip that is principally used for decoration. A wide range of moulding cutters are available.

multi-boring machine

A drilling machine capable of boring many holes in one operation in a piece of timber.

muntin

Vertical division between the rails in a door or panelling.

N

non-ferrous metals

Softer metals that do not contain iron, such as brass and aluminium.

O

ogee

This cutting profile term has architectural origins. It is a moulding having two curves which impart a wave like profile formed by one convex and one concave curve.

oilstone

A stone on which oil is applied for touching up cutting tools to hone them.

ovolo

This moulding has a convex surface (as opposed to a cavetto) formed from a quarter of a circle or ellipse.

P

panel

A board set in a frame, it can either be below, or above, or flush with, the face of the frame itself. Normally seen in panelled doors and furniture.

pass

In routing, it means one run of the router through the work. Several shallow passes of the router give a better finish than one deep one.

pattern

A shaped form used as a guide for repetitive cutting or making out.

peninsula tops

Kitchen worktops that are accessible from three sides like a breakfast bar.

peripheral speed

The speed of rotation at the extremity of the cutter tip.

pierce and trim

A single cutter designed to cut through a laminate overlay and then trim it back to the underlying shape.

pitch

A thick, sticky, resinous substance or residue often found in softwoods.

Plastazote (and **Esterzote**)

Dense foam compounds often used for packaging and in instrument cases. Good characteristics for machining with a router with sharp high speed steel tools providing the best quality of finish.

plunge
The plunge action of lowering the router cutter into the work. The feature of most modern routers is spring loaded columns for safe vertical movement with the power on.

plunge lock
The mechanism for quickly securing the plunge router down at a set depth.

plywood
A sheet material made by gluing thin layers of wood together with the grain direction of each layer running at right angles to the next one.

PTFE
Polytetrafluoroethylene. A dry lubricant, usually a spray, ideal for use on router bit shanks and collets.

PVA glue
Polyvinyl acetate glue, the most popular modern adhesive for woodworking. It dries under pressure in about two hours at 15 degrees Centigrade. Not a good gap filler. Relies on good surface-to-surface contact to produce a good joints.

PVC
Poly vinyl chloride, a type of plastic material.

Q

quirk
A step or flat area created with an ovolo cutter adjacent to the radius. This is often achieved by using a small bearing with an ovolo cutter. A larger bearing typically would not create the quirk giving only the radius.

R

rabbet cutter or **rebate cutter**
One of many kinds of edge-forming cutters which leave a square cornered edge.

radial arm routing
Using a special bracket to attach the router to a radial arm saw to effectively form an overhead stand.

radial relief
The amount of clearance behind the cutting edge of a cutter that prevents friction between the bit and the timber surface.

radius
Radius of a circle (half the diameter). Radius cutters produce part or half circular concave profiles.

rail
The horizontal member of a door, table carcass, or a chair frame.

rate of feed
The speed at which the cutter travels across the wood, either by feeding the router into the wood, or feeding the wood into the cutter .

re-honed
Rubbed with a sharpening stone to restore the cutting edge.

replaceable tips
TCT cutting blades held on to a cutter with locking screws so that they can be changed when blunt.

riser
The vertical board at the front of each step or tread in a staircase.

roller guide
Special accessory with a bearing fence allowing the router to follow curved edges.

rosette
A circular shaped decorative moulding often used at the corner joints of fireplaces and in cabinet making. Best produced using a purpose-made drilling tool fixed in a pillar drill.

roughing out
Quickly removing the bulk of the waste prior to the finishing cuts.

round-over cutter
One of the several round forming cutters which convert square edges, ends and corners of a board to a convex radius.

router table
Any routing system where the router is mounted in an inverted fixed position and the operator does not manually handle the router. Often provides a safe and accurate means of moulding or profiling workpieces.

S

sacrificial support strip
A waste batten clamped onto the work that is cut into to prevent break-out at the end of a cut.

sacrificial work pad
A waste board placed under the work which allows through cuts to be made.

scalloped
Cut-outs made in a series of regularly spaced circular scoops.

self-guiding cutter
A cutter with a guide bearing or pin which rides against the edge of a workpiece or pattern to limit its horizontal depth of cut. A bearing guide can be mounted on the end of a cutter or on the shank.

shank
The rounded shank of a cutter clamped into the router and held there by the collet.

shoulder cut
The cross-grain cut made on a joint like a tenon or lap joint.

ski supports
Additional supports used to control the router on uneven surfaces.

slotter
A cutter designed to produce slots in timber. Often used with a bearing guide.

snatching
When the revolving cutter picks up the work and tries to throw it off sideways, caused by touching the work whilst the cutter is revolving too slowly, see ***kickback***.

soft start
Slow start up without any inertial reaction when you switch on the router.

sole plate
Removable wearing surface covering the base of the router.

softwood
A term used to describe the physical hardness of various woods with low-to-medium impact resistance.

spelching
Damage at the end of a cut where the unsupported grain breaks away.

spike
A large nail, usually more than 4" (102mm) long.

spindle
Main shaft of the router with the collet on the end.

spindle lock
A device on the router shaft or collet that prevents rotation while installing or changing cutters. It enables one spanner only to engage this collet nut, when changing the tool.

spiral cutter
A special type of router cutter with helical or spiral cutting edges and grooves (flutes). Available with left hand fluting or right hand fluting to help raise chips out of the work.

staff bead

A return bead with a quirk at each side. Refers also to the beaded strip which holds a sash window in place.

stiles

The outer vertical members of a piece of framing.

stopped housing

A housing that does not run across the full width of a panel or workpiece.

straight-edge guide

An accessory that attaches to the router base, usually supplied as standard equipment. It helps maintain the cutting direction of the router in a continuous straight line.

stringings

Fine decorative inlays in the form of fine lines.

strings

Main side component of a staircase into which the treads are fixed.

stub tenon

A small tenon which does not go completely through the timber.

sub-base

A secondary additional base fitted under the base of the router. This may be introduced to increase bearing surface, or provide a means of guiding the router in various ways.

T

T-halving joint

A joint where one member crosses the middle of another at right angles, material being removed from both pieces such that the surfaces finish flush.

TCT

Tungsten carbide tipped, usually refers to grades of saw blades and router cutters. Much harder wearing and longer lasting than HSS. Tungsten tips are brazed onto the body of a router cutter.

template

Predetermined shape that acts as a guide for forming shapes.

template following guide

This is usually a circular guide bush or ring attached to the base or sub-base to help control the router while it is being used to rout irregular patterns and shapes.

tenon

A projection at the end of a piece of wood which locates into a slot called a mortise in another piece. This is a standard joint for many woodworking tasks.

through dovetails

A right angled joint where the pins and tails of the joint are exposed on both faces.

through housing

A slot across the width of a workpiece to receive, for example, a shelf.

tongue and groove joint

A conventional means for jointing wood members in wood flooring and wall panelling. Male and female formed interlocking edges, ensure the boards are dust proof and draught proof.

torus

A convex moulding of approximately semi-circular section, generally used as a moulding for the base of a cabinet.

trench

A channel or housing, called a 'dado'.

Tufnol®

A man-made plastic type material ideal for template making.

Tungsten

This is a metal found in a number of minerals, but chiefly in wolframite. In colloidal form it is used in the filaments of lamps. As tungsten carbide it is used in a wide variety of cutting tools to give them long cutting life.

up-cut shear

A straight bit with the cutting edges inclined slightly so that they lift the swarf clear of the cut.

veiner

A very fine pointed cutter used for engraving or letter cutting.

veneer

A thin sheet or layer of sliced wood, glued or bonded to a surface, usually wood or man-made board; to apply such a sheet to a surface.

weld back

Fusion of the hot swarf behind the cutter when machining materials such as acrylic.

workboard

A specially adapted board with a variety of built in mechanisms for holding the work.

workpiece

This is the board or component which is to be worked, machined, drilled, sanded, or routed.